D1554977

2

GENERAL AND APPLIED
ENTOMOLOGY

GENERAL AND APPLIED ENTOMOLOGY

THIRD EDITION

V. A. LITTLE

Professor Emeritus of Entomology
Texas A&M University

HARPER & ROW, PUBLISHERS
New York, Evanston, San Francisco, London

GENERAL AND APPLIED ENTOMOLOGY, Third Edition

Copyright © 1957 by Harper & Row, Publishers, Inc.
Copyright © 1963, 1972 by Van Allen Little

Printed in the United States of America. All rights
reserved. No part of this book may be used or repro-
duced in any manner whatsoever without written
permission except in the case of brief quotations
embodied in critical articles and reviews. For information address Harper & Row, Publishers, Inc.,
49 East 33rd Street, New York, N.Y. 10016.

Standard Book Number: 06-044023-6

Library of Congress Catalog Card Number: 79-181540

CONTENTS

PREFACE

Entomology is a fascinating science. Insects are more involved in the intricacies and complexities of the biological world than are any other group of animals. Insects will always be of interest because of their diverse habits, complex life cycles, interrelationships, behavior, adaptability, and their importance to the welfare of mankind. I disagree with any premise that insects may eventually engulf the human race; however, their importance must never be minimized. Man will always be capable of coping fairly well with his insect problems, but his methods will forever be changing or modified.

This textbook was written for students beginning a study of entomology. In the preparation of the text, I have kept the student in mind—his interest in and approach to the subject, and the type of information most worthwhile to him. Most students taking the subject will never have more than this one course. The most important question is "What subject matter should it include, and how should it be presented?" After more than 40 years of teaching a course in general and applied entomology, this text represents my views on the subject, and I hope many students will come to share my enthusiasm for it.

One must always keep in mind that entomology is the study of insects—their recognition, biology, and suppression of injurious species. Certainly, the study of taxonomy and the biological phases of insects is most important for the beginner. Next in importance are the applied phases of the science. However, I believe that morphology and physiology should be limited only to a working knowledge.

This vast assemblage of animal life (containing two-thirds of all species of animals) naturally has to be grouped systematically for study. Consequently, it is possible to discuss only a relatively few species. A general text can delve only lightly into the vast amount of accumulated knowledge of the science. Therefore, a selected listing of books having their own excellent bibliographies is included so that the student may pursue his studies further.

A number of insects of direct economic importance have been briefly discussed, and the entomogenous parasites and predators are included in their proper places, especially in the natural and biological control of insects.

Far-reaching changes in the science of entomology, specifically in the field of insect control, have occurred since the publication of the second edition of the text. This third edition updates the information and presents the important and perplexing problems facing the science today. In the endeavor to control pestiferous insects and to increase the food supply of an ever-hungry world through the use of insecticides, major problems involving ecology, pollution, and insect resistance have arisen. Consequently, more stress has been placed on those phases of control other than insecticides. To illustrate, the newer concepts of control such as sexual sterilization by radiation, chemosterilants, and the crossing of genetically incompatible strains are also discussed. All information pertaining to control has been taken from the most authoritative sources such as publications of the U.S. Department of Agriculture, Agricultural Experiment Stations, and the National Academy of Sciences. Most details of control are omitted because control measures vary so much in different parts of the country that one must depend largely on the recommendations of local authorities. Moreover, detailed information pertaining to dosages, application of insecticides, and precautions in their use are found on the manufacturer's label. When improperly used, insecticides can be hazardous to man and animals.

The suggested remedies made in this text are from publications of the U.S. Department of Agriculture and State Experiment Stations. They are given here as the current insect-control practices. However, control measures and insecticide recommendations change constantly. *The reader is warned that any use of remedies suggested is made at his own risk.*

Among other changes in this edition, keys to families have been eliminated. More satisfactory keys are found in laboratory manuals or in textbooks that are primarily taxonomic in nature. Because of the great current interest in environmental problems, Chapter 18, which gives some of the basic concepts of ecology and insect behavior, has been added.

I am indebted to a number of colleagues for the preparation and checking of this revision. Thanks in particular are due to the following: P. L. Adkisson, H. R. Burke, J. C. Gaines, R. L. Hanna, R. C. Hubbard, Jr., W. C. Nettles, F. W. Plapp, M. A. Price, N. M. Randolph, J. C. Schaffner, H. W. Van Cleave, J. K. Walker, Jr., S. J. Nemec, W. L. Sterling, J. G. Thomas, W. H. Newton, L. R. Green, B. G. Hightower, B. H. Cale, H. J. Rinehard, and R. L. Ridgway. Illustrations were obtained from many sources and from a number of people. I wish to thank again particularly those who helped with the drawings of earlier editions: Don Collins, C. O. Mohr, and Mrs. J. W. Dobson. Special thanks are due to Miss Gladys Kornegay and Mrs. Alicia Guffey for their typing and checking of the manuscript as well as for their proofreading.

V. A. LITTLE

College Station, Texas
February, 1972

GENERAL AND APPLIED
ENTOMOLOGY

CHAPTER 1
INSECTS AND RELATED ANIMALS: THE ARTHROPODA

The *Arthropoda* are the most extensive of all phyla of animals. Probably three-fourths of all species of animals are found in this vast and diverse group. The insects, class *Insecta*, constitute the greater part of the phylum.

This phylum possesses some of the characteristics of both higher and lower forms of animal life. Some characteristics held in common with higher animals are a triploblastic and bilaterally symmetrical structure, a coelomic cavity, and organ systems. They have in common with the phylum *Annelida* conspicuous segmentation of the nervous and muscular systems, particularly of the body. The class *Onychophora* (e.g., *Peripatus*) has both annelid and arthropod characteristics and represents a connecting link between the two. This group appears to have descended from a line closely related to the primitive ancestors of both.

In addition to insects, the Arthropoda include such common animals as spiders and crayfish. There is no other group with such diversity of habitats. Certain forms may be found on the tops of the highest mountains and others in the depths of the seas. They feed upon both plant and animal life, and are man's chief competitors for food as well as being disseminators of important diseases of animals and plants. However, not all are harmful by any means. There are many more beneficial species than harmful ones. Great numbers prey upon or parasitize each other. They are sources of food and commercial products for man, and an important food source for birds, mammals, and fishes. Many insects, particularly species of bees, are of great value in the pollination of plants, whereas other insects are of importance in the reduction of organic matter.

Arthropods are such a successful group primarily because of their structural and physiological characteristics. The possession of a chitinous exoskeleton, a segmented body, and jointed appendages has provided maximum mobility. Although chitin is found in some other forms of simpler animals, it is most important in this phylum. This exoskeleton is a remarkable protection against moisture, dryness, and other natural phenomena. At the same time it affords protection for the delicate inner structures, provides attachment for muscles, and supplies superior leverage. Chitin has been modified into such specialized structures as the appendages, chewing jaws, lenses for the eyes, sound and sensory organs, organs for defense, and other purposes.

The Arthropoda typically bear a pair of jointed appendages on each body segment. However, this characteristic is frequently modified because both segments and appendages may be adapted for specialized purposes. Adaptations have made possible greater efficiency and broader capacity for adjustment to diverse environmental conditions.

Aquatic arthropods usually breathe by some type of gills. Most terrestrial forms respire by means of a unique and very efficient system of air tubes which supplies oxygen directly to the tissues.

No group of invertebrate animals has such a great variety of sensory organs, ranging from simple ocelli to complex systems of hearing, touching, smelling, and balancing. Obviously these animals are quite aware of what is happening in their environment.

Reproduction is rapid. Many undergo marked metamorphosis in their development, and in a number of groups immature forms and adults have different food habits.

CLASSIFICATION

The phylum Arthropoda is so extensive and has such a large number of diverse groups that authorities are not well agreed upon their classification. A phylogenetic classification is not possible with the knowledge available at this time. The five most common classes are the *Crustacea* (crayfish, sow bugs, and shrimps), *Arachnida* (spiders, scorpions, and ticks), *Diplopoda* (millipedes), *Chilopoda* (centipedes), and *Insecta* (insects). However, there are other classes which are of interest to zoologists and geologists, or which contain species of some agricultural importance.

CLASS CRUSTACEA (CRAYFISH, SOW BUGS, AND SHRIMP)

The class Crustacea takes its name from the hard shells which cover their bodies (*crusta*, shell). Included in this class are such common representatives as crayfish, lobsters, pill bugs, crabs, and shrimps. Members of this class breathe by means of gills, with the exception of small forms that respire through the body wall. They are aquatic, or at least live in a moist environment. Two pairs of antennae are generally present on the head, and a number of pairs of legs—often modified for swimming—are attached to the body. Some forms are sessile. Malpighian tubes are lacking. In a number of cases the body segments are fused with the head to form a *cephalothorax* (head-body). (See Figure 1.)

Figure 1. A crayfish (Crustacea). (Courtesy of Carolina Biological Supply Co.)

Crustaceans live mostly in seas and fresh waters. Others, such as pill bugs and sow bugs, are terrestrial; they are found in humid places, in decaying organic matter, and in the soil. These may be chiefly nocturnal in habit. Crustaceans feed mainly as scavengers on decaying vegetable and animal matter. The bulk of zooplankton material in water consists of small crustacean life. Crustaceans supply much of the food for fish, and they are also a source of food for man (e.g., lobsters, shrimps, and crabs).

On the whole, the Crustacea are considered beneficial, but there are some harmful species. Barnacles, sessile marine forms, do much damage to shore installations, and impede the speed of ships by attaching themselves to the bottom of vessels. On rare occasions crayfish have been known to damage lawns and destroy field crops in humid regions where the soils have exceptionally high water levels. Sow bugs and pill bugs are pests in greenhouses, flower beds, and gardens. They may be controlled by use of prescribed sprays, dusts, and poison baits. Certain species of *Cyclops* serve as hosts of the broad tapeworm (*Diphyllobothrium latum*) and the guinea worm (*Dracunculus medinensis*).

CLASS DIPLOPODA (MILLIPEDES)

The Diplopoda are known as millipedes (Figure 2) or "thousand legs." They do not have as many legs as the name implies; however, they do have a large number of appendages for their body length and the number of segments. Their bodies are cylindrical and consist of 25–100 segments, most of which bear 2 pairs of legs. The head bears 2 antennae, 2 clusters of simple eyes,

Figure 2. A common millipede.

2 mandibles, and a pair of fused maxillae. A spiracle is located in front of each abdominal leg. These open into an air chamber from which tracheal tubes arise. There are 2 genital apertures which open behind the second pair of legs. In most species the append-ages of the seventh segment are specialized as copulatory organs. Eggs are laid in protected nests. Millipedes prefer dark, damp places under logs and homes. When disturbed they curl up into a ball. Their normal food is decaying organic matter, but sometimes they feed upon living plants and may become a local economic problem. *Julus* is a common genus.

CLASS CHILOPODA (CENTIPEDES)

The Chilopoda, like the Diplopoda, are terrestrial and breathe by means of air tubes. Unlike the millipedes, the body of centipedes is somewhat flattened dorsoventrally, and each body segment typi-cally bears one pair of legs (Figure 3). A pair of poison claws, located on the first segment behind the head, is used to paralyze insects and other small animal life which constitute the principal source of food. The head bears a pair of antennae, a pair of mandibles, and one or two pairs of maxillae. Two clusters of ocelli are located on the dorsal surface of the head. Some centi-pedes lay eggs, whereas others are viviparous. The class as a whole is usually considered beneficial, but some of the larger forms are capable of inflicting bites very painful to man. In temperate climates they are usually not more than 1½ inches in length. They may reach a length of 10 inches in the southern part of the United States, and some tropical species have been known to be a foot in length. *Scolopendrella* is a common genus. The house centipede (*Scutigera*) (Figure 4) has 15 pairs of long fragile legs, and is often seen in homes. Its food consists of flies and other insects, and it is considered harmless.

Figure 3. A southwestern centipede.

Figure 4. The house centipede (*Scutigera forceps*). (From Illinois Natural History Survey.)

CLASS ARACHNIDA (SPIDERS, SCORPIONS, AND TICKS)

The class Arachnida includes such common forms as spiders, scorpions, ticks, and mites. The name of the class is derived from the Greek word *arachne* which means "spider." This class is thought to be an isolated group of the Arthropoda. There is considerable variation in body organization, and it does not have the close-knit organization found in insects. The class appears to have developed from a very old group of arthropods that became differentiated from other forms of the phylum as early as the Cambrian Period.

The bodies of members of this group are usually composed of a cephalothorax and an abdomen. Antennae are absent, and eyes are simple. Respiration is by means of tracheae, book gills, or book lungs. The earliest Arachnida were aquatic, but the vast majority of present-day forms are terrestrial.

ORDER ARANEIDA (SPIDERS)

The Araneida form the largest order of Arachnida, and several thousand species are represented in North American fauna. Although a few species are poisonous to man, the group as a whole must be considered beneficial because its members prey chiefly upon insects (Figure 5).

Spiders may be readily distinguished from other Arachnida by an unsegmented abdomen attached to the cephalothorax by means of a slender stalk or pedicel. There are usually two to eight simple eyes, but in some cave-inhabiting forms eyes may be absent. Mouthparts consist of paired *chelicerae* and a pair of *palpi* (pedipalpi). The chelicerae represent the modified second antennae of the Crustacea. Spiders do not devour their prey, but crush it and suck the body fluids by means of a so-called sucking stomach. The palpi of the female are leglike structures, but they are enlarged and modified in the male for use in transferring sperm to the female in mating. On the ventral surface of the abdomen are located the spinnerets (silk-spinning organs). Opening on the spinnerets are four types of tubes through which four kinds of silk are spun, each of which is utilized for a different purpose. Anterior to the spinnerets is a single spiracle. Book lungs are accessory respiratory organs. They are sacs containing plates arranged like the leaves of a book. One or two pairs of book lungs are found in spiders and their openings are usually located on each side of the genital opening.

Spiders capture their prey by different means. Some species, such as jumping spiders and wolf spiders (Figure 5), stalk their victims. Crab spiders hide in flowers and pounce upon the insect visitors. Most spiders spin silken webs in which their insect prey is snared (Figure 6). The webs are of various types, characteristic of the spider group. The orb-weavers spin the well known orb webs. House spiders construct irregular webs. Others make funnel or triangular webs. When the prey is captured it is usually killed by the poison of the bite.

Figure 5. A wolf spider. (From Illinois Natural History Survey. Courtesy of C. O. Mohr.)

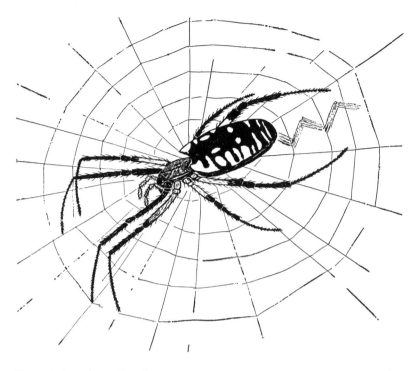

Figure 6. A garden spider (*Argiope aurantia*). (From D. J. Borror and D. M. DeLong, *An Introduction to the Study of Insects*. Copyright 1954 by D. J. Borror and D. M. DeLong. Copyright © 1964, 1971 by Holt, Rinehart and Winston, Inc. Used by permission of the authors and Holt, Rinehart and Winston.)

The mating habits of spiders are of interest to biologists. The males are generally smaller than the females, and can be recognized by the enlarged and modified palpi. In some species mating is preceded by a courtship performance; the males attempt to impress the females by dancing, circling, and showing off in other ways. Sometimes the females join in the display. In many species the females may kill and eat the males after mating. This is why the black widow spider is so named.

The female spider lays her eggs in a silken sac. Great care is taken of the eggs and young spiders. The sac containing the eggs may be carried by the female or attached to some object. Some young spiders are cannibalistic and devour the weaker individuals.

Spiders are wingless and must depend upon means other than flight for travel. They may crawl or be transported by other animals or by air currents. Young spiders frequently make use of air currents for dispersion, especially in the autumn. They crawl to a high point, elevate the abdomen, and spin out silken strands. When the silken threads create sufficient buoyancy in the breeze, the spider is carried away, frequently to considerable distances. Strands of silk floating through the air on clear autumn days are as much a part of the season as flocks of wild geese on their southward journey.

Spiders are feared because of their bites. It is difficult to induce most of them to bite, and only a few of the North American species are poisonous to man. Only the bites of the black widow spider (*Latrodectus mactans*) and the brown recluse (*Loxsceles reclusa*) are dangerously poisonous. Spiders bite with the chelicerae (fangs), which are normally provided with poison glands.

THE BLACK WIDOW SPIDER (*Latrodectus mactans*). The mature female black widow spider is deep black with red markings in the form of an hourglass on the underside of the abdomen (Figure 7). It measures about ½ inch in length. The male is much smaller than the female. The abdomen of the male is marked dorsally with three transverse white bands and a median red stripe. It has enlarged and modified palpi. The males are relatively shortlived.

The black widow spider is most frequently found where insects are abundant. During the summer it is quite commonly found underneath beehives. Occasionally it becomes relatively numerous in places flies frequent.

The poison of the black widow spider is reported to be a neurotoxin. Man, however, is seldom bitten by this spider. When bitten, excruciating pain is experienced and severe symptoms may

Figure 7. The black widow spider (*Latrodectus mactans*) hanging on web. (From Utah Agricultural Experiment Station.)

persist for several days. A physician should be consulted as soon as possible. In some cases fatalities have resulted. Approved household sprays containing malathion, chlordane, or ronnel applied where they are found will control both spiders and scorpions.

THE BROWN RECLUSE SPIDER (*Loxosceles reclusa*). This spider is another species which is of concern in many southern and midwestern states. Its bite may not be noticed for several hours, or an immediate painful reaction may occur, depending upon the sensitivity of the individual and the amount of poison, which is a hemotoxin, injected in the wound. Tissue around the bite usually is killed and slowly sloughs away. Healing may require several weeks. In case of a bite a physician should be consulted immediately.

The spider varies in color from yellow to dark brown and varies in length from ³⁄₁₀ to ½ inch. The males are somewhat smaller than the females. The legs are long, covered with short hairs and darker than the body. The species may be distinguished from other forms by three pairs of eyes arranged in a semicircle on the fore part of the head, a dark violin-shaped marking immediately behind the simple eyes, flattened carapace (hard shell covering of the cephalothorax), and short distinct median grooves.

This is a secretive spider that runs when disturbed. Most bites appear to occur when it is injured, and relatively few people are bitten by it. It may be found throughout the house. Frequent cleaning of the house and the use of approved household sprays are recommended to eliminate the spider.

TARANTULAS (*Dugesiella* spp. and others). Tarantulas are large hairy spides that are much feared by some people. They occur in the southwestern states, Mexico, Central America, and South America (Figure 8). The size of tarantulas varies from 1 to 3 inches in length. The native forms live in holes in the ground or under logs and stones.

The time required for the development of tarantulas is believed to be about 12 years. The adult females may live for another 12 years or longer. Popular opinion to the contrary, the bite of the species of tarantulas found in the United States is not poisonous to man. However, the bite of certain tropical species is toxic and produces local reactions.

ORDER SCORPIONIDA (SCORPIONS)

Scorpions are widely distributed in tropical and temperate climates, and within the United States they occur in the largest numbers in the Southwest. Probably more than 30 species occur in the United States. Members of this order are recognized by the jointed abdomen broadly joined to the cephalothorax and terminat-

Figure 8. A tarantula from southern Mexico. (Courtesy of General Biological Supply House.)

ing in a sting, and by the long palpi with the terminal segments forming strong pincers.

The sting of the common species of scorpions is painful, but the effects are not dangerous. The poison is a neurotoxin. In Mexico, however, five species are known whose sting may be fatal to small children. The poison injected by the sting of *Centruroides noxius* may be fatal to adults also. *Centruroides suffusus* is the commonly known Durango scorpion.

The biology of scorpions is not very well known. Scorpions are found in rotten logs; and under stones, bark, boards, and other similar places. Their food consists of insects, spiders, and other small animals which are usually stung before being devoured. The female of the common striped scorpion (Figure 9) produces about 30–40 young, which live, in their early stages of development, upon the back of the mother. However, they soon leave the female and fend for themselves, for the maternal instinct disappears rather early and they may be devoured by their own mother. Should it become necessary to control them around homes, garages, or other buildings, the same recommendations are made as for poisonous spiders.

ORDER PEDIPALPIDA (WHIP SCORPIONS)

Whip scorpions are tropical in habitat and are found only in the southern part of this country. In body build they have the general form of scorpions. They differ from the latter in the form of the front legs. They are elongated, with the tarsi divided into a number of small segments which produce a whiplike appearance. Also, members in one family bear a long whiplike appendage on the end of the abdomen and are commonly known as vinegarroons, because, when disturbed, they emit a fluid with a vinegarlike odor (Figure 10). They are thought by many to be poisonous, although no stinging organ is present. The fluid emitted could possibly cause some irritation on tender skin. Vinegarroons are also known as giant whip scorpions. The best known species is *Mastigoproctus*

Figure 9. A common scorpion.

Figure 10. A vinegarroon (*Mastigoproctus giganteus*).

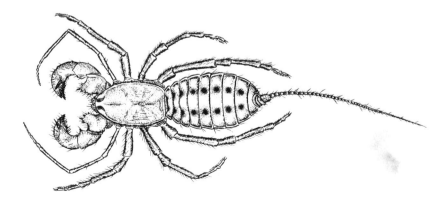

giganteus. Whip scorpions are predaceous and secrete themselves under logs, boards, and other objects.

ORDER CHELONETHIDA (PSEUDOSCORPIONIDA) (PSEUDOSCORPIONS)

Members of the order Chelonethida are small, rarely more than ⅛ inch in length, and have the general appearance of scorpions, but the abdomen is broad and flat, and they have no sting. Pseudo-scorpions live under stones and bark of trees, in homes between pages of books, and in similar places (Figure 11). They have the peculiar habit of running sidewise and backwards. Their food consists of small insects and mites. They may make use of large insects for transportation by clinging to their bodies. These animals have silk glands, the ducts of which are found on the chelicerae. The silk is used in the construction of overwintering cocoons.

ORDER PHALANGIDA (HARVESTMEN OR DADDY-LONGLEGS)

The common and widely distributed Phalangida are readily recognized by the compact oval body and the long ungainly legs. Daddy-longlegs, as they are most commonly called, feed on juices

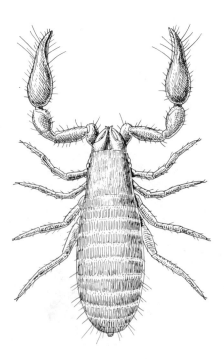

Figure 11. A pseudoscorpion (*Micro-bisium confusum*) enlarged. (From Illinois Natural History Survey.)

of plants, dead insects, and possibly on some living insects also. Their eggs may be laid in the soil, under stones, in cracks, and similar situations. Adults may overwinter in the South, but most species spend the winter in the egg stage in colder climates.

ORDER ACARINA (MITES AND TICKS)

The Acarina is the most important order of the Arachnida, for in this group are found a number of pests of both plants and animals. The Acarina may be separated from other Arachnida by the sac-like body with the abdomen not distinctly segmented and broadly joined to the cephalothorax. Mouthparts are for piercing and sucking.

Mites

Mites are generally quite small, many of them being microscopic. The taxonomy of the group is imperfectly known, but the number of species is indicated to be quite large. They are very abundant. Both plants and animals are attacked. Some are predators or parasites and others are scavengers. They may be found in the soil, rubbish, plant galls, under stones and bark, and in both fresh and salt water. Most species deposit eggs; however, a few are ovoviviparous, such as the straw itch mite (*Pyemotes ventricosus*). A six-legged larva is hatched from the egg. Following a period of feeding, the larva molts into a nymph with eight legs. The nymph feeds and molts one or more times before the adult stage is reached. The adult may be differentiated from the nymph by the presence of a genital pore. Only a few of the more important species can be mentioned here.

THE TWO-SPOTTED SPIDER MITE (*Tetranychus telarius*). The two-spotted spider mite (Figure 12) is an important pest of many plants. Among the more common hosts of this species are cotton, beans, peas, cucumbers, cantaloupes, arborvitae, and most flowers and greenhouse plants. The spider mite punctures the epidermis of the leaves with its mouthparts and sucks the plant juices. Leaves of lightly infested plants assume an ashy-gray stippled appearance, while those of heavily infested plants may turn reddish brown and later drop. The two-spotted spider mite is oval in outline and the female is about $\frac{1}{50}$ inch in length; the male is smaller. The color may be red, reddish yellow, yellow, greenish, or blackish. Normally a slight web to which the eggs are attached is spun on the underside of the leaf. In heavy infestations the entire plant may be enveloped by the web (Figure 13).

The life history of the spider mite is dependent upon climatic conditions. A generation may be completed in slightly more than a week under optimum conditions, while more than a month may elapse before the completion of a life cycle when conditions are not favorable. An average of about 50 eggs are laid by each

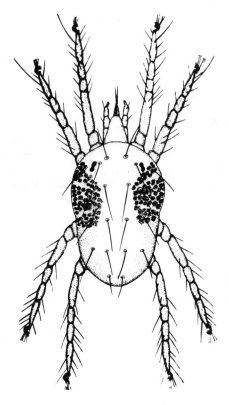

Figure 12. The two-spotted spider mite (*Tetranychus telarius*), highly magnified. (From Virginia Agricultural Experiment Station.)

Figure 13. Vetch plants heavily infested with spider mites. (From Texas Agricultural Experiment Station.)

female. A number of overlapping generations may occur in one season. Winter is spent on vetch (Figure 13), violets, geraniums, and other plants in the South. In the North it is reported that the mite overwinters in the soil.

Associated with the two-spotted spider mite are other closely related species which are extremely difficult to separate taxonomically. One of these is the carmine spider mite (*Tetranychus cinnabarinus*), which is now the most important cotton spider mite in Texas. It is very difficult to control.

A number of compounds are used in spider mite control. The product selected is dependent upon the crop and the measure of resistance, if any, to the compounds. Dicofol, parathion, ethyl parathion, malathion, and Azodrin are most commonly used (Figure 14).

Other common mites attacking cultivated plants are the citrus rust mite (*Phyllocoptruta oleivora*), citrus red mite (*Metatetranychus citri*), the pear leaf blister mite (*Eriophyes pyri*) (Figure 15), and the European red mite (*Panonychus ulmi*) (Figure 16).

A number of species of mites attack man and domestic animals. The more common species are chiggers, mange mites, scab mites, and the chicken mite.

CHIGGERS OR RED BUGS (*Eutrombicula alfreddugesi* and others). Humans become infested with chiggers in walking through grass,

Figure 14. Ash flower gall produced by a gall mite (*Eriophyes fraxiniflora*). (From Texas Agricultural Experiment Station.)

Figure 15. The pear leaf blister mite (*Eriophyes pyri*) greatly enlarged. (From Utah Agricultural Experiment Station.)

weeds, and other vegetation. Intense itching and red spots result from the feeding of these tiny red mites which are about ¹⁄₁₅₀ inch in diameter and barely visible to the naked eye (Figure 17). Only the larval or six-legged stage attacks larger animals. The mouthparts are inserted into the skin and a fluid is injected which dissolves the tissues upon which the chigger feeds. Following feeding, the larval chigger drops to the ground and later molts into the nymphal stage. In addition to man, chiggers attack snakes, turtles, rabbits, chickens, and other vertebrates. Nymphs and adults are associated with the soil, feeding upon insect eggs, small insects, and related organisms.

Chiggers may be controlled by spraying infested areas with chlordane, lindane, or toxaphene. Emulsion sprays provide more satisfactory control than those containing wettable powders. Dusting with sulfur is also recommended.

Chigger attacks may be prevented by treating the clothing with sulfur, diethyltoluamide, 622 mixture, or with indalone before going into infested areas. Swabbing chigger bites with a 50–50 mixture of chloroform and rubbing alcohol will kill the chiggers and relieve the severe itching; however, the chloroform will burn for a short while.

MANGE MITES. Mange or sarcoptic mites attacking man, hogs, horses, dogs, and other animals are varieties of the same species, *Sarcoptes*

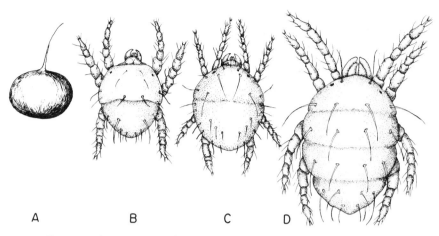

Figure 16. The European red mite (*Panomychus ulmi*). A. Egg. B. Larva or six-legged stage. C. Nymph. D. Adult. (Modified from Agricultural Research Service, USDA.)

Figure 17. Adult of a chigger (*Trombicula splendens*) on the head of a pin. (From Scientific Monthly, Vol. LXIX, No. 5, Nov. 1949, p. 287.)

scabiei. They feed in the skin and produce definite burrows in which the eggs are laid. The female human itch mite is about ⅟₆₀ inch in diameter, and the male is only one-half as large. The young female deposits 10–25 eggs in the burrow of the skin and the eggs hatch in 3–4 days. Following 3 molts the adult stage is reached in 10–12 days. The length of life of mites is a month or more.

Human itch is an old malady of man. In centuries past it was thought to be caused by bad blood or improper living. Benzyl benzoate formulations readily eliminate the itch when the remedy is properly used. Following treatment, clothing, towels, and bed clothing should be sent to the dry cleaners or laundered to eliminate the mites which may be infesting them.

Hog mange is quite common. Young hogs are usually most greatly affected by mange. When hogs are seen vigorously scratching and rubbing, and lice are not present, they are probably infested with mange mites. The skin on the head, neck, and back becomes rough, scabby, cracked, and pimpled. The life history of the mange mite on hogs is the same as the variety on human beings (Figure 18).

A spray or dip containing lindane at concentrations of 0.05 to 0.06 percent will control hog mange. Animals should not be treated within 30 days of farrowing or 60 days of slaughtering. Pigs under 8–10 weeks old should not be sprayed or dipped. Toxaphene sprays will control horse mange.

Sarcoptic mange of dogs may be treated with sulfur ointment, a solution of rotenone in alcohol or in a bland oil, or sprays or dips of lindane. Sarcoptic mange of dogs is not to be confused with follicular or demodectic mange. Follicular mange is very difficult to

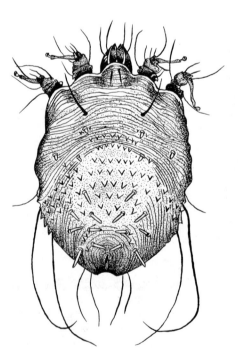

Figure 18. A sarcoptic mange mite (female) greatly enlarged. (From Agricultural Research Service, USDA.)

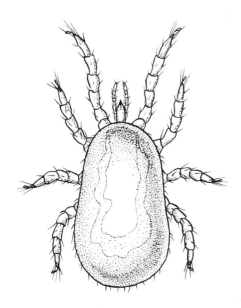

Figure 19. The chicken mite (*Dermanyssus gallinae*) enlarged. (Redrawn from W. B. Herms, *Medical Entomology.* Copyright 1950. Used by permission of The Macmillan Company.)

cure. Valuable animals should be placed under the care of a veterinarian as soon as follicular mange is discovered. Treating infected areas twice weekly with a rotenone solution, or sprays or dips of lindane are the most satisfactory treatments which may be prescribed for follicular mange.

SCAB MITES. Scab or psoroptic mites attack sheep, goats, cattle, and other animals. Unlike the sarcoptic mites that burrow in the skin, the psoroptic mites live at the base of the hairs. The skin is pierced by the mouthparts, producing an exudate which piles up, hardens, and forms a scab. All stages of the mites are found among the scabs.

The sheep scab mite (*Psoroptes equi* var. *ovis*) is the most important of the group. The first symptom of sheep scab is tagging of the wool and the rough, matted appearance of the coat. Infested animals rub vigorously and indicate symptoms of severe itching. Female mites lay about 15 eggs each. The life cycle is extremely short, about 9 days in duration.

Animals infected with sheep scab are subject to quarantine and the infection should be reported to the proper livestock official immediately.

THE CHICKEN MITE (*Dermanyssus gallinae*). This is an important pest of poultry, particularly chickens. The mite (Figure 19) is widely distributed and it is most troublesome in warm and dry regions. It feeds on the blood of its hosts and its capacity for harm is great. Young chickens and setting hens may be killed by the attacks. Chicken mites are ⅒₀ to ¼₀ inch long, grayish or red in color. They hide almost everywhere—in cracks and crevices, under boards and litter, in dry manure, and nests. They feed upon poultry chiefly at night. Only a relatively few mites will be found on the birds during the day.

Female mites deposit their white eggs in cracks, dry manure, and other similar places. Each female lays 25–35 eggs. Adults may live for several months. Only 7–10 days are required for a life cycle in warm weather, thus a large population may be built up in a relatively short time.

In mite control the first consideration is to clean the poultry house. Trash, litter, and droppings should be removed prior to the application of insecticides. Coumaphos, malathion, and carbaryl are recommended either as dusts or as sprays.

Ticks

Ticks are of economic importance because they suck the blood of their hosts and are vectors of a number of human and animal diseases. Mammals, birds, and reptiles are attacked. Ticks may be distinguished from mites by their larger size, leathery skin, and spiracles located behind the third or fourth pair of legs.

Ticks are classified into two families, the Ixodidae and the Argasidae. The *Ixodidae*, or hard ticks, are characterized by a dorsal shield or *scutum*, a *capitulum* (a false or specialized head, anteriorly borne), and *spiracles* located on a *stigmal plate* behind each fourth leg. The scutum of the female is small and is located directly behind the capitulum. In the male the scutum covers most of the dorsum which prohibits distention and limits its size. This results in marked sexual dimorphism. The Argasidae, or soft ticks, are distinguished from the hard ticks by absence of the scutum, ventrally located capitulum, leglike pedipalpi (palpi), and small stigmal plates behind the third pair of legs. Sexual dimorphism is not marked.

Mouthparts and accessory structures are borne by the capitulum (Figure 20). A pair of *chelicerae* project forward from the basal part of the capitulum, the *basis capituli*. Distally the chelicerae are provided with digits bearing recurved teeth. The *hypostome*, bearing recurved teeth, lies in a median position below the chelicerae. On the side of each chelicera is located a four-segmented palpus. When the tick feeds, both chelicerae and hypostome are pushed into the skin of the host.

There are four stages in the development of ticks; namely, *egg, larva* (seed tick), *nymph* (yearling tick), and *adult*. Eggs are usually laid in protected places on the ground. The active six-legged larva seeks its host in different ways. When a host is found, a succession of feeding and molting stages follows until the adult stage is reached. After feeding, the larva usually drops to the

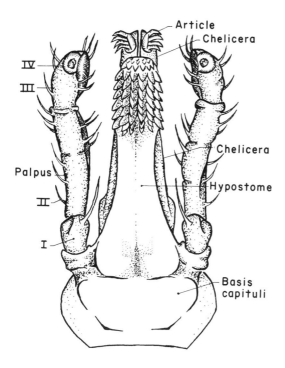

Figure 20. Ventral view of the capitulum of the lone star tick (*Amblyomma americanum*).

ground, molts, and becomes a nymph. The nymph has eight legs, as does the adult, but lacks the genital pore. The nymph now finds a new host, engorges, and generally drops to the ground and molts for the second time. A third host is found and the adult feeds to repletion. During this time the female is usually fertilized by the male. Following feeding and mating, the engorged female drops to the ground where it deposits the eggs and dies. The biology of the Argasidae differs from the account given in that there are several nymphal stages; the adult usually lives for a long while and feeds a number of times. Thus, more host animals are required for completion of the life cycle.

The life cycle of all species of ticks is similar; however, differences in the developmental cycle occur. Some species, such as the cattle tick (*Boophilus annulatus*), complete the life cycle on a single animal. These species are known as one-host ticks. In other species, such as the African red tick (*Rhipicephalus evertsi*), both larva and nymph develop on one host and the adult feeds on a second animal. They are two-host ticks. The lone star tick (*Amblyomma americanum*) and many other species require three hosts for development, leaving the host for each molt. They are referred to as three-host ticks. The fowl tick (*Argas persicus*) and most other members of the Argasidae are many-host ticks, requiring a number of hosts for completion of the life cycle.

FAMILY IXODIDAE. THE CATTLE TICK (*Boophilus annulatus*). The cattle tick once was not only the most common but the most important tick in the South. It has been eradicated in the United States with the possible exceptions of isolated areas in Florida and parts of Texas along the Mexican border. The cattle industry in the South was greatly handicapped until the cattle tick was eliminated.

The cattle tick is a vector of Texas fever, the causative organism of which is a protozoan (*Babesia bigemina*) which destroys the red blood cells of cattle. The tick obtains the organism in feeding. The parasite undergoes a growth cycle in the tick and developing eggs of the female become infected. A larva hatching from an infected egg can transmit the disease organism to a new host. This is the first known record of transovarial transmission of a parasite and also the first record of a tick being the intermediate host of a protozoan parasite. Cattle are the principal hosts, but the tick also attacks horses, mules, sheep, goats, deer, and buffaloes.

The parasitic phase of the life cycle of the cattle tick is completed on only one host. Molting and copulation occur on the host animal. Following copulation and engorgement, the adult female drops to the ground and deposits eggs. Each female lays 3000–5000 or more eggs. The eggs normally hatch in about 30 days. Usually a month is required for the tick to complete its parasitic cycle and drop from the host. Thus, a generation may be produced in about 2 months. Unfed larvae may live for as long as 8 months. Eradication of the cattle tick was feasible because it is a one-host tick and confines its attacks chiefly to cattle.

THE LONE STAR TICK (*Amblyomma americanum*). This tick is readily recognized by a white spot on the posterior margin of the scutum of the female (Figure 21A). It is widely distributed in the southeastern and south-central United States and occurs in greatest numbers in brush and wooded areas. This species shows little host preference. Both mammals and birds are attacked. Larvae, nymphs, and adults commonly attack cattle, horses, man, dogs, hogs, and other animals. Larvae and nymphs are found on small mammals, such as rodents, but adults rarely attack these animals. Birds of a number of species are common hosts of the larvae.

The lone star tick is quite important as a parasite and as a vector of human diseases. The tick is a predisposing factor in screwworm infestations in cattle, particularly in Texas and Louisiana. The parasite is a vector of Rocky Mountain spotted fever in Texas, Oklahoma, and probably other states. It transmits tularemia and is suspected of being a vector of American "Q" fever.

This is a three-host parasite and it normally completes one gen-

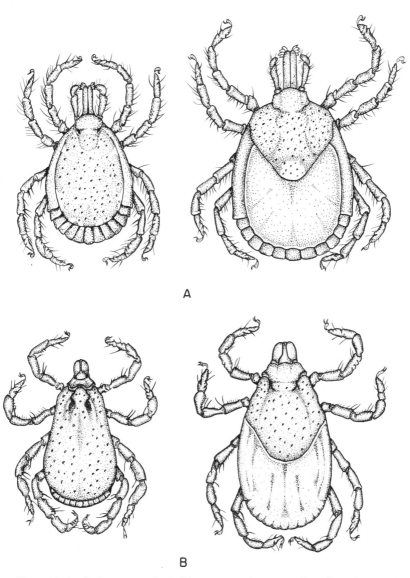

Figure 21. A. The lone star tick (*Amblyomma americanum*). Left, male; right, female. B. The brown dog tick (*Rhipicephalus sanguineus*). Left, male; right, female.

eration annually. The female lays 3000–4000 or more eggs. Nymphs and adults may live for more than a year without feeding.

THE BROWN DOG TICK (*Rhipicephalus sanguineus*). The brown dog tick is probably the most cosmopolitan species (Figure 21B). It is found in most tropical and temperate climates throughout the world. In 1912 this tick was reported only in south Texas. It is now widely distributed over the North American continent. The dog is the principal host; however other animals, such as cattle, horses, and occasionally man, are attacked. This three-host tick frequently becomes a serious pest in homes and kennels, where its reproduction may occur throughout the year. Females deposit 2000–3000 eggs and a generation of the tick may be completed in less than 2 months under favorable conditions. The brown dog tick is implicated as a vector in the transmission of several diseases.

THE GULF COAST TICK (*Amblyomma maculatum*). The Gulf Coast tick is found along the coast from Virginia into Texas with its range usually extending inland for about 150 miles. It is also present in the West Indies, Mexico, and South America.

Adults parasitize large animals such as cattle, horses, dogs, sheep, goats, wolves, and others. Larvae and nymphs are found principally on birds, but they will also attack small mammals. In those regions where the tick is abundant it is an important pest of cattle. The adults attach themselves chiefly inside the ears where their feeding may produce suppuration and scabs. The Gulf Coast tick is an important predisposing factor in screwworm infestations.

THE WINTER TICK (*Dermacentor albipictus*). The winter tick has a wide distribution in North America, but is most commonly found west of the Mississippi River. This is a one-host tick, attacking large animals such as moose, deer, elk, cattle, and horses. Ticks are found on the hosts only during the cooler parts of the year. The parasitic phase of the life cycle of the tick is completed about 6 weeks after attachment of the larva to the host. Following copulation and engorgement, the female drops to the ground, but it does not deposit its eggs until the next spring. Eggs hatch in 3–6 weeks. The larvae form a compact cluster and remain dormant during the warm season. With the first cool weather in autumn the larvae become active and attack their hosts.

THE AMERICAN DOG TICK (*Dermacentor variabilis*). This is a widely distributed North American species. Larvae and nymphs feed principally on rodents, such as mice; the adults attack dogs, men, cattle, horses, and other large mammals. Females deposit 4000–6500 eggs. Larvae may live for 11 months, nymphs 6 months, and unengorged adults for more than 2 years without food. The American dog tick (Figure 22) is an important vector of Rocky Mountain spotted fever in the East. This species also transmits tularemia.

Control of Hard Ticks (Ixodidae) on Animals
Arsenical dips, which were widely used in the past for the control of ticks on livestock, have been largely replaced by organic insecticides. Because most organic insecticides are toxic to animals, and

Figure 22. The American dog tick (*Dermacentor variabilis*). A. Male. B. Female. (From Agricultural Research Service, USDA.)

methods of determining the concentration of the insecticides in dipping vats are not generally accurate, spraying is preferred to dipping. Spraying of livestock also effects a considerable saving in time and labor. For control of ticks on beef cattle the following sprays are recommended: 0.5 percent toxaphene or 0.5 percent toxaphene combined with 0.03 percent lindane; 0.5 percent coumaphos, or 0.15 percent dioxathion. Milk and other dairy products may become contaminated with these chlorinated hydrocarbons, and their use is forbidden in the control of ticks on dairy cattle. Rotenone and pyrethrum sprays are recommended instead and repeated applications are necessary to reduce the tick population. Ciodrin may also be used. Ticks on dogs may be controlled with rotenone, carbaryl or dioxathion. Infested kennels should be sprayed with either of the two latter compounds.

FAMILY ARGASIDAE. THE EAR TICK (*Otobius megnini*). This tick (Figure 23A) is found chiefly in the Southwest where it is a pest of some importance. Domestic animals, particularly cattle and horses, are mostly attacked; however, wild animals sometimes are infested.

Larvae hatch from eggs which are laid on the ground. They are quite active and find their way into the deep folds of the ears of the host animals where they attach and feed. Seven to 12 days after attachment the larvae molt and become nymphs. There are 2 nymphal stages. Three weeks to several months following the first molt the second nymphal stage is completed, and the ticks

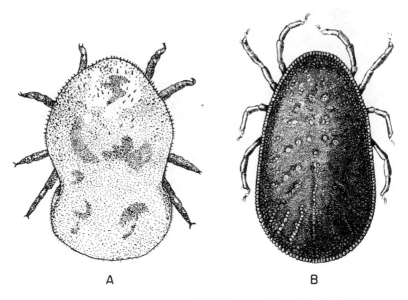

Figure 23. A. The ear tick (*Otobius megnini*). B. The fowl tick (*Argas persicus*). (From USDA.)

leave the host to molt into the adult stage. Adults do not feed, a characteristic which apparently does not exist in other species of ticks. Adults may live for more than a year. Each female lays an average of 800–1000 eggs.

Lindane applied inside the ears is used in control. Spraying with oil around salt and feed troughs will aid in elimination of the ear ticks in these breeding areas.

The genus *Ornithodoros* contains a number of species that transmit human and animal diseases. The American species are found chiefly in the Southwest where they are involved in the transmission of relapsing fever of man.

THE FOWL TICK (*Argas persicus*). This important pest of poultry (Figure 23B) is distributed in warm countries throughout the world. Chickens are the principal hosts; however, other domestic fowls such as turkeys, ducks and geese, and also wild birds are attacked. More than 600 eggs are laid by each female. Larvae remain attached to the host throughout this stage, which lasts about 5 days. Then they leave the host, molt, and become nymphs. There may be 3 nymphal stages. Nymphs and adults feed at night and hide underneath boards and other places of concealment during the daylight hours. Adults partake of several blood meals and the females deposit a batch of eggs following each engorgement. Under most favorable conditions, a generation may be completed in 30 days. Adults are reported to live for several years without food.

Carbaryl and malathion are recommended for control of the fowl tick in both the poultry house and other roosting places. The spray must be thoroughly applied wherever the pests are found. Sprays of chlordane or toxaphene may be employed outside the poultry house.

CLASS INSECTA[1] (HEXAPODA) (INSECTS)

The Insecta is the largest and most important class of the Arthropoda, with more than a half million known species. We are chiefly concerned in this book with the study of this class. The insect body is divided into three distinct regions: the head, thorax, and abdomen. The thorax bears three pairs of legs and usually two pairs of wings (Figure 24). Respiration is by means of air tubes. Although they live under greatly diverse conditions, insects must be classed as terrestrial animals.

See the table of General Characteristics of the Common Classes of Arthropoda.

[1] *Insectum,* cut into.

Figure 24. The eastern lubber grasshopper (*Romalea microptera*). (From Department of Entomology, Texas A&M University.)

General Characteristics of the Common Classes of Arthropoda

	Habitat	Breathe By	Body Divisions	Antennae	Legs
Crustacea (Crayfish, etc.)	Chiefly aquatic	Gills or body surface	Cephalo-thorax and ab-domen, or head and body	Generally two pairs	Numerous, may be modified for swim-ming
Arachnida (Spiders, mites, etc.)	Chiefly terres-trial	Air tubes, book lungs or body surface	Cephalo-thorax and ab-domen	None	Eight on cephalo-thorax
Diplopoda (Millipedes)	Terrestrial	Air tubes	Head and body	One pair	Many, typi-cally, two pairs per body seg-ment
Chilopoda (Centipedes)	Terrestrial	Air tubes	Head and body	One pair	Many, one pair per body seg-ment
Insecta (Insects)	Chiefly terres-trial	Air tubes	Head, thorax, and abdomen	One pair	Six on thorax

CHAPTER 2
ANATOMY AND PHYSIOLOGY OF INSECTS

EXTERNAL ANATOMY

In addition to the general characteristics of the phylum Arthropoda, which are common to all of its classes, adult insects have: (1) three body divisions—head, thorax, and abdomen; (2) three pairs of legs borne on the thorax; (3) usually two pairs of wings attached to the thorax; (4) one pair of antennae; (5) compound and simple eyes; (6) respiration by means of air tubes; and (7) reproductive organs opening near the caudal end of the abdomen (Figure 25).

THE EXOSKELETON

A general knowledge of the anatomy of insects is essential in distinguishing groups and individual species and understanding their way of life. Insects are well protected by the exoskeleton, which encases the individual like a suit of armor. Much of the success of these animals in competition with other forms of life must be attributed to this external skeleton. Protection is afforded against moisture, dryness, diseases, and natural enemies of many kinds. The exoskeleton protects the soft tissues within and serves as the place of attachment for the numerous muscles of insects. Leverage afforded by the exoskeleton is of the first class and is more efficient than that of animals with an endoskeleton. This superior leverage explains in part the remarkable relative strength of insects.

The exoskeleton is composed of three principal layers—*cuticula, hypodermis,* and *basement membrane.* The cuticula has a stratified appearance and consists of two distinct layers—an outer cuticula, *exocuticula,* and an inner cuticula, *endocuticula* (Figure 26). The exocuticula is covered on the outside by a thin layer about 1 micron thick known as the *epicuticula.* The most characteristic substance in the exocuticula and the endocuticula is chitin. This compound is a nitrogenous polysaccharide and is insoluble and resistant to the action of water, alcohol, and diluted alkalies and

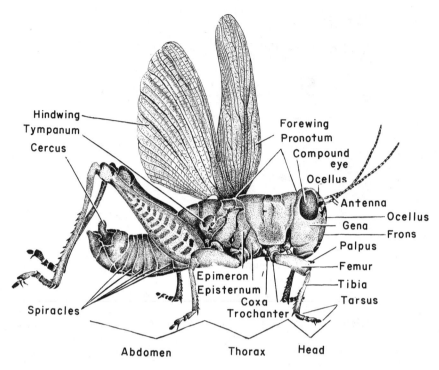

Figure 25. Lateral view of a grasshopper (*Melanoplus differentialis*). (From Department of Entomology, Texas A&M University.)

acids. The epicuticula is nonchitinous in nature. It is composed of substances that protect insects from excessive desiccation, humidity, and disease, thus enabling them to live under a wider range of environmental conditions. The hypodermis consists primarily of a single layer of cells that secrete the cuticula. The basement membrane is a thin, noncellular membrane that forms the inner lining of the hypodermis.

The body wall of an insect is made up of plates or *sclerites* which are usually hardened or sclerotized. The sclerites are separated by lines known as *sutures*. The sclerites and sutures have definite value in description and identification of insects. The surface of the body bears ridges, hairs, setae, spines, and scales. The body consists of three distinct regions—the *tergum* or dorsal portion, the *pleura* (singular *pleuron*) or sides, and the *sternum* or ventral region.

THE HEAD

The head is a heavily sclerotized, capsulelike, and unsegmented region which bears the *mouthparts, antennae,* and *eyes.* In the

Figure 26. Diagrammatic sketch of the body wall of an insect. Bm, basement membrane; Enct, endocuticula; Epct, epicuticula; Exct, exocuticula; Hy, hypodermis; Su, suture.

head of a generalized insect, such as the grasshopper, the parts are fairly distinct; for this reason the structures discussed here pertain to this insect (Figure 27). Among specialized insects some of these parts are greatly modified or lost through *fusion*. The *frons* or front extends from the region between the eyes to the *clypeus*. It bears the antennae and the median *ocellus*. A distinct suture separates the frons and the clypeus. The clypeus extends from the frons to the base of the labrum. The *genae* or cheeks are located on either side of the frons and below the eyes. The *vertex* is the highest point between the eyes. The *occiput* lies behind the vertex, eyes, and genae. Those parts that extend downward and back of the genae are known as the *postgenae*. The antennae, eyes, and mouthparts are the most important structures located on the head. They are discussed separately.

THE ANTENNAE

The paired antennae are located between and in front of the eyes. They vary widely in form and size and have considerable value in identification of insects. The function of the antennae is sensory; the sense of touch in particular is located here. In some instances at least, the senses of smell and hearing are located in the antennae also. The basal segment of the antenna is known as the *scape*. The second segment is the *pedicel*, and the remaining segments are collectively called the *flagellum*. A number of types of antennae are recognized (Figure 28). The more common types are:

1. *Setaceous* (bristlelike); the antenna gradually tapers to a point distally.
2. *Filiform* (threadlike); the segments are quite uniform in size.
3. *Moniliform*; the segments are similar in size and beadlike in appearance.

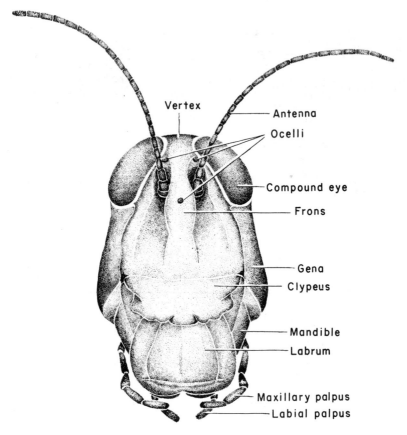

Figure 27. Front view of the head of a grasshopper (*Melanoplus differentialis*). (From Department of Entomology, Texas A&M University.)

4. *Serrate* (sawlike); the segments are somewhat triangular in shape and appear on one side like the teeth of a saw.
5. *Pectinate* (comblike); the antenna has the appearance of a comb.
6. *Clavate* (clubshaped); the segments are enlarged distally to produce a clubbed appearance.
7. *Lamellate*; the distal segments are expanded laterally to form thin plates.
8. *Aristate*; the distal segment is enlarged and bears a dorsal bristle.
9. *Plumose* (featherlike); most segments bear whorls of long hairs.

THE EYES

Typical adult insects have two types of eyes—*ocelli,* or simple eyes, and *compound,* or faceted eyes. When both are present there

are two compound eyes and usually three ocelli. In more specialized groups both types may be absent or the number of simple
eyes reduced. The ocelli are situated between the compound eyes
on the front of the vertex. They are usually quite small and have a
single lens for the entire eye. It is generally believed that these
simple eyes or photoreceptors increase the insect's responsiveness
to stimulation by light.

When a compound eye (Figure 29) is examined under magnification, it is found to consist of a large number of hexagonal
figures known as *facets*. The number of facets varies from a few
to as many as 50,000 in some insects. Each facet is the base of an

Figure 28. The more common types of antennae.

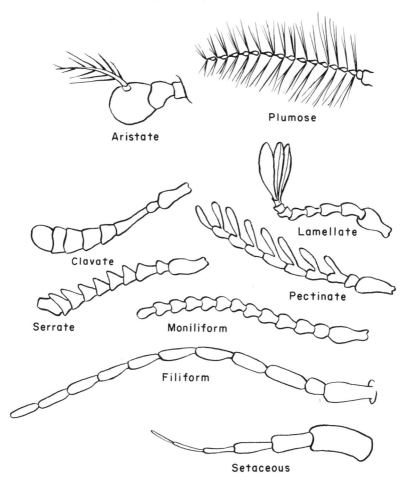

Plumose

Aristate

Lamellate

Clavate

Pectinate

Serrate

Moniliform

Filiform

Setaceous

Figure 29. Diagram of the vertical section of a part of a compound eye. BMb, basement membrane; CgCl, corneagenous cell; Cn, crystalline cone; Cor, corneal lens; I, lamia ganglionaris; Nv, nerve; OCh, outer chiasma; OR, ocular ridge; Ret, retinula; Rhb, rhabdom. (Redrawn from R. E. Snodgrass, *Principles of Insect Morphology.* Copyright 1935 by McGraw-Hill Book Co. Used with permission of McGraw-Hill Book Co.)

inverted pyramid which is a functionally separate eye element known as an *ommatidium*.

The facet is the lens or cornea of an ommatidium. Behind the cornea is a crystalline cone which rests upon the *retinula*. Usually lying at the sides of the crystalline cone are two hypodermal cells from which the cornea is secreted. The retinula, the sensory part of the eye, is composed of seven or eight elongated pigment cells, the inner surfaces of which form the optic rod, the *rhabdom*. The ommatidium extends to the basement membrane. Nerve fibers from the cells of the retinulae form the optic nerve. Each ommatidium is surrounded by pigment cells.

Two types of vision may be explained on the basis of differences in structure of the ommatidia. Images may be formed by apposition or superposition. In most day flying insects the ommatidia are so completely surrounded by pigmented cells that light is prevented from passing from one to the other. Hence, each ommatidium perceives only a small part of the object directly in front of it. The complete image is an apposition image.

In many nocturnal insects the ommatidia differ in morphological details from those of most diurnal insects. The ommatidia are more elongate. The retinulae are separated from the crystalline cones by a significant distance and the pigmented cells are concentrated forward between the crystalline cones. Hence, it is possible for a rhabdom to receive light rays from surrounding facets as well as from its own. Each elemental image is the result of the superposition of light from a number of facets. The compound image thus formed is known as a superposition image.

It is still not known how well insects can see. Their eyes cannot be moved or focused. Apparently insects are nearsighted and objects at some distance cannot be seen distinctly. Moving objects may be readily detected since a number of ommatidia would be successively stimulated. Insects can see color. Some have a perception of colors not visible to man, such as bands of ultraviolet rays. Certain insects are practically blind to red, while other insects can see this color.

THE MOUTHPARTS

Mouthparts of insects are of fundamental importance and deserve careful study. Insects feed on plants and animals in diverse ways, and their mouthparts have become modified for these purposes. This has resulted in the development of a number of types with much variation within each. Only representatives of the more important types of mouthparts can be considered here.

1. *Chewing type.* The chewing mouthparts, such as those of the grasshopper (Figure 30), consist of the *labrum* (upper lip), a pair of *mandibles* (primary jaws), a pair of *maxillae* (secondary

Figure 30. The chewing mouthparts of a grasshopper *(Melanoplus differentialis).* (From Department of Entomology, Texas A&M University.)

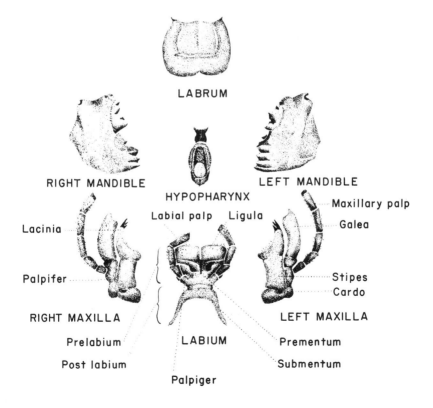

LABRUM

RIGHT MANDIBLE   LEFT MANDIBLE

HYPOPHARYNX

Labial palp   Ligula   Maxillary palp

Lacinia   Galea

Palpifer   Stipes
                                    Cardo

RIGHT MAXILLA   LEFT MAXILLA

Prelabium   LABIUM   Prementum

Post labium   Submentum

Palpiger

jaws), the *labium* (lower lip), the *epipharynx*, and the *hypopharynx* (tongue).

The *labrum* is a flaplike structure attached to the clypeus. The functions of the labrum are to close the front of the mouth cavity, protect the mandibles, and guide the food into the mouth. The *epipharynx* is not a well differentiated mouthpart in chewing insects; however, it is an important structure in other types. In the grasshopper's mouthparts it is identified as a swollen area on the ventral surface of the labrum.

The two *mandibles* are the parts that chew and grind the food. They may also be used in cutting, tearing, fighting, and, by the honeybee, in molding wax. The mandibles, together with the maxillae, move in a lateral manner and not as do the jaws of higher animals.

The paired *maxillae* are more complicated than the mandibles, and consist of several parts. The basal segment, known as the *cardo*, joins the maxilla to the head. This is joined to the central body of the maxilla, the *stipes*. On the outer side of the stipes is a more or less distinct sclerite known as the *palpifer* to which the palpus is attached. The *palpus* is an antennalike appendage usually consisting of several segments which bear tactile hairs and also probably organs of smell or taste. The *galea*, a variously shaped segment, and the *lacinia*, which bears teeth, are found attached to the distal end of the stipes. The toothlike parts of the lacinia may be employed in grasping, cutting, or chewing food.

The *labium*, or lower lip, closes the mouth cavity from below or behind. It has developed from two maxillalike structures which have fused along the median line. The lower lip is composed of the basal *postlabium* and the distal *prelabium*, separated by the line of flexibility. The prelabium is composed of a large central part (the *prementum*), lobed structures (the *ligula*), and a pair of *palpi*.

The *hypopharynx*, or tongue, arises from the floor of the mouth cavity, and it is usually attached to the inner wall of the labium. Its size and form is quite variable, and it is more or less covered with hairs. The *salivary glands* open through it. These glands are significant in the transmission of diseases by certain insects and also in the production of silk by the silkworm.

2. *Rasping-sucking type*. Rasping-sucking mouthparts are unique in that they are intermediate in their position between the chewing and the piercing-sucking types. Thrips (*Thysanoptera*) have this type of mouthpart, which is used to rasp the surfaces of plants and suck the exuded sap. The cone-shaped beak is composed of the clypeus, labrum, elements of the maxillae, and the labium. Within the beak are found the maxillae, hypopharynx, and the left mandible. The right mandible is not developed. The maxillae and the left mandible are styletlike in form. The food canal is between the labrum and the hypopharynx, and the saliva passes between the hypopharynx and the labium.

3. *Piercing-sucking type.* Piercing-sucking mouthparts are a very common and an extremely important type. The mouthparts have become greatly modified for puncturing the epidermis of plants or the skin of animals and sucking up the sap or the blood. The type is divided into several subtypes. Mouthparts of the stinkbug and the mosquito will be considered here.

MOUTHPARTS OF THE STINKBUG. If the mouthparts of the stinkbug are examined, a long four-jointed beak will be found lying between the legs when it is not in use (Figure 31). The main part of this beak is the labium. The labium has nothing to do with the actual sucking process; it acts only as a protective covering for the piercing-sucking organ lying within its folds. Its front surface is grooved throughout its entire length. Lying within this groove is a small, dark, needlelike structure which is responsible for the actual piercing and sucking. The labrum is an insignificant flaplike structure covering the groove of the labium at the base.

The needlelike structure is composed of four hairlike stylets fitted closely together. However, these stylets are not so firmly united that they cannot be separated. The outside pair of stylets are the mandibles, while the inner pair are the maxillae. Although quite small, the maxillae are doubly grooved on their inner faces; when these are brought together, they form two small tubes

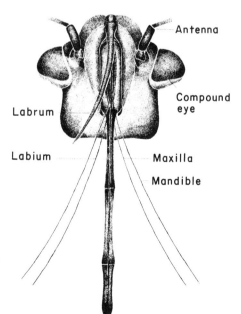

Figure 31. Head and piercing-sucking mouthparts of a stinkbug. (From Department of Entomology, Texas A&M University.)

extending their entire length (Figure 32). One tube is the food canal through which the liquid is taken. The second tube is the salivary canal through which saliva is pumped into the wound to facilitate the flow of food material.

MOUTHPARTS OF THE MOSQUITO. Mouthparts of the mosquito consist of the *proboscis*, which is composed of the elongate labium within which are ensheathed six stylets (Figure 33). The stylets are composed of the labrum-epipharynx, the hypopharynx, the two maxillae, and the two mandibles. The food canal is found in the labrum-epipharynx. Located below the labrum-epipharynx is the hypopharynx which is traversed its entire length by the small salivary canal. At the base of the labium are the segmented maxillary palpi.

4. *Sponging type.* Mouthparts of the housefly are an excellent example of this type (Figure 34). The fleshy proboscis, which consists chiefly of the labium, projects downward from the head. The labium is grooved on its anterior surface. Within this groove lie the labrum-epipharynx and the hypopharynx. The margins of the convex labrum-epipharynx and the concave hypopharynx form the food canal. Within the hypopharynx is the small salivary canal. Mandibles are absent. Maxillae have disappeared except for the palpi. At the end of the proboscis are two spongelike structures, the labella. The surfaces of the labella are traversed by capillary canals, *pseudotracheae*, which collect the liquid food and convey it to the food canal.

5. *Siphoning type.* This is the type of mouthparts found in moths and butterflies (Figure 35). The mandibles are absent, the labrum is greatly reduced, and only palpi and a small basal part of the labium remain. The maxillae are represented by rudimen-

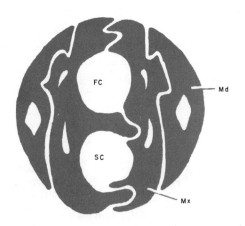

Figure 32. Diagram of a cross section of the mandibles and maxillae of the squash bug. Md, mandible; Mx, maxilla; FC, food canal; SC, salivary canal. (Modified D. G. Tower, Psyche, Vol. 21, 1914.)

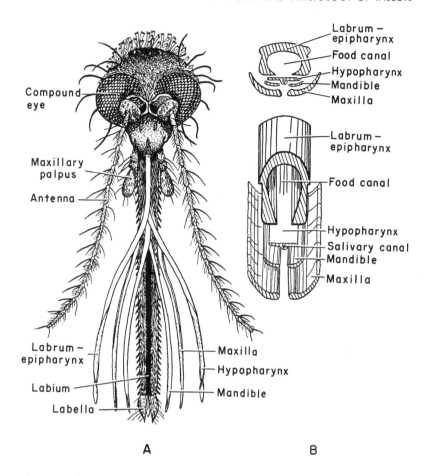

Figure 33. The piercing-sucking mouthparts of a female mosquito. A. Front view of the head with the stylets pulled out of the labium. B. Cross section of the mouthparts and an isometric view of their arrangement. (Redrawn from C. L. Metcalf, W. P. Flint, and R. L. Metcalf, *Destructive and Useful Insects.* Copyright 1951 by McGraw-Hill Book Co. Used with permission of McGraw-Hill Book Co.)

tary palpi and the modified galeae. The two galeae are greatly elongated and joined on their inner concave surfaces to form the long hollow proboscis. When the proboscis is not in use, it is coiled like a watch spring underneath the head. In feeding, the tip of the proboscis is dipped into the liquid and the food is drawn into the pharynx.

6. *Chewing-lapping type.* Chewing-lapping mouthparts are represented in the honeybee and bumblebee (Figure 36). The labrum and mandibles function as in the chewing type of mouthparts. The maxillae and labium are modified to form a proboscis.

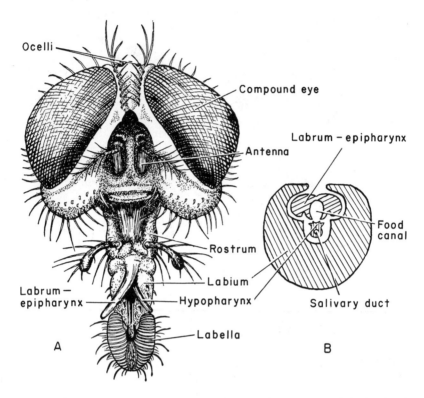

Figure 34. The sponging mouthparts of the housefly. A. Front view of the head and mouthparts with the proboscis pulled out. B. Diagrammatic cross section of the proboscis. (Redrawn from C. L. Metcalf, W. P. Flint, and R. L. Metcalf, *Destructive and Useful Insects.* Copyright 1951 by McGraw-Hill Book Co. Used with permission of McGraw-Hill Book Co.)

Figure 35. The siphoning mouthparts of a moth. A. Coiled proboscis; Ga, galea. B. Cross section of the proboscis; FC, food canal. (Redrawn from *Report on Cotton Insects,* 1879, USDA.)

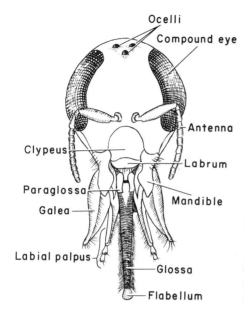

Figure 36. Chewing-lapping mouth-parts of the honeybee. (Redrawn and lightly modified from C. L. Metcalf, W. P. Flint, and R. L. Metcalf, *Destructive and Useful Insects*. Copyright 1951 by McGraw-Hill Book Co. Used with permission of McGraw-Hill Book Co.)

The glossa of the labium is greatly elongated and clothed with hairs. It forms a flexible tongue. A temporary food tube is formed by the galeae, labial palpi, and glossa fitting snugly together. Liquids are drawn up the tube by rapid movements of the glossa.

THE THORAX

Locomotion of insects is performed almost entirely by the thorax. Here are borne the legs and the wings (when present). The thorax is composed of three segments—the *prothorax, mesothorax,* and *metathorax.* Each segment bears a pair of legs. The first pair of wings arises from the mesothorax and the second pair is attached to the metathorax. The areas of the thorax are the *tergum* or *notum* (dorsal surface), the *pleura* (sides), and the *sternum* (ventral surface).

The thorax is quite specialized morphologically. In wingless orders the three segments are similar, but the mesothorax and the metathorax in wing-bearing orders have undergone marked modifications to accommodate functions of both legs and wings. The mesothorax and the metathorax are strongly united and form a compact body unit.

In the grasshopper the notum (tergal plate) of the prothorax resembles a sunbonnet and is known as the pronotum. It almost completely covers the prothorax and extends over part of the mesothorax.

Each pleuron of the mesothorax and the metathorax of the grasshopper is composed of two sclerites. The anterior sclerite is the *episternum* and the posterior plate is named the *epimeron*. The two sclerites are separated by a slanting suture. Two pairs of spiracles are borne by the thorax: the mesothoracic spiracle, located between the prothorax and the mesothorax, and the metathoracic spiracle, found above the second pair of legs. The sterna of the thoracic segments are composed of broad flat plates. The morphological features of the thorax are essentially the same in different groups of insects; however, marked modifications may have occurred.

THE LEGS

The legs of insects are variously modified according to the purposes for which they are used (Figure 37). In walking or running insects they are usually quite similar; otherwise many modifications may be found. Regardless of modifications, five divisions of

Figure 37. Legs of insects showing modifications for different uses. C, coxa; Tr, trochanter; F, femur; T, tibia; Ts, tarsus.

the leg are always present. These are, beginning with the division articulated with the body, the *coxa, trochanter, femur, tibia,* and *tarsus.*

The coxa frequently is found fitting in a cuplike depression of the body. It is generally freely movable. The trochanter is usually quite small, and the femur is the largest and most powerful division. The tibia is usually slender, quite long, and provided with downward projecting spines which aid in climbing and maintaining a footing. The tarsus usually consists of several segments and generally terminates in a pair of claws with one or more pads or cushions at their base or between them. A pad between the claws is usually known as an *arolium*, and pads at their base are designated as *pulvilli.*

THE WINGS

Insects are the only animals with wings, other than birds and bats. While adult insects have a definite number of legs, the number of wings varies from two pairs to none. Certain primitive groups represented by silverfish and springtails have no wings and bear no evidences of a winged ancestry. Other groups, such as lice and fleas, have lost their wings through the parasitic type of life they have followed. Flies and related insects have the second pair of wings modified into balancing organs known as *halteres*. Because the wings vary in shape, size, and texture, and are readily observed, the orders of insects are based on their characteristics.

A wing is an outgrowth of the body wall. It consists of two thin layers of the cuticula fused together except along certain lines where hollow riblike structures known as veins are formed. They serve to strengthen the wing and give it rigidity. The veins are named and are widely used in the classification and identification of insects. Research has shown that the venation of the wings of all winged insects is basically the same. Similarity in the wing venation is evident when the more generalized types are compared, and particularly when the wing pads of nymphs and pupae are examined. Veins have developed around the tracheae (air tubes) of the wing pads. The names of the veins of a hypothetical type of wing and abbreviations designating them are listed below, beginning with the vein nearest the anterior margin (Figure 38).

Name of Veins	Abbreviation
Costa	C
Subcosta	SC
Radius	R
Media	M
Cubitus	Cu
First Anal	1st A
Second Anal	2nd A
Third Anal	3rd A

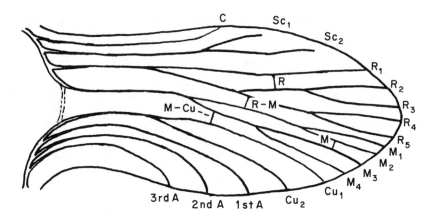

Figure 38. Venation in a hypothetical wing. (See p. 45 for key to lettering.) (Based on J. H. Comstock, *A Manual for the Study of Insects.* Copyright 1913 by Comstock Publishing Associates. Used with permission of Comstock Publishing Associates.)

Wings of insects seldom have the number of veins of the hypothetical type. Indications are that fusion rather than loss accounts for the greatest disappearance of veins.

THE ABDOMEN

The abdomen usually consists of a series of 10 or 11 ringlike segments which are quite similar, with the exception of those on the posterior end, which are modified. However, in many insects considerable reduction has occurred and only 5 or 6 segments are found. The female bears on the end of the abdomen an ovipositor which is adapted for egg deposition; cerci are present in the generalized groups. In the wasplike insects the ovipositor has been modified into a sting. External genitalia of the males may also be found on the extremity of the abdomen, along with the cerci of the more generalized orders. In the immature stages of insects, particularly caterpillars of Lepidoptera, prolegs are located on the abdomen. Nymphs of mayflies (Ephemeroptera) and larvae of some of the neuropteroid insects are other examples of immature insects with appendages on the abdomen.

Each abdominal segment usually is composed of a dorsal plate (tergum or notum) and a ventral plate (sternum). Along the lower margins of the dorsal plates of the abdomen are a series of paired openings known as *spiracles* which lead into the tracheae of the respiratory system. Six to eight pairs of spiracles are usually found on the abdomen.

INTERNAL ANATOMY AND PHYSIOLOGY

Although an insect may be very minute, its body organization and its ability to perform the essential functions of life are as perfect as those of man. Insects are unusual animals; their life processes and behavior differ decidedly from those of higher animals in a number of ways. A brief study of their internal anatomy and physiological processes affords some insight into the life of insects and the problems they present. Those students whose principal interest in the study of entomology is learning how to control insect pests may obtain from this study fundamental information which can be applied in solving practical problems.

THE DIGESTIVE SYSTEM

The alimentary canal is a tube extending throughout the body cavity from the mouth to the anus. It is divided into three parts— the foregut or *stomodaeum*, the midgut or *mesenteron* (*ventriculus*), and the hindgut or *proctodaeum*. A *cardiac valve* between the foregut and the midgut and a *pyloric valve* between the midgut and hindgut are usually present. The foregut and the hindgut are ectodermal in origin, arising from embryonic infoldings of the body wall. The midgut is derived from the endoderm. The system tends to be rather simple in some primitive forms and in larvae; because insect food consists of a great variety of materials, many modifications exist in most adults.

The foregut is usually divided into *mouth, pharynx, esophagus, crop,* and *proventriculus* (*gizzard*) (Figure 39). Its function is primarily storage, but it may grind and mix food. The mouth is located at the base of the space enclosed by the mouthparts. This is followed by a narrow *pharynx* and *esophagus.* It is difficult to differentiate between the two. Also, the esophagus and the crop,

Figure 39. Digestive system of a grasshopper (*Melanoplus differentialis*).

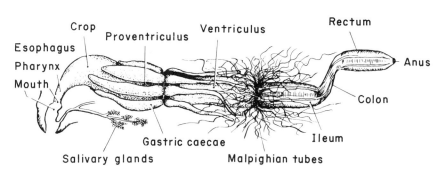

which is the main storage organ, can hardly be separated. The *proventriculus* is a gizzardlike structure, which in chewing insects may be lined with sclerotized ridges or teeth that grind and strain the food before it enters the *ventriculus* through the *cardiac valve.* The foregut does not produce any enzymes although some digestion of carbohydrates may occur from enzymes originating in the salivary glands or from enzymes regurgitated from the midgut. *Salivary glands* in their simplest form are blind-end tubes lying alongside the esophagus. They usually unite within the head to form a single duct, opening between the labium and the hypopharynx. In most insects they secrete saliva, but in Lepidoptera and Hymenoptera silk may be secreted. In blood-sucking insects an anticoagulin is also secreted.

Food material is generally not absorbed through the walls of the foregut, but apparently fats may be. Digestion is completed and most of the absorption of the food occurs in the midgut, which is a relatively large simple tube. Into its anterior region may open *gastric caeca*, blind-end tubes, in which there is much enzyme activity. Enzymes are abundantly present throughout the midgut. It is more alkaline in nature than the foregut. There is no cuticular lining of this section; however, in many insects, particularly when the food is solid material, there is a semipermeable structure known as the peritrophic membrane which envelopes the food and protects the delicate epithelial cells of the stomach walls. This membrane is not found in certain groups which subsist only on liquid foods.

The remaining contents of the ventriculus pass through the pyloric or proctodaeal valve into the hindgut, which is ordinarily divided into three parts—the *ileum, colon,* and *rectum.* All the functions of the hindgut are not completely understood. It is thought by some that absorption occurs in the ileum. The rectum collects and expels waste material. Water conservation is an important function of the rectum. Rectal pads are often present; in terrestrial insects these appear to remove water from the waste material and return it to the body. The rectum of dragonfly nymphs serves as a structure of respiration and locomotion. The walls are thin and supplied with tracheae. When water is drawn into the chamber and expelled forcibly, the recoil carries the insect forward.

All the digestive enzymes present in higher animals are generally found in insects, but not all may be found in any one species. Also, specialized enzymes may be found in some species which are not found in mammals. The types present are dependent upon the nature of the food of the particular insect. In insects which are general feeders, such enzymes as maltase, lipase, trypsin, and pepsin are produced. Enzymes of blood-sucking insects are mostly proteolytic. Some insects, such as termites and other cellulose feeders, require symbiotic microorganisms for digestion.

Insects have about the same nutritional requirements as other

animals. Amino acids are essential for protein synthesis. Carbohydrates are required for energy. Fats and oils are not considered
as absolute essentials. The only vitamins required are those of the
vitamin B complex and, for some insects that feed upon plants,
ascorbic acid.

THE EXCRETORY SYSTEM

The Malpighian tubes in insects are functionally equivalent to kid-
neys in vertebrates. They join the digestive tract where the mid-
and the hindguts unite. These are blind-end hollow tubes that
empty into the digestive tract. They generally lie free in the body
cavity. In some instances they are attached to the rectum by the
distal end. The number of tubes varies greatly in different groups
of insects. There may be as few as 2–6 or as many as 150 tubes.
If a large number are present, this is a result of branching of
the tubes.

Soluble waste products in the blood (hemolymph) are taken up
by the tubes. Generally the soluble nitrogenous products are converted into insoluble uric acid which is then discharged into the
hindgut. The excretion of this nitrogenous waste in an insoluble
form is a water conservation measure, the water being returned to
the blood. This water conservation mechanism is also found in
some other animals such as birds and reptiles. Mammals usually
excrete urea in solution. Those insects that live in a humid environment and do not need to conserve water also excrete this waste in
solution. Many aquatic insects and blowfly larvae excrete ammonia.
Also, certain wastes may be converted into pigments and deposited
in the body wall.

THE RESPIRATORY SYSTEM

Insects have a very efficient respiratory system. This is essential
for these small and usually very active animals with a high rate of
metabolism. Oxygen is carried directly to the tissues and cells by
tubes known as *tracheae* and *tracheoles,* and most of the carbon
dioxide is eliminated in the same way. Some of the carbon dioxide
is taken up by the hemolymph and escapes through the body wall.
The tracheal system may include large air sacs, particularly in flying insects. The tracheal tubes are derived from the ectoderm and
have an inner lining of a thin layer of cuticle which forms spiral
thickenings known as *taenidia.* These springlike spirals prevent
the collapse and provide elasticity to the tracheae. The tracheae
divide many times and terminate in tracheoles which ramify
throughout the body (Figure 40). They lack taenidia, are thin
walled, and may contain fluids. Through them oxygen is delivered
to the cells, and carbon dioxide is given off. Blood is not important
in respiration. However, in some larvae of the family Chironomidae hemoglobin is found in the blood.

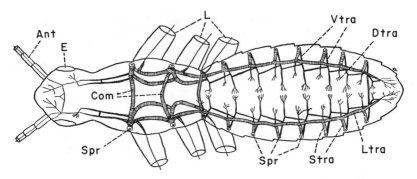

Figure 40. Diagram of a horizontal section of an insect showing the arrangement of the principal tracheae. Ant, antenna; com, commissural tracheae; dtr, dorsal trachea; e, compound eye; 1, legs; ltr, main longitudinal tracheal trunk; spr, spiracles; stra, spiracular tracheae; vtra, ventral trachea. (From D. J. Borror and D. M. DeLong, *An Introduction to the Study of Insects.* After H. J. Koble, *Einfuhrung in die Kentnis der Insekten*, Berlin, 1889. Used with permission of Holt, Rinehart and Winston and McGraw-Hill Book Co.)

Respiration is effected through a series of small paired openings known as spiracles which are located along the sides of the body. Basically two pairs of spiracles are found on the thorax and eight pairs on the abdomen. However, there is much variation in their number and exact location in different insects. Short transverse tracheae connect them to a large longitudinal trunk on each side, which in turn is connected to a lateral, a dorsal, and a visceral trunk. Commissural tracheae connect the system from each side in the dorsal and ventral regions.

Respiration is effected largely through diffusion with the help of body movements of some insects. Rhythmic movements of the abdomen, as in the grasshopper, may be observed. In Hymenoptera (bees) and Diptera (flies) the entire abdomen may slightly lengthen and shorten and in some insects there is a raising and lowering of the upper part of the abdomen. Observation of the spiracles shows that they do not open or close simultaneously. In the grasshopper air enters the thoracic and first two abdominal spiracles and escapes through the posterior abdominal spiracles. In flight all spiracles may remain open so that the maximum amount of oxygen may be obtained. The central nervous system controls the rhythmic opening and closing of the spiracles but individual spiracles may open when there is a local concentration of carbon dioxide.

Naturally a number of variations of the respiratory system are found. In small soft-bodied insects living under humid conditions and in water, and among some parasitic forms, spiracles may be actually lacking and respiration effected by diffusion through the body wall. Many aquatic insects have gills which are supplied with tracheae. There is considerable variation in their shape, size, and location. Some aquatic insects, such as mosquito larvae, breathe through a tube which is extended to the surface of the water. Other insects living in the water carry on their bodies a film of air which supplies more oxygen than is entrapped through diffusion of dissolved oxygen in the water.

In some mosquito larvae of the genus *Mansonia* the posterior end of the body is modified into a piercing organ which punctures air-filled cells of aquatic plants. Some internal parasites of other insects make connections with tracheae of their hosts.

THE CIRCULATORY SYSTEM

Insects have an open circulatory system; it is simple and very incomplete, consisting only of a dorsal tube (Figure 41). That part lying in the abdomen is chambered and is known as the *heart*; the anterior section which is not constricted is the *aorta*. The posterior end of the heart is closed, but a pair of openings (*ostia*), through which the blood may enter, is found on the lateral sides of each chamber. Valves prevent the blood or hemolymph from flowing out. Wavelike contractions force the blood forward through the *aorta*. The aorta may divide into several short branches in the head where the blood is released into the body cavity. The blood flows

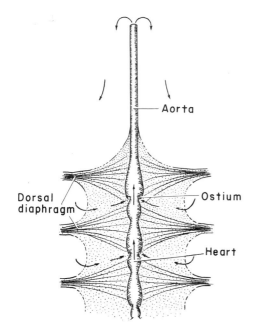

Aorta

Dorsal
diaphragm

Ostium

Heart

Figure 41. The dorsal blood vessel and the dorsal diaphragm. (Redrawn from R. E. Snodgrass, *Principles of Insect Morphology*. Copyright 1935 by McGraw-Hill Book Co. Used with permission of McGraw-Hill Book Co.)

rather freely throughout the body and will return again to the ostia. Dorsal and ventral diaphragms help direct and assist in the flow of the blood, but these may be indistinct or absent. Also, accessory pulsating organs may be present at the base of the appendages.

As the blood flows backward, bathing the tissues, food is picked up around the digestive tract and carried to the cells where it is needed. Hormones are also transported. Wastes, which are chiefly nitrogenous, are taken from the cells and are removed by the Malpighian tubes. Blood is not important in respiration. Hemoglobin is not known to be present in the plasma of insects, except in a few midge larvae. However, the blood may aid somewhat in the transportation and exchange of oxygen and carbon dioxide in the cells, inasmuch as both gases are soluble in it. The blood is usually light amber, but may be brown, yellow, or green, but seldom red.

A number of types of blood cells are present, and their functions are varied. They are important in destroying bacteria and disintegrating tissues; they may help to exclude parasites from the body cavity, plug wounds, and play a role in growth and metamorphosis.

THE NERVOUS SYSTEM

Insects have a central nervous system with a *brain* (*supraesophageal ganglion*) located in the head and a series of paired nerve centers lying in a median line along the ventral region of the body beneath the digestive tract. They are joined together by paired connectives or commissures (Figure 42). Embryological studies indicate a ganglion of a paired nature for each body segment, but in adult insects various degrees of coalescence exist. Both the brain and the subesophageal ganglion are composed of three fused ganglia each, and there may be three thoracic and as many as eight abdominal ganglia. However, there has been further fusion in many insects. As an example, in Hemiptera and in many Diptera one large thoracic ganglion not only innervates the thorax but the abdomen as well. Because the brain lies above the esophagus, it is quite frequently known as the supraesophageal ganglion. It is composed of the *protocerebrum* which supplies nerves to the compound eyes and ocelli, the *deutocerebrum* which controls the antennae, and the *tritocerebrum* which innervates the labrum and the *frontal ganglion*. The central part of the *sympathetic* or *stomodaeal* nervous system seems to be the *frontal ganglion*. Functions of all branches of the sympathetic nervous system are not fully understood. This system is concerned with supplying nerves to the digestive system, heart, reproductive system, and other structures. Most of its parts are located along the sides or on top of the stomodaeum. A median recurrent nerve connects with the frontal ganglion; it runs underneath the brain and along the dorsal sur-

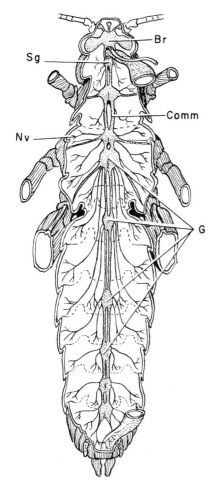

Figure 42. Central nervous system of a grasshopper (*Dissosteira carolina*). Br, brain (supraesophageal ganglion); Comm, commissure; G, ganglia; Nv, nerve; Sg, subesophageal ganglion. (Modified from R. E. Snodgrass, *Principles of Insect Morphology*. Copyright 1935 by McGraw-Hill Book Co. Used with permission of McGraw-Hill Book Co.)

face of the esophagus and here connects with a series of small ganglia and nerves.

A pair of large commissures joins the brain with the large nerve center, the *subesophageal ganglion,* beneath the esophagus. It is formed by a fusion of the mandibular, maxillary, and labial ganglia and it innervates the mouthparts and influences other motor activity. Thoracic ganglia innervate the legs and wings. The abdominal ganglia supply nerves to the abdominal muscles and appendages.

The basic unit in the nervous system of insects, as in other animals, is the *neuron,* which is composed of a cell body and a long filamentlike *axon.* The synapses are the junctions between the neurons. These are the integrating mechanisms of the transmission system. The impulse that travels through the axon is electrochemical in nature, and synaptic transmission appears to depend upon acetylcholine and the enzyme, cholinesterase. Interference of the nerve impulse transmission by organic phosphorus insecticides, which are anticholinesterases, leads to nervous disturbances and death.

THE MUSCULAR SYSTEM

Insects have a complicated muscular system. The muscles are distinctly cross striated and the fibers are strong. They may be grouped into skeletal muscles and visceral muscles. The skeletal muscles are arranged to produce movements of the mouthparts, antennae, legs, wings, and body segments. Most insects require five sets of muscles for the operation of the wings alone. Two types of muscles move the leg; one type moves the leg as a unit, and the other moves individual segments. A layer of visceral muscles covers the digestive tract and produces wavelike movements. Also, bands of this type of muscle surround the heart and produce pulsations. Movements of insects may be quite rapid, as represented by the vibration of wings in flight, or slow, as in the walking of *Phasmatidae* and certain beetles (e.g., *Zopherus* spp.), and the crawling of larvae.

THE REPRODUCTIVE SYSTEM

Normally insects are of two sexes. But among ants, bees, wasps, termites, and other groups, sexually undeveloped individuals may be found as workers. Both gynandromorphs and hermaphrodites are also known. Some insects (e.g., aphids) may reproduce for a number of generations without fertilization. This is known as parthenogenetic reproduction or parthenogenesis. Although this mode of reproduction is quite common among insects, it is not by any means the rule.

The reproductive system is located in the abdomen and most of the parts are bilaterally symmetrical (Figure 43). The paired *ovaries* lie in the upper front region of the abdomen. An ovary consists of a group of tubes known as *ovarioles*. The number of ovarioles varies from one in aphids to several hundred in some insects. Each ovariole, which is lined with epithelial cells, ends in an attachment thread or terminal filament. Within each tube may be found eggs in all stages of development, from the primordial germ cell to the mature egg. Growth of the egg is due mostly to yolk granules which are food reserves. The egg may be surrounded by nurse cells which aid in development and growth. By maturity a shell or *chorion* has been deposited by the epithelial cells. The sculptured pattern on the chorion is the imprint of these cells. On one end of the egg is an opening known as the *micropyle* through

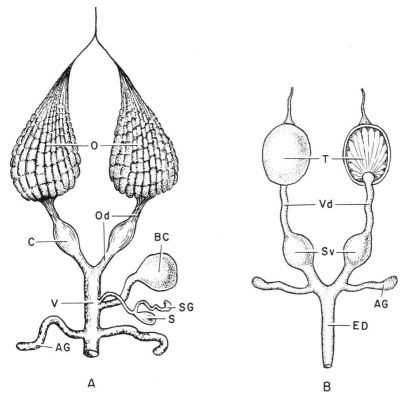

Figure 43. The reproductive organs of insects. A. female: AG, accessory gland; BC, bursa copulatrix; C, calyx; O, ovaries; Od, oviduct; S, spermatheca; SG, spermathecal gland; V, vagina. B. male: AG, accessory gland; ED, ejaculatory duct; Sv, seminal vesicles; T, testes; Vd, vasa deferentia. (Based on J. H. Comstock, *A Manual for the Study of Insects.* Copyright 1913 by Comstock Publishing Associates. Used with permission of Comstock Publishing Associates.)

which sperm enter and effect fertilization. The bottoms of the ovarioles form the *calyx*. From the calyx the egg passes into the lateral *oviduct*. The lateral oviducts unite, forming the common oviduct. The egg then passes into the *vagina* which opens into the egg-depositing structure, the *ovipositor*. There are two glands connected with the oviduct, the *spermathecal* gland, and the *accessory* or *colleterial glands*. The latter secrete material for covering the eggs or for sticking them to a support. When the egg passes the duct of the *spermatheca* it is fertilized. Queen honeybees can control fertilization of the eggs; the unfertilized eggs develop into males or drones and the fertile eggs produce workers or queens. Sperm can remain viable for long periods in the spermatheca.

A number of variations are to be found in the female reproductive system in the glands, ducts, and the number and shape of the ovarioles. Also, in a number of insects there is a special receptacle in which the spermatozoa is deposited. This chamber is known as the *bursa copulatrix* and is located to the side of the oviduct. In the higher Lepidoptera it is completely separated from the oviduct and is connected to it by a seminal duct.

The basic plan of the reproductive organs of the male is similar to that of the female. The *testes* are located in the body much as are the ovaries of the female. Each consists of tubelike follicles. Each follicle contains germ cells in all stages of development. The flagellate spermatozoa are found at the lower end of the follicle and the primordial germ cells at the distal end. Each testis opens into a seminal duct, the *vas deferens* (pl. *vasa deferentia*). The vasa deferentia are usually longer than the oviducts of the female and may be coiled or twisted. They pass downward and backward, and unite below the digestive tract to form the *ejaculatory duct*. *Seminal vesicles* for the storage of sperm may be found either in the vasa deferentia or in the ejaculatory duct. Also, various accessory glands associated with the ejaculatory duct may be present. The ejaculatory duct terminates within or on the penis or aedeagus.

There are also special external organs for mating and egg laying. The female bears an organ for use in egg deposition, the *ovipositor*. This structure is variously modified for specific purposes. In the stinging Hymenoptera it is associated with poison glands and modified into a sting. The external genitalia of the male consist of special clasping structures of some type, which are often quite complex in form.

HORMONES

Hormones are chemical substances produced by the insect endocrine system which control growth and development. The chief centers of the elaboration of these substances are associated with the central nervous system. In the head, neuroendocrine cells of the *pars intercerebralis* produce a hormone that is accumulated in the *corpora cardiaca,* from which it is released into the blood. It in turn stimulates the *prothoracic glands* to produce another hormone, *ecdysone*. Associated with the corpora cardiaca are the *corpora allata* which elaborate the *juvenile hormone*. The subesophageal ganglion also possesses neuroendocrine cells.

The functions of these hormones follow an orderly pattern controlled by the brain. Ecdysone, a growth and molting hormone, is also needed in the development of adult organs in the pupal period. The juvenile hormone, neotenin, counteracts the activity of ecdysone. It is responsible for the prevention of adult characteristics in immature stages, and is produced in smaller and smaller quantities as the insect approaches maturity. This change in the hormone balance allows the insect to complete its developmental cycle. Weismann's ring gland encircles the aorta behind the brain of circular-seamed Diptera. It elaborates a hormone that functions in the formation of the puparium. Within this organ are found tissues corresponding to those in the prothoracic gland, the corpus cardiacum, and the corpus allatum.

PHEROMONES

Pheromones, or ectohormones, are of considerable interest to research entomologists. These attractant substances are elaborated by external glands, and each has a specific effect on other members of the same species. The sex attractant substances which are pheromones may be secreted by one or both sexes and have been studied quite thoroughly. Glands in the last abdominal segment are the source of the sex attractant of unmated female moths. In many species of male butterflies the wings have special scales, *androconia,* which have basal glands that secrete a sex attractant. Other male Lepidoptera have glands on the legs. The bodies of certain species of cockroaches produce sex attractants. Both sexes of the yellow mealworm (*Tenebrio molitor*) secrete sex pheromones. Males of bagworms are attracted by pheromones to the wingless females within the bags.

Pheromones play an important role in the life of the honeybee. They provide marking scents which identify individuals and location. Pheromones secreted orally by the queen bee mark her presence; when licked by the workers they may retard ovary development and affect behavior of the workers. Species of beetles which live as guests in nests of termites and ants secrete substances that are attractive to the workers and cause the beetles to be accepted in the colonies.

CHAPTER 3
GROWTH AND METAMORPHOSIS OF INSECTS

Most insects undergo remarkable changes in form during the course of their development. The may beetle was once a grub; a butterfly develops from a caterpillar; and flies evolve from maggots. Knowledge of how insects grow and the changes (metamorphosis) they experience in attaining the adult stage is one of the basic essentials in the study of entomology, for this information enters into every phase of the science.

Insects develop from eggs which are formed from primordial germ cells in the ovaries of the females. Eggs are usually laid, and hatching occurs after a variable length of time. Those insects that lay eggs are termed *oviparous*. In some cases the eggs are retained in the body of the female until hatched. Such insects are *ovoviviparous*; that is, living young are deposited instead of eggs. Rarely, mature larvae are produced; this is known to occur in a few flies such as the sheep ked and the tsetse fly. They receive nourishment from the body of the female, a condition suggestive of *viviparous* reproduction of mammals.

The eggs of insects are small; although they may vary considerably in size, shape, color, and markings, they are more alike than the insects that laid them. They are covered with a shell, the chorion, which is formed by the follicular epithelium of the tubes of the ovaries. Fertilization occurs at the time the eggs are being laid. The stored spermatozoa enter the eggs through the micropyle, located on the proximal end. The duration of the egg stage may vary from a few hours to several months or longer. In some insects, namely, aphids, embryonic development occurs without fertilization of the eggs (parthenogenesis).

Although insect eggs are much alike, it is often possible to specifically identify them. This may be of much practical value in predicting outbreaks of certain pests, such as grasshoppers and the bollworm. In attempting to identify an insect in the egg stage, several things should be noted—shape, size, color and sculpturation, host, places of deposition, and whether or not they are laid singly or in clusters.

Insects usually multiply rapidly. The rate of increase is governed by the number of eggs laid, the length of a life cycle, and the rapidity with which generations follow each other.

The number of eggs an insect lays is as variable as insect life itself. The true female of certain aphids may lay one overwintering egg. The moth of the corn earworm may produce as many as 3000 eggs; the cotton leafworm moth averages about 600 eggs, while the queen of the honeybee may lay 1500–2000 daily for several weeks without cessation. The average number of eggs laid by all insects would probably be 100–200. All the eggs may be laid at one time; they may be deposited in batches, which are produced at varying intervals; or they may be laid in small numbers daily over a considerable period of time.

Eggs are generally laid where the newly hatched young have ready access to suitable food. After the eggs are deposited, the female usually pays no further attention to them and the young insects, upon hatching, must care for themselves.

Upon hatching from the egg, the young insect is usually quite unlike the adult into which it develops. The changes which occur during growth or development to the adult stage are termed *metamorphosis*. The young insect is quite small when it emerges from the egg. It feeds ravenously, but the extent of its growth is restricted by a rather rigid exoskeleton which encases the body. In order to continue to grow and develop, the insect must periodically replace the exoskeleton with one of larger size. This is accomplished by a process of shedding the outer skin, called *molting*. Prior to the time of each molt feeding ceases, and a molting fluid collects between the old and the newly formed cuticula. A slit in the old cuticula then appears, usually along the middorsal line of the head and thorax, through which the insect works its way out. The insect now has a soft elastic cuticula which is capable of further expansion to accommodate the increased size of the body. This new cuticula hardens after several hours, and the growth of the insect is again definitely restricted. Thus the insect develops by a series of growing stages, called *instars*, and *molts*. The number of molts is variable but quite constant for any one species. Insects ordinarily molt five or six times.

METAMORPHOSIS

All insects do not develop into the adult stage by the same series of changes or type of metamorphosis. Metamorphosis is grouped into four types, namely:

1. *No metamorphosis (ametabolous development)*. Stages of development: (a) egg, (b) young, (c) adult. Example, silverfish.
2. *Gradual metamorphosis (paurometabolous development)*. Stages of development: (a) egg, (b) nymph, (c) adult. Example, stinkbug.

3. *Incomplete metamorphosis (hemimetabolous development).* Stages of development: (a) egg, (b) nymph, (c) adult. Example, mayfly.
4. *Complete metamorphosis (holometabolous development).* Stages of development: (a) egg, (b) larva, (c) pupa, (d) adult. Example, housefly.

NO METAMORPHOSIS (AMETABOLOUS DEVELOPMENT)

When it hatches from the egg, the young insect with ametabolous development looks exactly like the adult except for size and differences in armature of spines and setae. The insect in each instar appears as in the preceding instar except for size and some minor differences (Figure 44). Some forms may molt after sexual maturity. In this respect they resemble the Crustacea. The young and adults live in the same environment, have the same types of mouthparts and feeding habits. This type of development is represented by the Thysanura (silverfish) and the Collembola (springtails). These groups of primitive insects are wingless, and there is no evidence to indicate that their ancestors possessed wings.

GRADUAL METAMORPHOSIS (PAUROMETABOLOUS DEVELOPMENT)

In those groups of insects with gradual metamorphosis, the newly hatched individual resembles the adult in general body form, but lacks wings and the external genital appendages (Figure 45). The young insect (called a nymph) undergoes a series of feeding stages (instars), which in each case is followed by a molt. With each successive molt the nymph resembles the adult more than it did in the preceding stage. Thus, step by step the adult stage is reached. The wing buds appear in the latter instars and are externally developed. Both nymphs and adults have the same type of mouthparts and food habits, and occur in the same habitat. Grasshoppers,

Figure 44. No metamorphosis (ametabolous development). A. Egg. B, C, D, E. Stages of young. F. Adult. Example: silverfish.

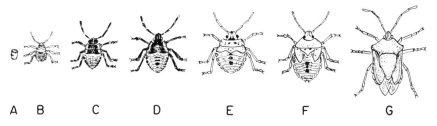

Figure 45. Gradual metamorphosis (paurometabolous development). A. Egg. B, C, D, E, F. Nymphal stages. G. Adult. Example: stinkbug.

squash bugs, and aphids are examples of insects with gradual metamorphosis.

INCOMPLETE METAMORPHOSIS (HEMIMETABOLOUS DEVELOPMENT)

Three orders of insects are characterized by hemimetabolous development—*Ephemeroptera* (mayflies), *Odonata* (dragonflies), and *Plecoptera* (stoneflies). The changes that occur during the immature stages (called *nymphs* or *naiads*) of these insects are more pronounced than in the case of insects with gradual metamorphosis, but are not nearly so great as the changes that occur in those forms which undergo complete metamorphosis (Figure 46). The immature stages of these insects are spent in water, while the adults are aerial. The nymphs breathe by means of tracheal gills, and their bodies are variously modified for the type of environment in which they live. The immature forms only slightly resemble the adults into which they develop. They also grow by a series of instars (growing stages) and molts. After the last molt the insects have fully developed wings fitted for an aerial life and a tracheal system for breathing oxygen from the air, together with other modifications of body structure.

COMPLETE METAMORPHOSIS (HOLOMETABOLOUS DEVELOPMENT)

Most species of insects undergo a complete metamorphosis, which includes four developmental stages; namely, *egg, larva, pupa,* and *adult* (Figure 47). The larva differs greatly in form from the adult into which it develops. It passes through a series of growing stages (instars) and molts, but, unlike insects with gradual metamorphosis, the larva does not resemble the adult any more closely following a molt than it did prior to it, but remains wormlike or grub-like in form. The larval stage is primarily a growing stage. All larvae have chewing or modified chewing mouthparts. Various names are applied to the larvae of insects of different orders. Beetle larvae are known as grubs, butterfly and moth larvae as caterpillars, and the larvae of flies are known as maggots. The wing pads, and in those groups which have footless larvae, the legs, develop internally and are everted at the time of pupation. Other changes in development also take place toward the close of the larval stage.

When the larva has attained maturity it ceases to feed, and following a period of inactivity transforms to the pupa. In this stage the insect usually remains inactive and does not feed, but undergoes marked physiological and morphological changes. It is in this stage that the processes of changing a wormlike body into that of a moth, fly, bee, or beetle are completed.

In the case of many insects, provisions are made by the larva for the protection of the helpless pupa. Some seek protection in the ground, others under the bark of trees; some spin cocoons (e.g., moths) or pupate in the last larval skin (e.g., flies).

Following the lapse of several days or months, the adult emerges from the pupal stage. Special provisions are always made by nature to enable the adult to escape from the pupa. The primary function of the adult insect is reproduction. In many insect groups the adults die soon after laying the eggs. Other insects live for a longer period, and some, such as ants and certain beetles, live for a long time.

The active stages of insects with gradual metamorphosis or none have identical mouthparts and feeding habits. In incomplete metamorphosis both the nymphs and adults have chewing mouthparts (vestigial in adult mayflies), but food habits and habitats are different. Those insects with complete metamorphosis may have entirely different types of mouthparts and food habits in the larval and the adult stages, or again, they may be similar. Larvae (caterpillars) of moths have chewing mouthparts and feed on a variety of materials, while the adults have siphoning mouthparts and normally feed on nectar of plants. Boll weevil larvae and adults both

Figure 46. Incomplete metamorphosis (hemimetabolous development). A. Egg. B, C, D. Nymphal stages. E. Adult. Example: mayfly.

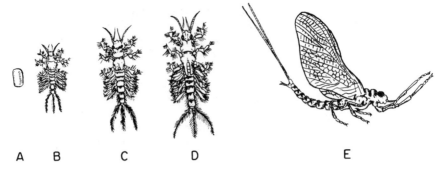

A   B   C   D   E

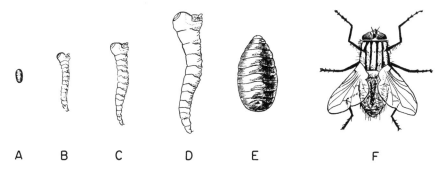

Figure 47. Complete metamorphosis (holometabolous development). A. Egg. B, C, D. Larval stages. E. Pupa. F. Adult. Example: housefly.

have chewing mouthparts and feed upon the fruit of the cotton plant. Flea larvae feed on inert organic material with their chewing mouthparts while the adults suck the blood of their hosts.

DIFFERENT LARVAL TYPES

Larvae of different insects with complete metamorphosis vary considerably in form (Figure 48). Many types of larvae exist, and some occur so commonly that names have been given them. Several of the most important types merit mention here.

SCARABAEIFORM

The scarabaeiform type of larvae is grublike. The white grubs of may beetles are the most common examples. They are almost cylindrical, curved, and bear short thoracic legs, but have no abdominal prolegs. Most of them are found in the ground, wood, or decaying organic matter. These larvae are sluggish and movement is slow.

CAMPODEIFORM

These larvae resemble certain members of the Thysanura. The body is elongate and flattened to some degree. Antennae and cerci are usually quite conspicuous and the legs are developed for running. Common examples are found among the Coleoptera and Neuroptera.

ERUCIFORM

Most larvae (caterpillars) of Lepidoptera are the eruciform type. The body is cylindrical; short thoracic legs are present, and the abdomen is provided with prolegs.

VERMIFORM

Larvae of this type are maggotlike. The body is elongate and legs are absent. Representatives are found in the Diptera, Hymenoptera, Coleoptera, and other orders.

DIFFERENT PUPAL TYPES

Three types of pupae are readily recognized. They are the *coarctate*, *exarate*, and *obtect* types (Figure 49).

COARCTATE

Coarctate pupae remain in the hardened larval skin (puparium), as do the pupae of most dipterous insects.

EXARATE

Pupae of this type have the legs, wing pads, and antennae free. Most pupae of insects with complete metamorphosis, Diptera and Lepidoptera excepted, are exarate pupae.

Figure 48. Common types of larvae. A. Campodeiform larva of a lacewing fly (Neuroptera, Chrysopidae). B. Scarabaeiform larva of a May beetle (Coleoptera, Scarabaeidae). C. Vermiform larva of a housefly (Diptera, Muscidae). D. Eruciform larva of a moth (Lepidoptera, Phalaenidae).

A   B   C   D

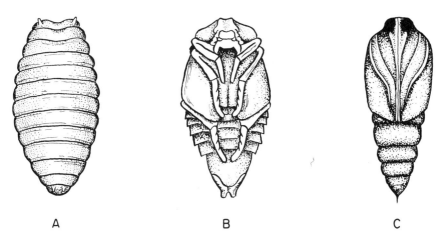

Figure 49. Principal types of pupae. A. Coarctate type, such as pupae of flies. B. Exarate type, such as pupae of beetles. C. Obtect type, such as pupae of moths.

OBTECT

These pupae have the legs, antennae, and wing pads glued to the body, such as pupae of Lepidoptera.

CHAPTER 4
THE CLASSIFICATION
OF INSECTS

In the preceding chapters a brief account has been given of the systematic position, morphology, physiology, and types of development of insects together with general methods of control of harmful species. With this information as a background, it is now essential to consider the classification and biologies of insects. In science, as in all other progressive enterprises, some logical system of grouping or classifying according to the types, quality, or the needs of the materials concerned is necessary. A natural system of classification is followed in the science of biology, of which entomology is a part. It is believed that in the world of living things all animals and plants had a common origin—that they have evolved into the present-day forms and complexities of development through the processes of evolution. The chief factors of evolution are variations, mutations, natural selection, and heredity.

Since the days of Aristotle many able biologists have devoted much time to the study and classification of plants and animals. The greatest of these early biologists was Carolus Linnaeus, a Swedish naturalist. He proposed the present-day system of classification based upon the natural relationships among living organisms. The names used to designate the different forms were Latin, a dead language. This was a fortunate procedure as the language is not subject to change and is the basis of a number of our present-day languages. At present these Latin names are in general use, so that either animal or plant forms may be recognized by name designation throughout the scientific world. Common names of insects usually are not known except locally. Although Latin names are of little value to the layman, they are indispensable to the scientific worker who must identify species, conduct research, and compile and disseminate information pertaining to them.

Several times more species of insects exist than all other animal forms combined. Upwards of a million species are believed to exist. The number is so great that insects must be studied largely as groups because no one has the time or the mental capacity to learn all of them. Except for common species, he must content himself with recognizing the order, family, and perhaps the genus to which an insect belongs. If a worker is sufficiently conversant with the characteristics and general biologies of these groups, oftentimes he has most of the essential information needed regarding an insect.

As mentioned earlier, insects constitute the largest class of the phylum *Arthropoda*, the *Insecta*. When Linnaeus classified the insects he established the orders of insects on the basis of wing characteristics and named them accordingly. For example, all two-winged insects (flies) were named *Diptera*,[1] and those insects wih the first pair of wings consisting of hornlike, veinless wing covers, beetles, were designated as *Coleoptera*.[2] This proved to be a very desirable system of classification as it facilitated the identification of an insect to the order, and made the names easier to learn. This system of naming the orders has been continued as far as possible to the present time.

Linnaeus assigned the insects to only seven orders which he named *Aptera* (wingless arthropods), *Hemiptera* (true bugs), *Neuroptera* (net-veined insects), *Coleoptera* (beetles), *Lepidoptera* (scale-winged insects), *Diptera* (flies), and *Hymenoptera* (bees, wasps, and others). Inasmuch as little was known concerning the biologies and the morphology of the arthropods at that early day, dissimilar groups naturally were placed in the same order. As an example, the Linnaean order, Aptera, contained not only all wingless insects, but crustaceans, arachnids, millipedes, and centipedes as well. The crustaceans, arachnids, millipedes, and centipedes certainly belong to different classes on the basis of anatomical characteristics. Such a great diversity of morphology, method of development, and habits exists among the wingless insects that it was necessary to divide this group into several orders. Thus reclassification necessarily has occurred, and a number of new orders have been established. Twenty-five orders are recognized for the purposes of this text. Some of these orders are of only slight importance and will be treated very briefly.

The class Hexapoda may be naturally divided into two subclasses, the *Apterygota* (those insects without wings) and *Pterygota* (those insects with wings). The subclass Apterygota is made up of those insects, such as silverfish and springtails, which are primitively wingless; that is, there is no evidence that their ancestors ever had wings. Conversely, the members of the Pterygota bear wings, or in case of the absence of wings, as with bedbugs or animal lice, there is evidence that they descended from winged ancestors. The wingless condition of these groups is the result of a parasitic way of life.

The subclasses and orders of insects as considered here are as follows.

[1] *Dis*, two; *pteron*, wing.
[2] *Coleos*, sheath; *pteron*, wing.

1. Subclass Apterygota. Primitive wingless insects; there is no indication that they developed from winged ancestors.
   Order Thysanura—the silverfish
   Order Collembola—the springtails
2. Subclass Pterygota. Winged and wingless insects; if wingless the condition is an acquired one.
   Order Ephemeroptera—the mayflies
   Order Odonata—the dragonflies and the damselflies
   Order Plecoptera—the stoneflies
   Order Orthoptera—the cockroaches, grasshoppers, katydids, and others
   Order Isoptera—the termites
   Order Dermaptera—the earwigs
   Order Embioptera—the embiids
   Order Zoraptera—the zorapterons
   Order Psocoptera—the psocids
   Order Thysanoptera—the thrips
   Order Mallophaga—the chewing lice
   Order Anoplura—the sucking lice
   Order Hemiptera—the true bugs
   Order Homoptera—the aphids, scales, and others
   Order Coleoptera—the beetles
   Order Strepsiptera—the stylopids
   Order Neuroptera—the corydalis, aphis lion, and others
   Order Mecoptera—the scorpionflies
   Order Trichoptera—the caddisflies
   Order Lepidoptera—the moths and butterflies
   Order Diptera—the flies
   Order Siphonaptera—the fleas
   Order Hymenoptera—the wasps, bees, and others

KEY[3] TO ORDERS OF COMMON INSECTS (ADULTS)

1. Functional wings present	2.
Wings absent or vestigial	27.
2. With 1 pair of wings	3.
With 2 pairs of wings	5.
3. Wings net-veined; halteres absent; mouthparts vestigial (certain mayflies)	**Ephemeroptera,** *p. 77*
Wings with veins but not net-veined; halteres present; sucking or vestigial mouthparts	4.
4. Wings with reduced venation; caudal filaments present; minute, delicate insects (males of Coccidae)	**Homoptera,** *p. 146*
Wings with longitudinal and a few cross veins; caudal filaments absent (flies)	**Diptera,** *p. 318*

[3] A key is a device made to aid in the identification of insects. It is made up of distinquishing characteristics involving wings, legs, mouthparts, shape, size, color, and other markings. The key is in couplet form; there is a choice between two contrasting characteristics. In use of the key begin with couplet 1. Upon examination of the specimen, decide into which category it fits and proceed from there. For example, if wings are present proceed to couplet 2. With two pairs of wings one is directed to couplet 5. Decisions are made between contrasting characteristics until one is encountered which provides the name of the order.

5. Front and hind wings unlike in texture — 6.
Front and hind wings similar in texture, membranous — 12.

6. Front wings reduced to slender clubs; hind wings large, triangular in form, folding fanlike; very small parasitic insects stylopids or twisted-wing parasites) — **Strepsiptera,** *p. 230*
Both front and hind wings normally developed — 7.

7. Front wings thickened at base, membranous and usually overlapping apically; piercing-sucking mouthparts (true bugs) — **Hemiptera,** *p. 122*
Front wings of same texture throughout — 8.

8. Front wings horny, veinless sheaths (elytra) — 9.
Front wings parchmentlike or leathery — 10.

9. Front wings usually covering abdomen; abdomen without movable forcepslike caudal appendages (beetles) — **Coleoptera,** *p. 174*
Front wings short, not covering end of abdomen; abdomen with movable forcepslike caudal appendages (earwigs) — **Dermaptera,** *p. 105*

10. Hind wings folded fanlike; chewing mouthparts (cockroaches, grasshoppers, and others) — **Orthoptera,** *p. 86*
Hind wings not folded fanlike; piercing-sucking mouthparts — 11.

11. Beak arises from anterior ventral portion of head (certain true bugs) — **Hemiptera,** *p. 122*
Beak arises from posterior ventral portion of head (cicadas, leafhoppers, and others) — **Homoptera,** *p. 146*

12. Wings with many longitudinal veins and cross veins; netveined, at least basally — 13.
Wings with branching veins and with relatively few cross veins — 19.

13. Front and hind wings approximately equal in size — 14.
Front and hind wings unequal in size — 17.

14. Head prolonged into a trunklike beak (scorpionflies) — **Mecoptera,** *p. 237*
Head not prolonged into a trunklike beak; mouthparts in normal position — 15.

15. Each wing with a jointlike structure, the nodus, near the middle of each front margin; tarsus with 3 segments (dragonflies) — **Odonata,** *p. 80*
Nodus absent on middle front margin of wings; tarsus with 4 or 5 segments — 16.

16. Front and hind wings long, narrow, and similar with venation weakly developed except in costal and anal areas; wings held flat over body; tarsus with 4 segments; colonial insects (termites) — **Isoptera,** *p. 100*
Wings large, leaflike, strongly veined, held rooflike over the body; 5-segmented tarsus (aphis lions, dobsonflies, and others) — **Neuroptera,** *p. 234*

17. Front wings larger than hind wings; 2 or 3 long, many-segmented filamentous caudal appendages on abdomen (mayflies) — **Ephemeroptera,** *p. 77*
Hind wings larger than front pair and folded in plaits when not in use — 18.

18. Front and hind wings of same texture; body depressed and elongate, sides subparallel; nymphs develop in water (stoneflies) — **Plecoptera,** *p. 83*

Front wings parchmentlike and somewhat thicker than hind pair; body variable in form but when depressed sides not subparallel; terrestrial insects (grasshoppers, cockroaches, and others) **Orthoptera,** *p. 86*

19. Wings fringed with long hairs or covered with long hairs or scales   20.
    Wings without long hairs or scales   23.

20. Wings usually completely covered with scales; mouthparts adapted for sucking (moths and butterflies) **Lepidoptera,** *p. 242*
    Wings fringed with long hairs or covered with long hairs   21.

21. Base of abdomen constricted and joined to the thorax by a narrow segment (certain minute parasitic wasplike insects) **Hymenoptera** (in part), *p. 369*
    Base of abdomen not constricted; broadly joined to the thorax   22.

22. Wings and body usually clothed with long hairs, wings held rooflike over the body; mouthparts vestigial; tarsus with 5 segments and with claws (caddisflies) **Trichoptera,** *p. 240*
    Wings long, narrow with 1 or 2 veins or none, and fringed with long hairs; tarsus with 2 segments without claws and terminates in a retractile bladderlike structure; minute insects (thrips) **Thysanoptera,** *p. 110*

23. Piercing-sucking mouthparts enclosed in a sheathlike beak, which arises from posterior ventral portion of head (cicadas, aphids, and others) **Homoptera,** *p. 146*
    Mouthparts adapted for chewing, or chewing and lapping, arising from normal position   24.

24. Tarsus with 4 or 5 segments; front pair of wings larger than the hind pair (bees, ants, and others) **Hymenoptera,** *p. 369*
    Tarsus with 2 or 3 segments   25.

25. Cerci absent; wings held rooflike over body; veins prominent but somewhat reduced (psocids) **Psocoptera,** *p. 108*
    Cerci present; small frail insects, body less than 3 mm in length   26.

26. Wings subequal in size; tarsus with 3 segments (embiids) **Embioptera,** *p. 106*
    Hind wings smaller than front wings; tarsus with 2 segments (zorapterons) **Zoraptera,** *p. 107*

27. Abdomen with one or more anteriorly located ventral appendages; mouthparts usually retracted with only the tips visible   28.
    Abdomen with anteriorly located ventral appendages absent; the only abdominal appendages consisting of posteriorly located cerci and genitalia   29.

28. Abdomen with no more than 6 segments; collophore or ventral tube usually present on ventral surface of first abdominal segment; springlike structure usually present on ventral surface of fourth abdominal segment; cerci absent (springtails) **Collembola,** *p. 75*
    Abdomen with 10 or 11 segments terminating in a pair of many-segmented cerci or unsegmented forcepslike appendages; styli situated on ventral side of abdomen (silverfish, bristletails) **Thysanura,** *p. 72*

29. Sedentary, scalelike, attached to host; usually covered with waxy secretions (scale insects) — **Homoptera,** *p. 146*
    Not sedentary, not scalelike; capable of locomotion — 30.
30. Mouthparts modified for chewing — 31.
    Mouthparts modified for sucking — 40.
31. Head terminating in broad deflexed beak (scorpionflies) — **Mecoptera,** *p. 237*
    Head not terminating in a deflexed beak — 32.
32. Base of abdomen constricted and joined to thorax by a narrow stalk (ants, gall wasps, and velvet ants) — **Hymenoptera,** *p. 369*
    Base of abdomen not constricted; broadly joined to thorax — 33.
33. Abdomen with movable forcepslike caudal appendages (earwigs) — **Dermaptera,** *p. 105*
    Abdomen without movable forcepslike caudal appendages — 34.
34. Hind legs enlarged for leaping or jumping (wingless katydids and crickets) — **Orthoptera,** *p. 86*
    Hind legs not so modified — 35.
35. Small, louselike in form; usually flattened and leathery — 36.
    Size variable but not louselike; usually not flattened — 37.
36. Antenna with 5 or fewer segments; parasitic on birds and mammals (chewing lice) — **Mallophaga,** *p. 115*
    Antenna with 9 or more segments; not parasitic (book lice) — **Psocoptera,** *p. 108*
37. Tarsus with 2 segments (zorapterons) — **Zoraptera,** *p. 107*
    Tarsus with 3–5 segments — 38.
38. First segment of front tarsus greatly enlarged; tarsus with 3 segments (embiids) — **Embioptera,** *p. 106*
    First segment of front tarsus normal; tarsus with 3–5 segments — 39.
39. Small, softbodied, stocky; live in colonies usually in soil or wood (termites) — **Isoptera,** *p. 100*
    Exoskeleton heavily sclerotized, body elongate or oval; large insects not in colonies (cockroaches, walking sticks) — **Orthoptera,** *p. 86*
40. Body compressed laterally; legs long and stout, modified for jumping (fleas) — **Siphonaptera,** *p. 363*
    Body not compressed laterally; legs not modified for jumping — 41.
41. Tarsus without claws, terminating in a retractile bladderlike structure; very small insects (thrips) — **Thysanoptera,** *p. 110*
    Tarsus with well developed claws — 42.
42. Antenna concealed in a pit, not visible from dorsal view (Pupipara) — **Diptera,** *p. 318*
    Antenna exserted dorsally, visible — 43.
43. Mouthparts retractile; tarsus with 1 claw (sucking lice) — **Anoplura,** *p. 117*
    Mouthparts form a beak; tarsus with 2 claws — 44.
44. Beak arises from anterior ventral portion of head (bed bugs) — **Hemiptera,** *p. 122*
    Beak arises from posterior ventral portion of head (aphids and others) — **Homoptera,** *p. 146*

An order of insects is based on three primary characteristics:

1. Wings present or absent; if present, the type and structure.
2. Type of metamorphosis.
3. Type of mouthparts.

In addition, one or more minor characteristics are given which aid in readily identifying the insect to the order. As an example, the order Coleoptera is characterized by the horny, veinless wing covers that usually meet in a straight line down the back when the insect is at rest. Coupled with this major characteristic in the beetles is a stout body. This combination of characters readily places the insect in the order Coleoptera.

Most insects may be identified to an order on sight. When the order to which an insect belongs is recognized, the type of mouthparts and the type of metamorphosis are known. This knowledge is of basic value because it provides information regarding the type of feeding and the stages of the insect that may be involved. A knowledge of the general biology of the order supplies still further information. If the family of the insect is known, some information concerning such points as life history, feeding habits, hosts, and reproduction may be available. For example, consider the boll weevil. A brief observation identifies the insect as belonging to the order Coleoptera. The mouthparts throughout this order are of the chewing type regardless of the presence of the snout. The metamorphosis is complete. The stages of development are then known to be egg, larva, pupa, and adult—larva and adult being the active stages. The larva is known to have the same type of mouthparts and generally feeds upon the same hosts as the adult. The boll weevil belongs to the family *Curculionidae*. All family names of animals end in *-idae;* thus, the family names may be readily recognized anywhere. Members of the Curculionidae are provided with snouts for use in feeding primarily within the tissues of the host plants. Hence, they are as a group specialized in their feeding habits. This immediately suggests that it may be difficult to poison the insect by the application of insecticides. The Curculionidae not only have specialized feeding habits but are usually specialized with respect to food plants as well. For all practical purposes the boll weevil may be considered as restricted to cotton as its source of food. The plum curculio feeds upon peaches, plums, apples, and related hosts and never feeds upon cotton. The acorn weevil breeds in acorns and the hickory weevil attacks hickory nuts and pecans.

The green stinkbug may be taken as another example. The presence of four wings, with the front pair thickened at the base, with the apical portions membranous and overlapping while the insect is at rest, and the large triangular scutellum on the broad flat back identify the insect as belonging to the order *Hemiptera.* When the order is recognized, the mouthparts are known to be of the piercing-sucking type and the nature of feeding indicated. The

stages of development are known to be egg, nymph, and adult—
the nymph having the same type of mouthparts and feeding habits
as the adult. This insect belongs to the family *Pentatomidae*. If the
biology of the family is adequately known, one may surmise the
number of generations produced annually; perhaps also the overwintering stage and other pertinent information.

A knowledge of the orders of insects and the characteristics of
each provides more information than any other basic fact of the
science of entomology. Knowledge of the families is also of great
value. However, there are so many different families of insects that
one can become acquainted with comparatively few in a general
course of entomology.

A family is subdivided into genera and species. The scientific
name of an animal or a plant consists of the name of both the
genus and species. This practice of naming insects is known as the
binominal system of nomenclature. The scientific name of the boll
weevil is *Anthonomus grandis* Boh. Here the first word of the
combination is the genus name, which should always begin with a
capital letter; the second word is the species name and the first
letter is never capitalized. The abbreviation "*Boh.*" (for Boheman)
is the name of the describer of the species and, excepting technical
discussions, this name is usually omitted. Scientific names are
either italicized or underscored.

CHAPTER 5
SUBCLASS APTERYGOTA

ORDERS THYSANURA AND COLLEMBOLA

The Apterygota are primitively wingless insects, and there is no morphological or biological evidence to indicate that they descended from a winged ancestry. Another primitive feature of this subclass is the presence of rudiments of abdominal appendages, particularly the styli in the Thysanura (bristletails). The members of this order are therefore of special interest as they furnish some evidence to the ancestry of insects (Figure 50).

Apterygota are generally small insects, some being only ½ mm long; however, some of the larger forms are known to approach 50 mm in overall length. The insects in this group develop with only slight morphological changes, and they are considered as having no metamorphosis (ametabolous development). The mouthparts are formed for chewing. In some forms the mouthparts are almost concealed by the overlapping folds of the cheeks. About 2500 species of Apterygota are known to science.

ORDER THYSANURA [1]
BRISTLETAILS, SILVERFISH, FIREBRATS

The chief characteristics of the members of this order are:

1. Primitively wingless or without evidence of a winged ancestry.
2. Mouthparts formed for chewing.
3. Development without metamorphosis, the adult stage attained by the young with little change in body form except size.
4. Abdomen composed of 10 or 11 segments, terminating in a pair of many-segmented cerci or unsegmented, forcepslike appendages.
5. Styli situated on the ventral side of the abdomen.

Insects of this order are commonly referred to as bristletails because of the presence in most species of either two or three long

[1] *Thysanos*, tassel; *oura*, tail.

Figure 50. The silverfish (*Lepisma saccharina*). (From USDA.)

filamentous appendages at the tip of the abdomen. The paired appendages are called cerci. When a third, median, appendage is present, it is a prolongation of the eleventh abdominal segment. In certain species of bristletails the cerci are not jointed filamentous appendages, but are much shorter and stouter, and are forcepslike structures.

The Thysanura are considerably larger than the other members belonging to this subclass. The abdomen is composed of 10 or 11 segments. The latter bear on the ventral surface slender two segmented appendages known as styli. These are believed to be vestigial abdominal legs. The number of styli varies in different species; they are also present on the ventral side of the thorax in certain forms. The eyes of the insects of this order may be perfect, degenerate, or entirely absent. In some species the body is covered with scales.

The life history of bristletails is imperfectly known. Upon hatching from the egg the young resemble the adult except in size and in some other minor details. The silverfish and firebrats are known to molt in a manner similar to other insects. In fact, they may molt a large number of times and may continue to molt after attaining sexual maturity.

Only two members of Thysanura are of much economic importance in the United States. They are the silverfish or "slicker," and the so-called firebrat.

SILVERFISH (*Lepisma saccharina*). Silverfish are soft-bodied insects about ½ inch in length with three long taillike appendages at the apex of the abdomen (Figure 50). These insects are covered with scales which give them a uniform silvery or gray color. The presence of these scales and the feeding habits have probably suggested the name "fish-moths" which is frequently applied to them. These insects are nocturnal in habit and prefer to secrete themselves in dark places. They are rarely seen until disturbed. When disturbed they are very active and quickly dart to safety, usually eluding capture.

In homes silverfish may be found from the basement to the attic. They feed upon materials with a high starch or sugar content, such as wallpaper, book bindings, pastes, and paper sizing (Figure 51). They may seriously damage starched clothing and lace curtains. Sometimes these insects also attack such thin fabrics like rayon. Perhaps the most extensive injury done by these insects is in loosening wallpaper from the walls and eating holes in it.

Eggs of the silverfish are laid in cracks, crevices, or folds of the food materials. The eggs are not glued to any object but roll freely like those of a flea. Egg to adult development may occur in 7–9

Figure 51. An envelope almost destroyed by silverfish. (From USDA.)

months in tropical regions, but about 2 years are required to complete the life cycle in temperate climates.

Although silverfish and bristletails produce but few eggs and develop slowly, they may maintain a relatively high population since the mortality rate is low and the life span protracted.

FIREBRAT (*Thermobia domestica*). The firebrat closely resembles the silverfish in general appearance, but the body dorsally is mottled with light and darker spots. This insect thrives best under conditions of relatively high temperatures and is usually found in heated basements, about furnaces, and in bakeries. Its food and biology are similar to that of the silverfish.

Control measures for silverfish and firebrats should be applied primarily in those parts of a building where the insects are developing in the largest numbers—usually the basement or the attic. If this is not done, reinfestations will continue in other parts of the building.

Chlordane, malathion, or diazinon sprays or dusts will control both pests. To be effective the insecticide should be applied on baseboards, in closets, bookcases, and other places where the insects hide or will be forced to crawl over the deposit. The spray should be applied so that the surfaces treated are thoroughly moistened. Control measures may not produce immediately noticeable results, but a gradual reduction of the pests may be expected when insecticides are thoroughly applied.

ORDER COLLEMBOLA [2]
THE SPRINGTAILS

The chief characteristics of this order of insects are:

1. Primitively wingless or without any evidence of winged ancestry.
2. Mouthparts of the chewing type, but only the tips of the mandibles are visible.
3. Metamorphosis is slight or absent as in the Thysanura.
4. Abdomen composed of not more than 6 segments.
5. Collophore or ventral tube usually present on the ventral surface of the first abdominal segment.

The common name "springtail" has been applied to members of this order because of a springlike structure which is usually present on the ventral side of the fourth abdominal segment. This springing organ is called the *furcula*. When the furcula is suddenly released against the surface upon which the insect is resting, the insect is propelled through the air. On the ventral aspect of the third abdominal segment there is usually a pair of appendages forming a structure known as the catch or *tenaculum*, which holds the furcula when not in use. A *collophore*, or ventral tube, is usu-

[2] *Colla*, glue; *embolon*, bolt, bar. The name is derived from the presence of a collophore.

ally present on the ventral surface of the first abdominal segment. It is provided with two eversible sacs which secrete a sticky substance. This substance enables the insects to cling to smooth surfaces.

Springtails are minute insects, rarely more than ⅕ inch long (Figure 52). Although seldom observed by the layman, they may occur in enormous numbers on the surface of stagnant water, in decaying vegetable matter, in mushroom houses, or other damp places.

In general, springtails are not considered to be of much economic importance. However, they may do serious injury to tender leaves of garden crops and mushrooms. Dusting with rotenone or malathion provides satisfactory control of these insects.

Figure 52. Springtails (Collembola). A. *Isotoma andrei.* B. *Sminthurides lepus.* (Courtesy of H. B. Mills and the Iowa State University Press.)

A   B

CHAPTER 6
SUBCLASS PTERYGOTA

ORDERS EPHEMEROPTERA, ODONATA, AND PLECOPTERA

Most insects belong to the Pterygota. This subclass is composed of all insects which bear wings in the adult stage. Also, certain wingless insects such as lice and fleas are included here, since biological and morphological studies clearly show that these forms have descended from a winged ancestry. These apterous insects have lost their wings by degeneration.

Morphologically and biologically, the Pterygota are a diverse group. Incomplete, gradual, and complete metamorphosis occur among the members. The mouthparts may be formed for chewing, sucking, sponging, or lapping, with various modifications or adaptations depending upon the type of food consumed. The only abdominal appendages present are cerci and genitalia. These differences, among others, are so great that the members of Pterygota must be studied under a number of separate orders.

ORDER EPHEMEROPTERA [1]
MAYFLIES

The Ephemeroptera are characterized by:

1. Two pairs of membranous wings, triangular in shape and net-veined; the hind pair (sometimes absent) always much smaller than the front pair.
2. Mouthparts of the adults vestigial, fitted for chewing in the nymphs.
3. Incomplete metamorphosis.
4. Two or 3 elongate, many-segmented, filamentous appendages at the tip of the abdomen.

Mayflies are commonly found in the vicinity of ponds, lakes, or streams. The adults are readily recognized by the rather large net-veined triangular shaped front wings and their frail bodies

[1] *Ephemeros*, lasting but a day; *pteron*, wing.

(Figure 53). The hind wings are smaller and absent in some species. They are softbodied, with inconspicuous antennae and bear at the tip of the abdomen two or three long, many-segmented filamentous appendages. These insects are attracted to lights and at times huge numbers are found around street lights in towns and cities located near large bodies of fresh water.

Mayflies attract the attention especially of scientists and fishermen. Scientists are interested in the short life span of the adult, which may not extend more than a day or two, and the molting habits and the biology of the various species; whereas the fisherman's interest has been aroused by the feeding of fish upon them. Fishermen have vainly tried to use the adults as bait, but their bodies are too fragile for this purpose. A number of artificial lures resembling mayflies, fashioned out of feathers, wire, and silk are used by fishermen.

The swarming and mating flights of mayflies have been described by several writers. These flights consist only of males and usually occur at twilight. The cloud of insects rises and falls in the air in endless repetition. Females dart into the swarm, are seized by the males, and the pairs fly away together to a nearby bush or other resting place. Soon after mating the females return to the water, lay their eggs, and die.

The various species swarm at different times. Some swarm only at a certain time, while swarms of others may be seen several times during the season. The swarming flights usually occur between sundown and dark.

The nymphs of mayflies live in relatively clean water. All species are found in an aquatic environment for which they are adapted. Typical immature forms are elongate and bear on the end of the abdomen two or three caudal filaments. In these characteristics they resemble the adults. The nymphs usually have paired tracheal gills located along the sides of the first seven abdominal segments. These are provided with numerous tracheae which obtain oxygen from the water. The gills vibrate in a shuttle-like manner. The nymphs have functionally chewing mouthparts and feed on decaying vegetable matter and small plant life. They may molt a number of times, and as many as 27 molts have been observed in at least one species.

The life history of mayflies is imperfectly known. Certain species are thought to have two generations annually while the period of development of others is longer. Probably most species produce one generation a year. These insects overwinter as nymphs. When the nymphs reach maturity they float to the surface of the water, cast their skins, and the winged forms quickly fly away and alight on some nearby object. This is not a true adult or *imago;* it is known as a *subimago.* Shortly thereafter the subimago molts. This is the only insect with functional wings that molts as a subimago. The mouthparts of the adult are vestigial and they probably do not partake of any food. The digestive tract

A

B

C

Figure 53. Mayfly adult and nymphs. A. Adult of *Hexagenia limbata*. B. Nymph of *H. limbata*. C. Nymph of *Ephemerella argo*. (From Illinois Natural History Survey.)

is filled with air which gives the insect added buoyancy in flight. Soon after the final molt the females mate and then return to the water to oviposit. The number of eggs laid may range from several hundred to several thousand.

The life of a mayfly is fraught with many dangers. The nymphs are fed upon by fishes, water beetles, frogs, and other enemies. The subimago may be devoured as it emerges from the water. Birds, spiders, dragonflies, frogs, and other enemies feed upon them on land; and as the females dip into the water in the process of egg laying, many are eaten by fish before this final mission of life is accomplished.

Mayflies are important in the economy of fresh waters. Much organic matter which otherwise would pollute streams, lakes, and ponds is destroyed by the nymphs. They constitute an important source of food for a number of animals, especially fish. They are the most abundant insects in some waters.

Several families and more than 500 species of mayflies are now recognized in North America. The nymphs of certain species of mayflies serve as intermediate hosts of nematode parasites of fish, frogs, and salamanders.

ORDER ODONATA [2]
DRAGONFLIES AND DAMSELFLIES

Members of the order Odonata are recognized by:

1. Four net-veined, membranous wings; the hind pair as large or slightly larger than the front pair; and a nodus or notch near the middle of the front margin of each wing.
2. Well developed chewing mouthparts.
3. Incomplete metamorphosis.
4. Adult usually with large head and large eyes, and long slender body.
5. Antennae short, awlshaped, and inconspicuous.

Dragonflies and damselflies are known to practically everyone and are generally of interest to the layman. They are commonly found in the vicinity of lakes, stock tanks, and streams, where the eggs are laid and the immature stages develop. However, the dragonflies are strong fliers and may frequently be found considerable distances from water.

The Odonata are divided into two distinct and readily recognizable suborders, the *Anisoptera* (dragonflies) and the *Zygoptera* (damselflies). The dragonflies are much larger and are strong flying and soaring individuals (Figure 54). When at rest the wings are held horizontally and at a right angle to the long axis of the body. The head is large, broad, subglobose, and concave posteriorly. The compound eyes often cover the greater surface of the head, each of which in certain species may contain more than 30,000 facets. Due to the curvature of the surface of the head, the large eyes enable the insects to see in almost every direction. The damselflies are rather delicate insects, and are weak fliers. When at

[2] *Odous*, tooth.

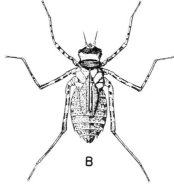

Figure 54. A. An adult dragonfly (*Platythemis lydia*). (From Department of Entomology, Texas A&M University.) B. Nymph of a dragonfly (*Macromia magnifica*). (From C. H. Kennedy, Notes on the Life History and Ecology of the Dragonflies (*Odonata* of Washington and Oregon), Proceedings of the U. S. National Museum, 1916, Vol. 49, p. 259.)

rest their wings are held parallel over the long axis of the body. The head is transverse with prominent compound eyes borne on lateral prolongations.

Odonata have three ocelli; antennae are short and awllike, and the mouthparts are strongly mandibulate. The insects are predaceous and catch their prey in flight. The modified legs are held in such a way that a basket is formed into which the food is scooped.

The dragonflies are also known as mosquito hawks and devil's darning needles. The name mosquito hawk is naturally derived from the habit of the adults of feeding on mosquitoes and similar small insect life. Superstition is responsible for the name of devil's darning needle, as the impression exists among some that the insects may sew up the eyes and ears of sleeping children. Needless to say, these insects are perfectly harmless.

Damselfly is quite an appropriate and descriptive name for the members of this beautiful and delicate group of insects that flit and flutter over the water surface (Figure 55). However, they are also known as snake doctors by many because of the superstition that they administer to ill or injured snakes. Country boys are often admonished in killing snakes to thoroughly macerate their heads or else a snake doctor will stitch up the wounds and nurse the serpents back to health. These insects have long slender bodies and are often beautifully colored.

With the exception of one group, odonates mate during flight. A peculiarity of the order is that the copulatory organs of the male are found on the ventral side of the second and third abdominal segments. Prior to mating the seminal fluid is transferred to a cavity located here. In mating the male grasps the female by the

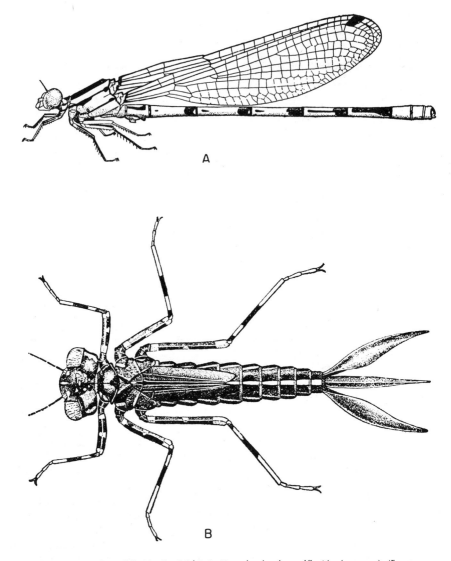

Figure 55. A. A damselfly (*Argia vivida*). B. Nymph of a damselfly (*Argia emma*). (From C. H. Kennedy, Notes on the Life History and Ecology of the Dragonflies (*Odonata* of Washington and Oregon), Proceedings of the U. S. National Museum, 1916, Vol. 49, p. 259.)

prothorax or head with its clasping organs and the female bends its abdomen around to reach the copulatory organs of the male. United dragonflies flying over water are commonly seen. Eggs are laid in the stems of aquatic plants, logs, or directly in the water. The eggs hatch into immature forms known as nymphs which have little resemblance to the adults. They are found on the bottom of bodies of water, in mud, on submerged plants, or in debris. The nymphs feed upon aquatic insects as well as other small animal life, including young fish. The labium is greatly elongated and jointed, bearing hooks at the apex. It is used in reaching out and capturing the prey. When not in use it is folded backward and conceals the mandibles, thus forming a masklike structure over the face. Damselfly nymphs respire through three leaflike tracheal gills located at the end of the abdomen. These tracheal gills also are used in swimming. In dragonflies the rectum of nymphs is modified into a tracheal gill. Its walls are thin and abundantly supplied with tracheae and tracheoles. Water is drawn into this chamber and alternately expelled. If the water is expelled forcibly, the recoil carries the insect forward, thus providing a means of locomotion.

Few life history studies have been made of the odonates. The nymphs molt a number of times; when fully grown they leave the water and attach themselves to a weed stem, tree trunk, or other object for the final molt from which the adult with fully developed wings emerges. The cast skins of emerged dragonflies are common objects in and around the water's edge. Some species may have more than one generation annually. In others more time is required for a life cycle. It is thought that the usual life cycle requires 1 year. The winter months are usually spent in the nymph stage.

The Odonata are generally considered beneficial insects. The adults feed on all forms of small insects. They will prey on any insect that is not too large for them to overcome. Larger species of dragonflies may feed on honeybees and become pests of some importance around apiaries. Nymphs are quite beneficial in feeding upon noxious insects breeding in water, and they are of some value as a source of food for fish. Conversely, however, they prey upon small fish. Fish produce so many young, however, that this habit of feeding upon them could not be considered of any importance except possibly in hatcheries.

More species of Odonata exist than is commonly realized. Upwards of 5000 species have been recorded. They occur in greatest numbers in warm climates. Certain species are intermediate hosts of flukes, which attack waterfowl, poultry, frogs, and other animals.

ORDER PLECOPTERA [3]
STONEFLIES

Members of the Plecoptera may be characterized by:

1. Usually 2 pairs of membranous wings exceeding length of body; hind pair much larger than front pair and folded in plaits when at rest; a number of cross veins usually present.

[3] *Plecos*, plaited; *pteron*, wing.

2. Mouthparts mandibulate but frequently vestigial in the adult.
3. Incomplete metamorphosis.
4. Antennae and cerci long.

Stoneflies are soft-bodied insects, small to moderate in size, and generally drab in appearance; the predominant colors are gray, black, brown, and green. In build the body is elongate, and flattened with parallel sides (Figure 56). Members of the order are poor fliers and are usually found near their breeding places. The adults usually have poorly developed mouthparts and probably do not partake of any food, but some species have well developed mandibles and are known to cause injury in feeding on buds and leaves. Two pairs of membranous wings are usually present which lie flat on the body when not in use. The hind wings are generally broader than the front pair, and fold in plaits over the abdomen

Figure 56. A stonefly (*Isoperla confusa*). A. Adult. B. Nymph. (From Illinois Natural History Survey.)

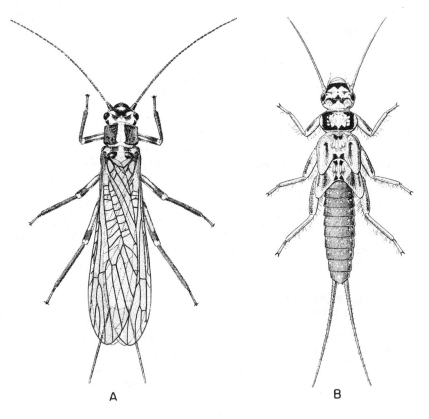

A   B

when at rest. They have a moderate number of veins but a number of cross veins may be present.

Eggs, often several thousand in number, are dropped in a mass by the female in the water. Here they hatch into nymphs which live under stones, logs, or masses of debris in swiftly running or other well aerated water. Most of the nymphs feed on vegetable matter, but some feed on insects and other aquatic invertebrates.

The nymphs have the general body conformation of the adults and are usually somewhat more brightly colored. Respiration is generally effected by means of tracheal gills which are usually located at the base of each leg. However, the nymphs of some of the smaller species respire through the thin body wall of the ventral surface. The nymphs leave the water when fully grown and attach themselves to nearby objects where the final molt occurs. Their cast skins are commonly observed around the breeding places. The adults may live for several weeks. The life history of stoneflies is not very well known. The smaller species complete a life cycle in 1 year, while the larger forms require more time.

Stoneflies are of little economic importance. Most nymphs feed on organic material of vegetable origin and are thus of some value as scavengers; others are predators on small aquatic animal life. They constitute a source of food for freshwater fish, which is of some importance.

Some 1500 species of stoneflies are known, but less than 300 of these occur in North America.

CHAPTER 7
ORDERS ORTHOPTERA
AND ISOPTERA

ORDER ORTHOPTERA[1]
COCKROACHES, GRASSHOPPERS, CRICKETS, KATYDIDS, AND OTHERS

Members of the Orthoptera are characterized by:

1. Two pairs of wings, sometimes absent or vestigial; front wings more or less parchmentlike with distinct venation, hind pair membranous and folded fanlike when at rest.
2. Mouthparts of a typically chewing type.
3. Gradual metamorphosis.
4. A pair of cerci present.

The order Orthoptera contains some of the more common and better known insects, such as grasshoppers, katydids, crickets, and cockroaches. It is one of the larger orders of insects, comprising more than 30,000 species of which about 2000 occur in North America. Some of the more important pests, such as grasshoppers and cockroaches (Figure 57), belong here, as well as katydids and crickets, those major contributors to nature's orchestra of the long summer evenings.

This group of insects is so diverse in morphology and habits that it is difficult to cite specific characteristics. There is some justification in the tendency to subdivide the order. Mouthparts of all members are mandibulate. The grasshopper's mouthparts are usually selected for study of a generalized chewing type. Metamorphosis is gradual, with the nymphs and adults feeding on the same materials and occurring in the same general habitat. With the exception of a single family, the Mantidae, the members of which are predaceous, the Orthoptera are mostly all feeders on plants or plant products.

Members of the Orthoptera typically bear two pairs of net-veined wings. The two pairs of wings differ in structure. The front wings (known as tegmina) are more or less thickened and

[1] *Orthos*, straight; *pteron*, wing.

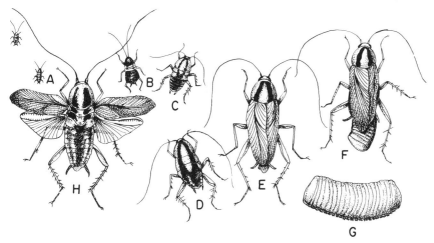

Figure 57. The German cockroach (*Blatella germanica*). A, B, C, D. Nymphs. E. Adult. F. Adult female with egg case. G. Egg case (ootheca). H. Adult with wings spread. (From USDA.)

parchmentlike. The hind wings are somewhat thinner and are usually broader in the anal areas and are folded fanlike when at rest. In some species the wings of the adult are small or wanting. The nymphs of short-winged grasshoppers, katydids, and crickets may be readily separated from the adults because their wing pads are inverted, with the hind pair on the outside and with the outer surfaces corrugated. The males of those families composed of grasshoppers, katydids, and crickets have modifications on their wings for making sounds of a more or less musical nature. These insects are sometimes called the musicians of the insect world. The sounds are made to attract the opposite sex. Grasshoppers produce sound by rubbing the two pairs of wings together in flight, or by rubbing the hind femora against the front wings when the insect is at rest. Their auditory organs are located on the first abdominal segment. In the common cricket each front wing (tegmen) bears near its base a file, a scraper (a hardened area), and vibrating areas (tympana). The file of one wing scrapes on the hardened area of the other and sets the tympana in vibration. The auditory organs are found on the front tibiae. The sound-making organs of the katydids are similar to those of the crickets, but only one functional file is present in common representatives of the family, and this is on the left tegmen. As with the crickets, the auditory organs of katydids are located on the front tibiae.

Orthopterous insects have several biological characteristics in common. Most members have only one generation annually in the more temperate climates. Exceptions are found, particularly in certain species of cockroaches. Most Orthoptera overwinter in the egg stage, but cockroaches may overwinter in all stages if conditions permit. Many lay their eggs in packets or capsules; some deposit their eggs singly.

Family Blattidae (Cockroaches)

Cockroaches are known to practically everyone and a description of them is scarcely necessary. The body is oval and depressed. They are brown or brownish black in general color; however, green cockroaches are known. The head is bowed downward and almost completely covered by the pronotum as viewed from above. The mouthparts project backward between the front legs. The antennae are long and slender and are used as tactile organs. Two pairs of fully developed wings are usually present; however, in some cases they may be short or entirely lacking. In some species the female is wingless or has vestigial wings, but fully developed wings are present in the male.

Cockroaches thrive best in tropical or subtropical climates. More than 2000 species are recorded in the world, of which about 70 different kinds are known to occur in the United States; most of these are found in the southern states. Only a few native species occur in the northern part of the United States. This is a very ancient group of insects. Fossil remains indicate that they were most abundant in the Carboniferous Age (more than 200,000,000 years ago).

Cockroaches prefer a warm, dark, and humid environment. They are secretive and feed during the night. Certainly the ancients were acquainted with their feeding habits as they called them *lucifuga*, meaning light-fleeing. The name cockroach is derived from the Spanish, *cucaracha*.

Only a few species of cockroaches have taken up their abode in the habitations of man and thereby have become pests. They are practically omnivorous feeders. Their food consists of most kinds of plant and animal products—the foods of man, garbage, sewage, binding and sizing of books, and wallpaper paste. They are not only destructive through their feeding activities, but their fetid odor may be imparted to foods over which they crawl. Their filthy habits suggest the probability of spreading diseases, such as dysentery and typhoid, although positive proof is lacking. Some cockroaches may serve as intermediate hosts of certain parasitic worms of birds and mammals.

A wood cockroach (*Cryptocercus punctulatus*) found in the southeastern states is of interest because it has developed a type of true social life and is capable of digesting cellulose as termites do, with the aid of certain protozoans in its digestive tract. A colony consists of several generations of individuals living together in decaying logs where they feed on the rotten wood.

The most important domestic species of cockroaches are the American cockroach (*Periplaneta americana*) (Figure 58A), the

Australian cockroach (*Periplaneta australasiae*), the Oriental cockroach (*Blatta orientalis*) (Figure 58B), the brown-banded cockroach (*Supella longipalpa*) (Figure 58C), and the German cockroach or croton bug (*Blattella germanica*). All of these species originally came from the tropics and have been introduced into the United States through channels of commerce.

Most cockroaches deposit their eggs in brown beanlike capsules (*oothecae*). The oothecae are usually carried for several days protruding from the abdomen of the female and are then secreted in a secluded spot. The German cockroach differs from the other common species in carrying its ootheca until almost time for the eggs to hatch.

The American cockroach attains a length of about 1½ inches and is reddish brown with a light brown band around the lateral and posterior margins of the pronotum. The length of the life cycle from egg to adult requires from a year to 1½ years. Adults may live for longer than a year. During this time females will deposit 50 or more egg capsules which normally contain 16 eggs each. This species has migratory habits. It may come into the home on its own volition from stores, garbage dumps, and sewer lines. In the southern states it is capable of rather long flights.

The Australian cockroach is of less importance than the American cockroach but this cosmopolitan species may become locally abundant. It may attain approximately the size of the American cockroach. The general color pattern is similar but it can be distinguished by the presence of a yellow mark extending about one-third the length of the front wing along the costal margin.

The oriental cockroach is shining black, occasionally dark red-

Figure 58. Common cockroaches. A. The American cockroach (*Periplaneta americana*). B. The oriental cockroach (*Blatta orientalis*). C. The brown-banded cockroach (*Supella longipalpa*), relatively enlarged to show markings. (Modified from USDA.)

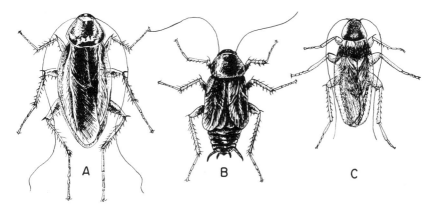

dish brown, and about 1–1¼ inches long. The male has fully developed wings and is capable of flight, while the wings of the female are greatly reduced in size and are nonfunctional. The species has about the same life cycle as the American cockroach. A seasonal cycle is suggested by the emergence of a preponderance of adults in the spring. This insect is considered the filthiest of cockroaches.

The German cockroach is one of the most common pests of the home, grocery, and cafe. It measures about ½ inch in length and is light brown with two dark stripes on the pronotum. This form is known as the water bug and also the croton bug. Due to its small size it is frequently brought into the home with groceries. Migrations from nearby infested places also occur.

Unlike other common species, the female of the German cockroach carries the ootheca until the eggs are about ready to hatch. It is quite prolific and under conditions of high temperatures three or more generations may be completed annually. Adult females may live for about 9 months.

The brown-banded cockroach is a comparatively recent introduction into the United States, where it is now quite widely distributed. It first was confined to the southern part of the country but later it spread northward and became established in heated buildings. It has the general appearance of the German cockroach but is slightly smaller. The sexes differ in that the male is longer, narrower, and has fully developed wings; while the female is darker, broader, and has short, nonfunctional wings. Two light transverse bands are present across the back. These markings are more distinct on the nymphs than on the adults.

Unlike the German cockroach, the brown-banded cockroach does not tend to confine itself to the kitchen and bathroom, but may be found throughout the home. This species is often found in elevated situations such as shelves in closets and behind pictures and molding. Egg capsules may be deposited in almost any secluded spot, often among linens and clothing. The female life span averages about 200 days, and there may be two generations annually.

Cleanliness and guarding against infestations is the first step in the control of roaches. Proper protection of foods and disposal of food scraps and garbage should be practiced. Also, care should be exercised to prevent the introduction of the pests in bags of groceries. Cracks or other entrances around plumbing should be sealed.

Cockroaches may be controlled by treating with chlordane, dieldrin, or malathion the dark corners, cracks, and crevices underneath sinks, and other hiding places where cockroaches congregate or frequent in search of food. Numbers of cockroaches frequently congregate in basements and underneath buildings. These places may need proper insecticidal treatment before the pests can be eradicated from the buildings. With heavy infestations of the

American cockroach, the use of yellow phosphorus paste may be advisable as a supplemental control measure.

Family Mantidae (Praying Mantids, Devil's Horses)

Mantids are common insects, particularly in the South (Figure 59). They constitute the only family of *Orthoptera* which is beneficial, since all of the members are predaceous on other insects. They are even cannibalistic and readily eat each other. These large to medium sized insects are readily recognized by the elongate prothorax on which is borne the first pair of grasping legs. The ventral side of both femur and tibia of each front leg is armed with spines and the tibia is capable of being folded back on the femur, thus forming an efficient grasping organ. The second and third pairs of legs are long and similar, and are used for walking.

Mantids, like cockroaches, are found in largest numbers in tropical and subtropical regions. More than 600 species are known, but only about two dozen are found in North America. These insects are green or brown or with a mixture of the two colors. Wings may be fully developed, abbreviated, or wholly absent. In some mantids the wings simulate the leaves of plants.

The common name of praying mantid has been applied to this insect because of the habit of holding its grasping front legs in a pious attitude while waiting for prey. This attitude has suggested the name of a common species, *Mantis religiosa*. Superstition has it that the brown saliva of mantids will cause blindness to man and kill a mule, and that the dead insects, when eaten in hay, will kill mules and horses. The common walking stick is implicated also in the latter superstition.

Eggs are laid in a mass (*ootheca*) arranged in a definite pattern of rows and glued together (Figure 60). These brown oothecae are rather commonly observed glued to branches of trees, fence

Figure 59. The Carolina mantid (*Stagmomantis carolina*). (From Illinois Natural History Survey.)

Figure 60. Egg capsule (ootheca) of a mantid.

posts, or other objects. The eggs are often destroyed by a hymenopterous parasite which emerges soon after the time the young mantids should have emerged. The winter season is spent in the egg stage. Only one annual generation of the insects has been observed.

Family Phasmatidae (Walking Sticks)
The common name applied to these insects aptly describes them (Figure 61). They usually simulate in both body conformation and general color a twig of a tree or a stem of grass upon which they are commonly found. Nature has done such an excellent job of camouflaging their presence that they are usually passed by unseen. Their movements are very slow and deliberate.

Only one North American species has wings. Some of the tropical forms are broad and resemble the leaves of the trees upon which they are found. About 700 species of walking sticks are known, and occur mostly in the tropics. One species found in the East Indies and Borneo measures nearly 13 inches in length and is thought to be the world's largest insect. Walking sticks feed entirely on vegetation. They have been known to become so numerous as to defoliate trees, but such occurrences are rare.

No provisions are made for the protection of the eggs. The females drop eggs at random to the ground, where they remain through the winter months and hatch the next season. Parthenogenesis is common. Only one generation is produced each year.

Family Acrididae (Grasshoppers, Locusts)
Members of this family are commonly known as grasshoppers. The term locust is most frequently applied to the migratory forms. Grasshoppers are readily recognized by antennae usually shorter than the body, tarsi of three segments, auditory organs located on

the first abdominal segment, and the presence of a short stout ovipositor.

Among the grasshoppers are found some of the most important pests of mankind. They have destroyed the crops of man from Biblical days to the present time. And they, in turn, have been used to some extent as food by man in certain parts of the world.

About 8000 species of grasshoppers are known. Of this number more than 600 occur in North America. All of these species cannot be considered as destructive forms. Only a small percentage of this number ever increases in numbers large enough to seriously damage crops and other vegetation; however, every section of the country has its predominant forms which, on occasion, may prove to be pests of importance.

Grasshoppers usually have only one generation annually; however, some species, such as the American grasshopper (*Schistocerca americana*), may be two brooded. As a rule the winter is passed in the egg stage; but certain species, such as *Schistocerca damnifica* and *S. americana,* may overwinter as adults, or in the nymphal stage (*Chortophaga viridifasciata*). With few exceptions, eggs of grasshoppers are deposited in the ground. In general the females lay 100 or more eggs, which hatch in the spring. Maturity is reached during the summer. There are usually five nymphal instars, but occasionally a sixth is observed. Grasshoppers are found in greatest abundance and are most destructive in prairie lands with an annual rainfall of less than 25 inches.

Every continent has its species of migratory locusts. The most important migratory locust found in North America is the Rocky Mountain locust (*Melanoplus spretus*). The most severe insect losses to agriculture ever suffered in this country were inflicted by this insect in the Great Plains regions a generation ago. The destruction of crops was so great that hardships unknown to present-day farmers were experienced. These insects increased in indescribable numbers and migrated by flight for hundreds of

Figure 61. A walking stick (*Diapheromera femorata*). (From Illinois Natural History Survey.)

miles, leaving denuded and desolate areas behind them. Occasional outbreaks of this insect still occur. The best known of all migratory locusts is the desert locust (*Schistocerca gregaria*), of which accounts are found in the Bible. It occurs over large areas of the Middle East and plagues still occur as in Biblical days. *Locusta migratoria* is another species of much importance in these regions. Conditions producing the migratory phase of grasshoppers and others are not fully understood. The theory is advanced that this phase is produced when overcrowding occurs in the natural breeding grounds.

Although the Rocky Mountain locust is found throughout most of the United States, it is considered a pest of importance only in the Great Plains region. The solitary phase of this species is known as the lesser migratory grasshopper (*Melanoplus sanguinipes*).

One of the most destructive grasshoppers throughout the Mississippi Valley region is the differential grasshopper (*Melanoplus differentialis*) (Figure 62A). This brownish to olive green grasshopper is one of the largest economically important forms, measuring about 1½ inches long. Associated with the differential grasshopper in most of this region is the two-striped grasshopper (*Melanoplus bivittatus*), which approaches it in size. The red-legged grasshopper (*Melanoplus femurrubrum*) (Figure 62B), is

Figure 62. A. The differential grasshopper (*Melanoplus differentialis*). B. The red-legged grasshopper (*Melanoplus femurrubrum*). (From USDA.)

A

B

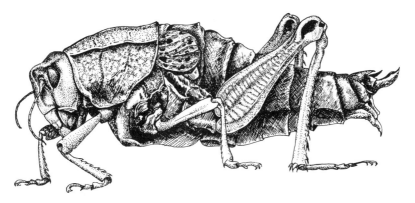

Figure 63. The lubber grasshopper (*Brachystola magna*).

quite widely distributed and it is often of considerable economic importance.

The American grasshopper (*Schistocerca americana*) and the Carolina grasshopper (*Dissosteira carolina*) are two of the most widely distributed and best known species. Only on occasion do they become local pests. The American grasshopper is almost 3 inches long, reddish brown with dark brown spots on the tegmina. When disturbed it often finds refuge in trees. The Carolina grasshopper is most often seen along dusty roadsides and margins of fields. It is readily recognized by the black hind wings which are bordered with yellow.

The lubber grasshopper (*Brachystola magna*) (Figure 63), is a native of the Southwest. This is a large, brown, clumsy grasshopper with wings reduced to mere pads. On account of its slightly humped appearance this species is often called the buffalo grasshopper. It cannot fly, but its hind legs are greatly enlarged and it is a strong hopper. Its counterpart, the eastern lubber (*Romalea microptera*), occurs in the Gulf states. This large species is yellow and black and the short hind wings are red and bordered with black. Locally, both species may become pests of importance. In addition to these grasshoppers, a number of other species may become pests of limited importance in various parts of the country.

Since the grasshoppers of most economic importance overwinter in the soil in the egg stage, fall and winter plowing will destroy many of them. In localities where acreages of pasture and wasteland are very extensive, this practice will not likely prove of much value.

When a heavy emergence of grasshoppers is indicated by surveys, farmers must prepare to poison them. For most satisfactory results grasshoppers should be poisoned over large areas. Control is most economically and efficiently done by poisoning the insects soon after hatching and before they move into the crops. Toxaphene, malathion, and carbaryl are recommended for their control.

Under conditions where vegetation is sparse or not very attractive to the insects, especially in the more arid sections of the country, poison baits may be as effective as dusts and sprays and are much more economical. A number of bait formulas have been recommended and used through the years.

Family Tettigoniidae (Katydids and Meadow Grasshoppers)

Insects of the Tettigoniidae are represented by the katydids, false katydids (Figure 64), meadow grasshoppers, cone-headed grasshoppers, and others. They may be recognized as belonging to this family by antennae as long or longer than the body, four-segmented tarsi, and a female ovipositor that is sword-shaped and exserted. The predominant color of these insects is green, but some brown forms occur. Some are wingless, such as the shield backed grasshoppers and the camel crickets. Eggs of the tettigoniids are laid singly on leaves or twigs (Figure 65) of trees and shrubs, in cracks of bark, within tissues of plants, or in the soil.

The katydids and false katydids are the chief music makers of this family. In this respect they rival the crickets. It is the true katydid (*Pterophylla*) that incessantly repeats, "katy did, katy didn't," during the late afternoon and night.

Very few members of this family have been recorded as pestiferous, although katydids have been known to injure orange trees and have been observed to denude completely rather large areas of post-oak forests. The most important exception is the Mormon cricket (*Anabrus simplex*) (Figure 66). This is a large, wingless, dark brown insect found in the Great Basin region of the Rocky Mountains. It often occurs in epidemic proportions and causes considerable damage to range and cultivated plants. In 1848 an outbreak of this insect occurred in Utah. Hordes of the pest threatened the complete destruction of the crops of the Mormon settlement, but flocks of sea gulls made a timely appearance and

Figure 64. A false or broad-winged katydid (*Microcentrum rhombifolium*). (From Illinois Natural History Survey.)

Figure 65. Eggs of a false or broad-winged katydid deposited on a twig.

Figure 66. The Mormon cricket (*Anabrus simplex*). A. Male and B. Female. (From USDA.)

devoured the insects. In appreciation the Mormons erected a monument to commemorate the event.

When Mormon crickets are about half grown, they start migrating. The same measures may be employed in their control as for grasshoppers.

Family Gryllidae (Crickets)

The friendly chirping of crickets is a familiar sound to nearly everyone. They are the principal music makers among the Orthoptera. The best known of all crickets are the field crickets and the house or hearth crickets.

Most crickets have a lance-shaped ovipositor, three-segmented tarsi, usually long antennae, and are usually winged. The front wings (termina) lie flat on the body and are bent abruptly downward to cover the sides of the body. Some forms are wingless. Most crickets have only one generation annually, and overwinter in the egg stage. The eggs are laid singly in the soil.

The field crickets (*Gryllus spp.*) (Figure 67A), are probably the most widely distributed species; it occurs in both North and South America. This black or brown jumping cricket with its prominent antennae and ovipositor is a most familiar insect. In cold climates it usually overwinters in the egg stage and produces one generation annually. In its southern range the insect may be more or less active throughout the year and may produce as many as three generations in a season. It feeds on both plant and animal materials rather indiscriminately, and cannibalism may occur. Field crops sometimes suffer damaging attacks. The species is known to attack clothing and other household belongings. In the fall it frequently enters homes and becomes a pest. Attracted by the lights, it may migrate into towns and cities and cause considerable

---

Figure 67. A. Last instar of a field cricket (*Gryllus sp.*) (From USDA.) B. The snowy tree cricket (*Oecanthus fultoni*) and egg punctures in a berry cane. (From the University of California Division of Agricultural Sciences.)

A   B

Figure 68. The northern mole cricket (*Gryllotalpa hexadactyla*). (From Illinois Natural History Survey.)

annoyance. The dusts, sprays, and poison baits used in grasshopper control are recommended for control of the cricket. The European house cricket (*Gryllus domesticus*) is now established in the eastern part of the United States.

The tree crickets are frail, light green or yellow insects about ½ to ¾ inch long. *Oecanthus fultoni* (Figure 67B) is the best known species. These insects are found on the foliage of trees and shrubs. Their song is commonly heard throughout the night in the summer and fall. This high-pitched song or note is monotonously reverberated and the rapidity of the note is correlated with the prevailing temperature. All of the songsters in the neighborhood stay in tune. Should an individual stop to rest and then begin again, it is always in time with the others that have continued the music. Tree crickets are beneficial because they prey upon aphids. Conversely, the females may do material damage in laying their eggs. They make a series of deep punctures for the purpose of laying eggs in the twigs of trees, berry canes, and other plants, causing the twigs to die. The female has an unusual habit of packing a bit of her own excrement around each egg after it is laid.

The mole crickets differ markedly in appearance from the ordinary crickets (Figure 68). These differences are so great that some authors place them in a separate family. The most striking difference lies in the structure of the fore tibiae which are modified into digging organs and resemble the foot of a mole. These crickets are brown and the larger species are longer and stouter than the common field cricket. They burrow in the soil like moles, disturb seedbeds and young seedlings, and feed on the tender roots of growing plants. The European species (*Gryllotalpa gryllotalpa*) has the unusual habit (for an insect) of guarding its eggs and newly hatched young. This species has become established in the eastern United States. It is thought that the completion of a generation requires 3 or 4 years. The Puerto Rican mole cricket or

"Changa" (*Scapteriscus vicinus*) and the southern species (*Scapteriscus acletus*) are found in the South and are pests of some importance. The northern mole cricket (*Gryllotalpa hexadactyla*) is not so abundant. These indigenous species require only 1 year for the completion of a generation. Treatment of the soil with chlordane in the form of a spray or a dust is recommended for the control of mole crickets should their damage become serious.

ORDER ISOPTERA [2]
TERMITES

The order Isoptera is characterized by:

1. Winged members with 2 pairs of long, narrow wings, similar in form, size, and texture, which lie flat on the back when not in use.
2. Chewing type mouthparts.
3. Gradual metamorphosis.
4. Live in colonies under a caste system.

Termites are also known as "white ants" because of the usual grayish-white color and their social habit of life. Their resemblance to ants is only that both live in colonies and have some habits in common. In termites the abdomen is broadly joined to the thorax instead of being constricted (wasp waisted) at the base, as in ants. The wings of termites are similar, whereas the hind wings of ants are smaller and have fewer veins than the front pair. Termites spend their lives in the soil, wood, or earthen tunnels; while ants may be commonly found running about on top of the ground.

Termites occur in greatest numbers in the tropical and subtropical parts of the world where their destructive capacity is best known, but they also are found throughout most of the temperate regions. About 2000 species are known, of which more than 50 forms have been recorded in North America.

Termites vary in color, size, shape, and mode of life. Wings are present only in the sexually mature males and females during the swarming season (Figure 69). The wings are long, narrow, semitransparent, and extend at least one-half their length beyond the end of the abdomen. Both pairs of wings are similar and are broken off along a suture at the base after swarming. Mouthparts are of a generalized chewing type, as found in grasshoppers and cockroaches. The termite workers, and probably the soldier caste as well, are blind. The winged sexual forms have pigmented compound eyes and also two ocelli. Metamorphosis is gradual and there is no pupal or quiescent stage, such as ants and numerous other insects have.

A number of castes of termites have been recognized, but not all are ever found in the colony of any particular species. Male and female individuals of each caste are known. The castes present

[2] *Isos*, equal; *pteron*, wing.

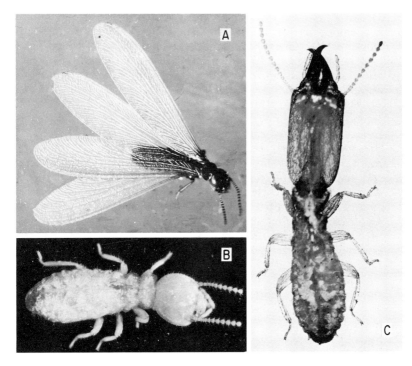

Figure 69. Subterranean termites. A. Winged sexual adult. B. Adult worker. C. Adult soldier. (From USDA.)

in colonies of the more common species include primary queens and kings, complemental queens and kings, workers, and soldiers.

Usually during the spring or fall, but at other times when conditions are favorable, the winged sexual members of a colony swarm from the colony. Normally only a few individuals of the dry-wood termite leave the parent colony at a time, but the flights from the colonies of subterranean termites consist of large numbers. Following a short flight the wings are broken off, the individuals separate in pairs, and a cell is excavated in the soil or wood. Only then do the queens and kings mate. The relationship of the queens and kings is on a permanent basis and repeated matings occur. The king assists the queen in excavating the new home and rearing the first brood. After the first workers are produced, the sole duty of the queen is to lay eggs. Queens of native species become enlarged but the abdomens do not become so distended that the power of locomotion is lost, as in some tropical forms. Also, queens of native species do not lay nearly so many eggs as tropical termites. The first offspring of a young colony consist of workers and a few soldiers. About a year is required for their development. The winged sexual forms are not produced in a colony until it is at least 2 years old. Workers do most of the work of the colony. The soldiers resemble the workers but they may be distinguished by their large heads and mandibles. Workers are not present in colonies of nonsubterranean termites, and nymphs perform their duties.

Termites constitute one group of nature's scavengers. They convert logs, stumps, branches, and other plant material to humus. In this service they are beneficial to man. In his use of wood materials man too frequently provides both food and shelter for termites. There has been no sudden increase of termites in this country. They are widely distributed insects and will attack suitable wood products whenever conditions are favorable. The principal food of termites is the cellulose of wood. Feeding is primarily on dead wood, but living plants may be attacked. Most species of termites contain in their digestive tracts low forms of life, especially protozoans. They secrete enzymes which digest the food for the termites.

The two groups of termites of most economic importance are the dry-wood termites and the subterranean termites. The dry-wood termites establish their nests in the tunnels and galleries they make in the wood upon which they feed (Figure 70). In the United States, damaging infestations occur only along the southern boundaries of the southernmost states and on the Pacific Coast. They are more destructive in the tropics. Solutions of pentachlorophenol are recommended for the treatment of wood infested by dry-wood termites.

Probably 95 percent of the termite damage in the United States is done by subterranean species belonging to the genus *Reticulitermes*. *R. flavipes* is the most common species. Colonies of these

Figure 70. Workers of the common termite exposed in decaying wood. (Prepared by the Clemson University Cooperative Extension Service's Entomology-Plant Pathology and Agricultural Communications Sections, Federal Extension Service Cooperating.)

insects may be found in the ground wherever food is available and moisture conditions are suitable. They require much moisture, which they obtain from the soil. Food consists of wood or wood products in the soil, in contact with the ground, or that which may be reached by means of tubes which they may construct. These termites are most destructive in the South, but damage may occur throughout most of the United States.

For the protection of pilings, bridge timbers, power and telephone poles, cross ties, and other timbers that are used in contact with the soil against termite damage and rots, chemical treatment is essential. These timbers should be treated under pressure with coal-tar creosote, pentachlorophenol, or other approved chemical compounds.

In the prevention and control of the common subterranean termites in buildings it is essential to remember that they maintain their colonies in the ground where requisite moisture conditions are found and food is available. Although the common termites may be feeding well above the surface of the ground, they are obliged to return to the colony in the soil. The most important steps in the prevention of termites in buildings are to create conditions unfavorable to termites and isolate the building as completely as possible from the ground. The soil of the building site may be treated with chlordane, dieldrin, pentachlorophenol, or other chemical compounds. The lot should be graded so that water will not run or puddle underneath the structure. All stumps, pilings, stakes, wooden forms, and scraps of wood should be removed from the soil and building site. Adequate ventilation must be provided to maintain a dry condition underneath the house. Wooden floors should be at least 18 inches from the closest contact with the ground.

Another essential requirement is that no wood should come in contact with the ground. The foundation should be constructed of concrete, stone, or brick. If stone or brick is used, a good grade of cement mortar should be used to ensure the closing of all cracks. Metal termite guards will materially aid in termite prevention if properly installed but constitute no guarantee of permanent protection. The sills and possibly the floor joists should be chemically treated to prevent termites as well as rots.

Concrete porches and chimneys often afford ready access for the entrance of termites into buildings. Concrete porches should preferably be of hollow construction, but if the concrete is poured on an earthen fill, the soil next to the foundation should be removed after the concrete has set. Chimney foundations should be of open construction and a high grade of cement mortar used between the bricks to prevent cracks. Concrete floors are no assured protection against termites, since they may enter such buildings through expansion joints and cracks in the concrete.

When a building becomes infested with termites, control may involve the expenditure of considerable labor and money. Corrective measures may have to be taken. These may involve improvements in drainage and ventilation, and removal of wood which is in contact with the ground.

Soil poisoning is the most satisfactory treatment for the control of subterranean termites. Several chemical compounds have been found satisfactory for this purpose. Pentachlorophenol, dieldrin, and chlordane are among the more efficient and better known products used. No termite treatment can be considered permanent. Annual or semiannual inspections should be made and the treatment repeated in those places where termites may reappear.

CHAPTER 8
ORDERS DERMAPTERA, EMBIOPTERA, ZORAPTERA, PSOCOPTERA, AND THYSANOPTERA

ORDER DERMAPTERA [1]
EARWIGS

Characteristics of the order Dermaptera are:

1. Winged members with 2 pairs of wings; front pair short, leathery, without venation and meet in a straight line down the back when at rest. Hind wings membranous, broad, with veins radiating from a center, folded both lengthwise and crosswise when at rest.
2. Chewing mouthparts.
3. Gradual metamorphosis.
4. A pair of forcepslike cerci at the end of the abdomen.

The common name of earwig was given these insects in Europe because of the superstition that they would crawl in the ears of sleeping persons. The name could have come from "ear-wing" as the hind wings have a slight resemblance to an ear. This is a rather small order of insects, about 1000 species, occurring mostly in warm countries. Less than 20 species are reported from North America. Earwigs are rather narrow and elongate insects (Figure 71). They may be confused with rove beetles by the novice, but may be readily distinguished from the latter by the forcepslike appendages on the end of the abdomen. Earwigs are nocturnal in habit, hiding during the day in the most convenient places. They feed chiefly on decaying materials and occasionally on living plants; some forms are carnivorous. Although flowers, foliage, and fruits of plants may be attacked, the injury usually is not very important.

The eggs are laid within a cell in the soil in a protected place and the female watches over them until they are hatched. She continues her maternal care for a short time after hatching. The nymphs undergo four to six instars before attaining maturity. In temperate climates only one generation occurs annually.

[1] *Derma*, skin; *pteron*, wing.

Figure 71. Adult female of an earwig (*Labia minor*). (From Illinois Natural History Survey.)

Some earwigs have stink glands opening on the abdomen. These glands emit an illsmelling liquid which probably has a repelling effect on natural enemies.

The European earwig (*Forficula auricularia*) has been introduced into the United States and is now established on the eastern and western seaboards. It feeds upon a variety of plant and animal materials, but it is of more concern as a nuisance in households.

ORDER EMBIOPTERA [2]
EMBIIDS OR WEB-SPINNERS

Embiids are characterized by:

1. Wings, when present, 2 pairs, similar in structure, elongate and membranous.
2. Chewing mouthparts of primitive type.
3. Gradual metamorphosis but deviates somewhat from usual type.
4. Small insects with elongate and somewhat flattened bodies.

The order Embioptera comprises a small and rarely encountered group of insects (Figure 72). About 70 species of the order are represented in the fauna of the warmer climates of the Americas.

[2] *Embios*, lively; *pteron*, wing.

These small, feeble insects are found living gregariously in silken tunnels underneath stones, logs, bark of trees, and similar environments.

The silk with which their small tunnels are constructed is secreted from glands located in the enlarged basal segment of the tarsus of the forelegs.

All females are wingless; the males usually have two pairs of elongate, membranous wings with reduced venation. Some species develop parthenogenetically. The insects feed on plant materials of many kinds, preferably fungi.

Overwintered nymphal forms of embiids attain the adult stage in the summer months. Apparently the females lay only a small number of eggs. The latter are deposited in the silken tunnels; and after a comparatively short incubation period, hatch into nymphs which develop slowly. Only one generation annually has been observed.

ORDER ZORAPTERA [3]
ZORAPTERONS

The name Zoraptera is inappropriate for this small inconspicuous group of insects, as it was based upon wingless forms only. Sub-

[3] *Zoros*, pure; *apterous*, without wings.

Figure 72. Embiids or web-spinners (*Oligotoma saundersii*). A. Winged male. B. Wingless female. (Adapted from E. O. Essig, *College Entomology*. Copyright 1942. Used by permission of The Macmillan Company.)

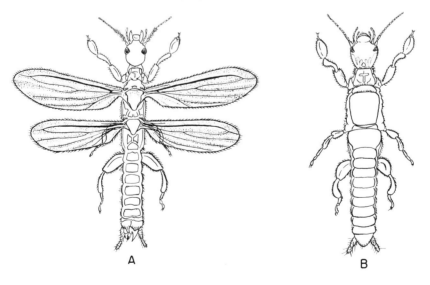

A   B

sequent discoveries have shown that winged members also occur in the order. These are among the rarest of insects; less than 20 species are known, of which only 2 are found in the United States. Both of these species occur in the South.

Zorapterons (Figure 73) are quite small, measuring 1½–3 mm in length; both winged and wingless individuals may be found in the same colony. The winged forms have two pairs of wings which contain only a few veins. The wings are broken off as in the case of termites. The wingless forms are blind. Metamorphosis is gradual, and the mouthparts are of the generalized chewing type.

The insects are found under bark, in rotten wood, and in piles of sawdust. They live in colonies which contain 25–100 individuals each. Zoraptera feed as scavengers or probably as predators on small arthropods.

ORDER PSOCOPTERA [4]
PSOCIDS, BOOK LICE

Psocids have the following characteristics:

1. Winged representatives of the order with 2 pairs of wings held rooflike over the body when at rest, front pair larger; veins prominent.
2. Mandibulate mouthparts.

[4] *Psoco*, rub, small; *Pteron*, wing.

Figure 73. A zorapteron (*Zorotypus guineensis*). (Adapted from E. O. Essig, *College Entomology.* Copyright 1942. Used by permission of The Macmillan Company.)

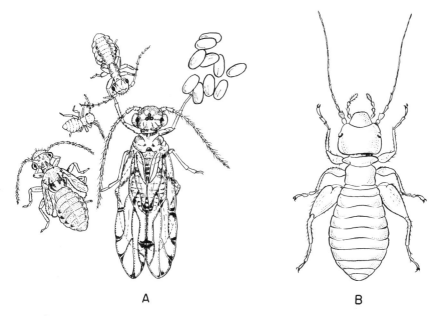

Figure 74. A. The ten-spotted psocid (*Peripsocus californicus*); eggs, nymphs, and adult. (From E. O. Essig by permission of The Macmillan Company.) B. A book louse (*Liposcelis divinatorius*). (From the University of California, Division of Agricultural Sciences.)

3. Gradual metamorphosis.
4. Antennae slender, and as long or longer than the body.

Psocids (Figure 74A) are small and inconspicuous insects and are rarely noticed by the layman. The best known are the light-colored and wingless forms which are commonly called book lice (Figure 74B). Book lice are usually found feeding on paste and paper of unused books and in birds' nest where their food consists of feathers and other waste material.

Most species of psocids are found outdoors and normally possess two pairs of wings. The front wings are larger than the hind pair and the wings at rest are usually held rooflike over the abdomen. They are usually dusky or mottled in appearance. The insects resemble aphids in general appearance, and are often mistaken for them by the novice.

Psocids are most often found on the bark of trees, or under lichens and fallen leaves. Here they feed on fungi, algae, dead plant tissues, and other waste materials. Eggs are laid singly or in small groups and may be covered with a silken web. Certain species are gregarious in habit and live under silken webs. One southern species (*Archipsocus nomas*) spins conspicuous webs on tree trunks and larger branches.

Certain book lice are capable of making a faint ticking sound somewhat like that of a watch. This sound can be heard only in the still of the night, and is called the deathwatch by superstitious people in the belief that it presages the death of some member of the household. It is believed that the insect produces the sound by tapping the abdomen against a resonant support such as a thin piece of paper. Small wood boring beetles of the family Anobiidae also make a similar ticking sound by striking their heads or jaws against the sides of their tunnel.

Book lice sometimes become so abundant in dwellings that control measures are necessary. Sunning books, papers, and furniture will usually free such articles of the pest. Heating the rooms to a relatively high temperature will likewise prove effective in eliminating the insects. Ordinary household sprays are quite effective in control of book lice.

The biology of Psocoptera is imperfectly known. They usually overwinter outdoors in the egg stage, but in heated buildings breeding of book lice may continue throughout the year. More than 1000 species are known of which about 150 species occur in North America.

ORDER THYSANOPTERA[5]
THRIPS

General characteristics of the Thysanoptera are:

1. Two pairs of wings, often absent, long narrow, membranous and fringed with long hairs, particularly on posterior margin.
2. Mouthparts modified for rasping and sucking.
3. Gradual metamorphosis which differs from the usual type in that a quiescent (pupa) stage precedes the adult.
4. Tarsi are 1- or 2-segmented, each with a retractile bladderlike structure on the end.
5. Minute insects, usually less than 1/8 of an inch long.

Although quite numerous, thrips are seldom noticed because of their minute size. They are most readily found in flowers, e.g., primroses and legumes. When they get on the hands and arms of persons they may bite tender skin and cause some discomfort.

Thrips (Figure 75) are slender in form and seldom measure more than 2 or 3 mm in length. Some have functional wings; others may be apterous or possess short nonfunctional wings. The normally developed wings are long and narrow, with few or no veins and are fringed with hairs, particularly on the posterior margin. This fringe of hairs aids in flight and compensates, at least in part, for the small area of the membrane. The wings lie flat on the body when not in use. The antennae have six to nine segments; the compound eyes are relatively large, and the abdomen is ten-segmented.

[5] *Thysanos,* fringe; *pteron,* wing.

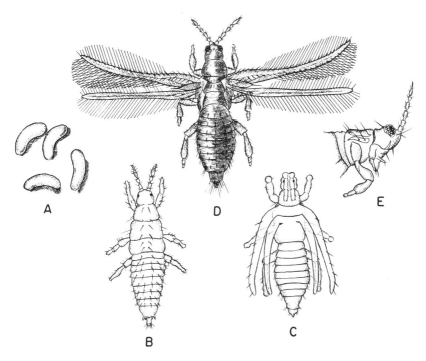

Figure 75. The pear thrips (*Taeniothrips inconsequens*). A. Eggs. B. Larva. C. Pupa. D. Adult. E. Side view of head to show mouthparts—all greatly enlarged. (Adapted from USDA.)

The tarsi of thrips are quite distinctive in structure. They are one- or two-segmented, usually devoid of claws, and terminate in a cup-shaped depression. Within the latter is a bladderlike organ which is protruded when the tarsus is in contact with an object and retracted when it is not in use.

The mouthparts are of a rasping and sucking type, and are somewhat peculiar in structure. They are in the form of a blunt cone and are situated far back on the underside of the head. The rasping and piercing operation is performed by the needlelike maxillae, assisted by the left mandible. The right mandible is vestigial.

Metamorphosis of the Thysanoptera is gradual but deviates from the usual type in that a quiescent stage precedes the adult. The first two or three instars are similar in appearance and in feeding habits to the adults. These are known as larvae. Then follows a prepupal stage in which wing pads suddenly appear but the insect remains fairly active. In the fourth instar the wing pads and antennae are enlarged; the insect is completely inactive and does not feed. Some species even have a fifth instar. This type of development is not typically gradual metamorphosis, nor is it complete. It may be regarded as intermediate between the two types of development.

Although sexual reproduction is the rule, parthenogenesis is quite common. In some species males are quite rare; in others, parthenogenesis may occur even though males are commonly found.

Thrips commonly feed on plants, particularly the flower parts. They may occur in most species of flowers and attack a wide range of cultivated plants. A number are pests of flowers, greenhouse plants, and such crops as onions, pears, cotton, and citrus. Injury is produced by puncturing and rasping the surface of leaves, buds, stems, and flowers. All thrips are not phytophagous. Some are predators on mites, such as the red spider mite; small insects; and insect eggs. About 4000 species of thrips are known, of which some 500 are recorded from North America.

THE ONION THRIPS (*Thrips tabaci*). This insect (Figure 76) is an important pest of onions. Often entire fields of the plant are destroyed by its attacks. It is a widely distributed pest, occurring throughout the United States, Canada, and Europe. Stems of infested onions assume a silvery appearance caused by the removal of juices from the cells. As the infestation continues, the stems turn brown and die. The heaviest concentrations of the insects are found between the sheaths and stems of the plants. A number of other plants also serve as hosts, e.g., numerous weeds, cotton, melons, turnips, cucumbers, and tomatoes.

The onion thrips is yellowish and about ½₅ inch in length. The females have fully developed wings, but the males are wingless and occur in much smaller numbers. Females regularly reproduce asexually. The larvae develop through 4 instars; the last 2 are passed without food in the ground. A life cycle varies in length from 15 to 30 days, and a number of generations may be devel-

Figure 76. Onion thrips (*Thrips tabaci*). (From USDA.)

oped in one season. Winter is passed as adults or larvae in protected places. Feeding may occur throughout this season in the South.

Weeds in the immediate vicinity of fields should be destroyed to prevent the buildup of infestations on these hosts. Applications of diazinon, malathion, parathion, and related insecticides either as sprays or dusts are recommended in the control of the pest.

THE FLOWER THRIPS (*Frankliniella tritici*) and the TOBACCO THRIPS (*Frankliniella fusca*). The yellowish to dark brown adults are about ½₅ inch in length. They attack a wide range of plants, such as many weeds, flowers, wheat, the strawberry, alfalfa, clover, and cotton. In the South they are pests of importance of cotton in the early season. Both flower and vegetative buds are attacked, as are the leaves and flowers. Destruction of the terminal buds of the young cotton plants results in distorted and abnormal growth of the plants. At 87° F the flower thrips may complete a life cycle in 10 days. When the temperature is lowered to 73° F the life cycle is lengthened to 18 days, and at 61° F the time is increased to 27 days. The length of a life cycle of the tobacco thrips is somewhat longer; about 3 more days are required for each temperature condition. Both species produce female offspring only after fertilization, and eggs from unmated females develop only into males. A number of generations are produced annually. Control measures recommended for the onion thrips are suggested for these species.

THE CITRUS THRIPS (*Scirtothrips citri*). This small yellowish insect is a pest of importance in the more arid regions of California and Arizona. Injury is produced through feeding on the buds, new growth, and fruit of citrus trees. Young trees may be retarded and the growth distorted as a result of the feeding injury. The value of the fruit is reduced because the skin is scarred and often ringed due to the feeding when the fruit is small. Many deciduous fruits and numerous other plants also serve as hosts of the insect. A new generation may be produced in 2 or 3 weeks. Winter is passed in the egg stage deposited in the leaves and stems of host plants. Applications of sulfur dust or sprays of parathion will control the pest.

THE GLADIOLUS THRIPS (*Taeniothrips simplex*). The gladiolus thrips is a pest of importance. Feeding of the insects causes a characteristic "silvering" of the leaves. The flowers may be deformed and spotted, and the spikes and corms injured. Lilies and iris are other hosts.

The insect is brownish black and about ¹⁄₁₆ inch long. It overwinters on the corms except in warm climates when hibernation may occur outdoors. Some breeding may occur on corms in storage at temperatures above 60° F. A generation may be completed in 2–4 weeks during the warmer seasons.

Corms free from infestation should be used. Gladioli should not be grown in soil infested by the insect the previous year. Some varieties of gladioli are reported to be resistant to the pest. Thrips on corms may be eliminated by dusting them with chlordane. The insect on growing plants may be controlled by applications of chlordane or toxaphene dusts or sprays.

THE PEAR THRIPS (*Taeniothrips inconsequens*). This small, dark-colored insect passes the winter in the ground and emerges in the spring as the fruit buds are swelling. It works its way between the bud scales and feeds on the delicate parts, thus causing the buds to shrivel and die. The leaves, flowers, and fruit are also injured. Eggs are deposited chiefly in the young leaves, fruit stems, and small fruit. The egg-laying period lasts about 3 weeks. The eggs hatch in about a week, and the larvae feed on the leaves and young fruit for 3 or 4 weeks and then drop to the ground to enter the soil and complete the life cycle. Adults do not emerge until the next spring. The life history of this insect is unlike that of other thrips as only one generation is developed each year and its activity is limited to a rather short period during the spring. Other hosts are fruits such as prunes, cherries, apples, apricots, and grapes. Timely sprays of malathion or diazinon effectively control the pest. Thorough and deep cultivation of the soil in late summer or early fall will destroy many of the larvae in the soil; however, care must be taken to prevent injury to the trees in plowing.

CHAPTER 9
ORDERS MALLOPHAGA AND ANOPLURA

ORDER MALLOPHAGA [1]
CHEWING LICE

The Mallophaga are characterized as:

1. Small wingless insects which live as ectoparasites of birds and mammals.
2. Metamorphosis gradual but approaching an ametabolous condition due to the parasitic habits.
3. Mouthparts formed for chewing, but modified.
4. Body considerably flattened and hard; the head generally large and the eyes degenerate.

The chewing or biting lice have been generally known as bird lice because they are found chiefly on these hosts. Since quite a number of species also occur as parasites of mammals, the common name cannot be considered quite appropriate for the order as a whole.

The Mallophaga feed primarily on the feathers, hair, skin scales, possible blood clots, and other materials on the hosts. Recently certain species have been found obtaining blood by puncturing the base of young feathers. This method of feeding, however, does not appear to be of much importance. The principal injury produced is through constant irritation of the hosts. Birds dust themselves in the attempt to obtain relief from the parasites. Chewing lice are not known to be vectors of any diseases.

The tarsi of chewing lice infesting birds terminate in a pair of claws which are adapted for clinging to feathers (Figure 77). All lice on mammals, with the exception of rare species found on kangaroos, wallabies and wombats, bear only one tarsal claw which folds against the tibia. The clasping organ thus formed is admirably adapted for clinging to hair. Chewing lice may also cling to the hair and feathers by means of the mandibles.

[1] *Mallos*, wool; *phagein*, eat.

A   B

Figure 77. Common poultry lice. A. The body louse (*Menacanthus stramineus*), male. B. The shaft louse (*Menopon gallinae*), female. (From Agricultural Research Services, USDA.)

Mallophaga are quite specific in their host relationships. Most species parasitize only one host or closely related forms. The entire life cycle of these parasites is spent on the host animal and they are transferred from one individual to another mainly by contact. If a host dies, the lice also perish unless another host is readily available.

The life histories of relatively few species are known. The eggs, commonly called "nits," are glued near the base of the feathers or hair by a cementlike substance secreted by the female at the time of oviposition. The eggs hatch into nymphs which pass through several molts before the adult stage is attained. The duration of a life cycle depends upon the species concerned, and so far as is known may vary from 3 to 7 weeks.

More than 2500 species of Mallophaga are known, of which several hundred are found in North America. Over 40 species have been reported infesting poultry, 7 of which are quite common. The more common species found on chickens are the body louse (*Menacanthus stramineus*), the head louse (*Cuclotogaster heterographus*), and the shaft louse (*Menopon gallinae*). Young chickens may be killed by heavy infestations of lice. As most young chickens are now grown in brooders, there is small likelihood of louse infestations becoming established. Injury to older chickens is produced mainly through irritation caused by the parasites feeding and crawling over their bodies. Many poultrymen are more concerned with the discomfort experienced when the lice crawl on them in caring for the birds than the injury produced. Pigeons often become heavily infested with the small pigeon louse (*Goniocotes bidentatus*) and the slender pigeon louse (*Columbicola columbae*).

In poultry louse control, coumaphos, carbaryl, and malathion are recommended. These compounds also aid in control of other pests. (The feed and water of poultry should not be contaminated with these insecticides.)

Cats may suffer irritation from infestations of *Felicola subrostrata*. A powder containing rotenone is recommended for the control of the pest on cats. Dogs may harbor a small species (*Trichodectes canis*). Rotenone and malathion powders will readily eliminate this parasite on these animals.

Livestock are also subject to infestations of chewing lice. Horses become infested with *Bovicola equi*, and cattle with *B. bovis*. Sheep may become heavily infested with *Bovicola ovis*. *Bovicola caprae* and *B. hermsi* are harbored by goats. Control measures for chewing lice on domestic animals are the same as those recommended for sucking lice under the order Anoplura.

ORDER ANOPLURA[2]
SUCKING LICE

The order may be described as:

1. Small depressed wingless insects which live as ectoparasites only on mammals.
2. Mouthparts formed for piercing-sucking; head narrow and usually pointed in front.
3. Metamorphosis gradual but approaching an ametabolous condition due to the parasitic habits.
4. Eyes vestigial or wanting.

The order Anoplura is composed of blood-sucking lice. These are important parasites because they subsist on blood of mammals

[2] *Anoplus*, unarmed; *oura*, tail.

and are vectors of various diseases. Sucking lice attack only mammals and are never found on birds, as are the chewing lice (Mallophaga). This is a small order of insects, consisting of less than 300 species.

The mouthparts are fitted for piercing and sucking, and are retracted within the head. The apex of the mouth is encircled with small hooks which are attached to the skin during feeding activities. The piercing and sucking organs consist of several stylets which are forced into the skin. The homologies of these parts are uncertain. The legs are fitted for grasping. Each tarsus ends in a single claw which folds back on a thumblike projection of the tibia, thus forming an efficient organ for clinging to the hairs of the host.

The Anoplura, in common with the chewing lice (Mallophaga), are obligatory ectoparasites, and are quite restricted to specific hosts. Under normal conditions the entire life cycle is spent on one animal. The parasites are transferred from one animal to another chiefly by bodily contact.

THE HEAD AND BODY LOUSE (*Pediculus humanus*). The most important sucking louse is the head and body louse of man (Figure 78). The species was formerly considered as two, the head louse and the body louse, but research has established that they are varieties

Figure 78. A. The body louse (*Pediculus humanus*). B. Egg of *Pediculus humanus* attached to a human hair. (From J. Smart, *Insects of Medical Importance.* Copyright 1943. Used by permission of British Museum of Natural History, London.)

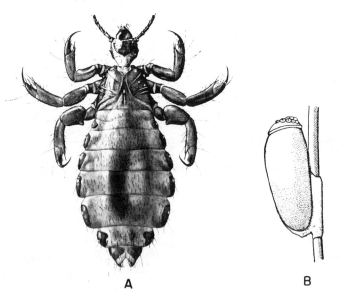

A   B

of the same. Head and body lice occur on man where overcrowding and substandard living conditions exist. Infestations of body lice become particularly prevalent during war conditions. The use of DDT powder efficiently controlled the pest during World War II and eliminated sporadic outbreaks of typhus fever.

The head louse inhabits the head, but it is said the louse may also be found on other hairy parts of the body. It averages 2 or 3 mm in length and is somewhat smaller than the body louse. The eggs (nits) are cemented to the hairs and hatch in about a week. A complete life cycle from egg to egg is about 3 weeks. Head lice may be eliminated by dusting lightly with MYL powder or rotenone.

The body louse occurs on most parts of the body, particularly on the back and chest. Normally the eggs are laid in the seams of the clothing, but also they may be attached to hairs. Body lice are commonly found on soldiers, sailors, prisoners, and others who live in overcrowded quarters and do not have the opportunity of changing clothing and bathing regularly. The life cycle of the body louse is similar to that of the head louse, but the former is more prolific, since more eggs are laid by the female.

Head and body lice are to be feared as vectors of relapsing fever, trench fever, and the dreaded epidemic form of typhus fever. During and following World War I, typhus fever swept over large areas of Europe and Asia, and caused the death of millions of people. The application of DDT powder under the clothing and on the head readily eliminates these lice. However, during the war in Korea, lice in that area were not effectively controlled with DDT, and other insecticides, such as lindane, had to be used. MYL powder or malathion may be used.

THE CRAB LOUSE (*Phthirus pubis*). This species is distinctive in its crablike appearance (Figure 79A). It is nearly as broad as long and is about 1½–2 mm in length. A related species, *Phthirus gorillae*, occurs on the gorilla. The crab louse inhabits particularly the pubic and perianal regions of the body. The eggs hatch in about 7 days. Fewer eggs are laid and the life cycle is somewhat longer; therefore it is not so prolific as the head and body louse. The insect is not known to carry any disease. MYL or malathion dust may be used for control.

Sucking Lice of Domestic Animals

Sucking lice are important pests of domestic animals. The hog louse (*Haematopinus suis*) (Figure 79B) is a common pest of hogs. It is the largest of all Anoplura and measures ⅕ inch in length. Four species of the order commonly infest cattle. Of these, the short-nosed cattle louse (*Haematopinus eurysternus*) (Figure 80A) is probably the most important in the United States. The cattle tail louse (*Haematopinus quadripertusus*) is a relatively recent introduction into the United States. This form appears to be spreading

Figure 79. A. The crab louse (*Phthirus pubis*). B. The hog louse (*Haematopinus suis*). (From J. Smart, *Insects of Medical Importance*. Copyright 1943. Used by permission of British Museum of Natural History, London.)

Figure 80. A. The short-nosed cattle louse (*Haematopinus eurysternus*), female. B. The long-nosed cattle louse (*Linognathus vituli*), female. (Courtesy of G. F. Ferris.)

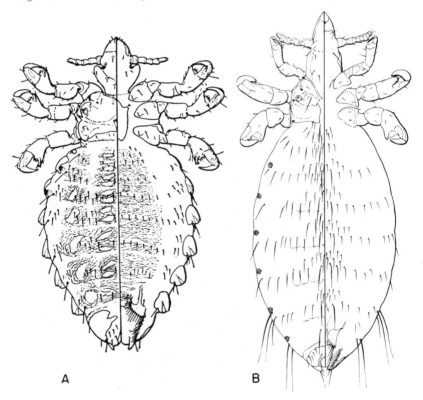

and it is assuming greater importance. Two other species which occur on cattle are the long-nosed cattle louse (*Linognathus vituli*) (Figure 80B) and the blue louse (*Solenopotes capillatus*). Horses and mules may become infested with *Haematopinus asini*. Two species, *Linognathus ovillus* and *Linognathus pedalis*, occur on sheep in the United States. Heavy infestations of *Linognathus stenopsis* occur at times on goats. Dogs may suffer from infestations of *Linognathus setosus*.

Lice on domestic animals may be controlled without difficulty. Sprays or dips containing coumaphos, malathion, or lindane will control hog lice. These parasites on beef cattle may be controlled by use of one of several insecticides, such as toxaphene, dioxathion, malathion, lindane, or coumaphos. The same compounds may be employed in control of sheep and goat lice. Ciodrin and pyrethrins are designated for use on dairy animals.

CHAPTER 10
ORDER HEMIPTERA[1]

BUGS

The Hemiptera are distinguished from insects of other orders by having:

1. Two pairs of wings almost always present; the front wings, the hemelytra, with exceptions, thickened at the base with the apical portions membranous and overlapping when not in use.
2. Mouthparts typically piercing and sucking, without palpi, and arising from the front part of the underside of the head.
3. Gradual metamorphosis.
4. A plate usually triangular in outline, the scutellum, located between the base of the wings.
5. Body build usually broad and flattened dorsoventrally.

Any insect or animal resembling an insect is known by the layman as a bug. But the name "bug" can be correctly applied only to a member of this large and important order of insects (Figure 81). Bugs are among the more common insects. They are widely distributed throughout the world, but they reach their greatest numbers and diversity of form in the tropical regions. They vary in size from extremely small insects to individuals measuring 4 or 5 inches in length. Hemipterous insects are chiefly terrestrial, but some are aquatic and others are semiaquatic in habitat.

Bugs are generally considered as plant feeders and a number of important plant pests belong to this order. Some, however, are predaceous, feeding on other insects, and others are parasites of man and animals.

In Hemiptera the body is normally broad and somewhat flattened dorsoventrally. The thorax and abdomen are broadly joined. Between the base of the wings there is usually a large triangular plate known as the scutellum. In some groups this plate covers most of the body behind the pronotum.

[1] *Hemi*, half; *pteron*, wing.

Figure 81. The harlequin bug (*Murgantia histrionica*). A. Eggs with newly hatched nymphs. B and C. Nymphs. D. Adult.

Wings are usually present, and four in number. They lie flat upon the body when not in use. The hind pair is membranous and covered by the front pair when the wings are folded. The front pair is thickened and corneous on the basal portion and membranous apically. The membranous parts of the front wings overlap when they are at rest. The corneous nature of the basal portion of the front wings is similar in texture to the elytra of beetles, hence they are known as hemelytra (half-wings). The divisions of the basal portion and the venation of the membranous apices of the hemelytra are of much value in the taxonomy of the order (Figure 82).

The mouthparts of Hemiptera are typically piercing and sucking. Insects with such mouthparts puncture the epidermis of plants and the skin of animals with the slender stylets and take up the sap or blood as food. The structure of the mouthparts and the manner in which they function are discussed on page 37. Obviously no type of stomach poison could ever function in the control of insects with such mouthparts. When chemical control of pests belonging to this order is needed, contact poisons and fumigants must be employed.

Most bugs secrete disagreeable odors for protection from their natural enemies. The scent glands of the bedbug are located on the dorsal surface of the first three abdominal segments. In stink-

Figure 82. Diagrammatic illustrations of front wings (hemelytra) of Hemiptera. A. *An-thocoridae.* B. *Coreidae.* C. *Miridae.* D. *Pyrrhocoridae.* E. *Reduviidae.* F. *Nabidae.* C, cuneus; Cl, clavus; Co, corium; E, embolium; M, membrane.

bugs and squash bugs these glands open on the dorsum of the abdomen of the nymphs and the ventral surface of the thorax of the adults.

Family Pentatomidae (Stinkbugs)
Stinkbugs are relatively large insects with five-segmented antennae and a large-sized scutellum, triangular in shape, narrowing posteriorly. Members of this family are generally plant feeders and suck the sap of leaves, stems, and fruit. Some are predaceous, such as the two-spotted stinkbug (*Perillus bioculatus*) which feeds almost entirely on the Colorado potato beetle (adults, larvae, and eggs). Others are both predaceous and phytophagous, e.g., the green stinkbug (*Acrosternum hilare*).

Stinkbugs overwinter as adults, yet in the southernmost parts of the United States certain species may remain more or less active throughout the winter. Eggs are laid on end in clusters or in rows on the host plants. The total number of eggs laid varies from 100 to several hundred. The generations produced in a season may range from 1 to 5, the number depending upon the species and climatic conditions.

THE HARLEQUIN BUG (*Murgantia histrionica*). In the South this insect (Figure 81) is a pest well known to every truck farmer and gardener. It occurs as far north as Washington, Ohio, Wisconsin, New Jersey, and New York, but rarely produces much damage in the northern range of its distribution. This insect inflicts considerable damage and often destroys entire crops of cabbage, mustard, turnips, and other cruciferous plants. Other plants are occasionally attacked. Sap and chlorophyll are taken from the leaves with the piercing-sucking mouthparts, and heavily infested plants may appear as if they have been scorched by fire.

This conspicuous black and red or yellow-checkered bug is about ½ inch in length. Because of its markings it is also known as the calico back, terrapin back, and fire bug. Another common name, Lincoln bug, was applied by the farmers because, a native of Central America, it was first found in Texas during the Civil War.

Eggs are usually laid on the underside of the leaves and are arranged in two-row clusters of about 12 each. They are laid on end and measure ¹⁄₂₅ inch in height; are white and banded by 2 black rings. In warm weather the eggs hatch in 4 or 5 days. The nymphs pass through 5 instars before attaining the adult stage. During the warmer parts of the season a life cycle may be completed in 40–60 days. Adults are long lived and may live for several months. During this time each female may lay more than 100 eggs. The insects overwinter as adults under crop residues, grass, brush, and other debris. In its southern limits some activity and breeding may occur during mild weather throughout the winter. As many as three complete generations and a partial fourth have been recorded.

In control of the harlequin bug it is important that crop residues and hibernation places be destroyed. Trap crops are of some aid in combating the insect. Rows of mustard, kale, or rape may be planted prior to the main crop and the bugs allowed to collect on them. These plants, together with the bugs, are then destroyed by spraying with oil or by burning. Endosulfan and parathion are recommended in control of this pest.

THE SOUTHERN GREEN STINKBUG (*Nezara viridula*). This insect (Figure 83) is a widespread and well known pest of peas, beans, cotton, tomato, pecan, citrus, and other field and garden plants. The feeding punctures of this and related species may result in the destruction or partial destruction of cotton bolls, peas and beans in the pod, and deformation of the fruit of tomatoes and peaches. The kernels of pecans often have discolored spots and are bitter to the taste. This disorder, known as kernel spot, is caused by the feeding of this and other hemipterous insects before the nuts mature. Azinphosmethyl and parathion sprays and dusts are recommended as control measures. The elimination of alternate host plants and hibernation quarters is also advisable.

The green stinkbug (*Acrosternum hilare*) is a closely related species which causes similar injury. The conchuela (*Chlorochroa*

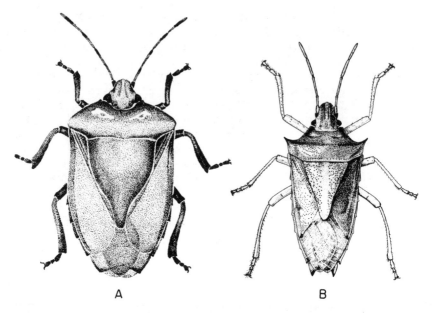

Figure 83. Common stinkbugs. A. The southern green stinkbug (*Nezara viridula*). (From Department of Entomology, Texas A&M University.) B. The rice stinkbug (*Oebalus pugnax*). (From USDA.)

---

ligata) and the Say stinkbug (*Chlorochroa sayi*) are important species in the Southwest.

Family Coreidae (Squash Bugs)
Representatives of the Coreidae have four segments in both beak and antenna; ocelli are present, and the membrane of the hemelytron has many veins which arise from a transverse basal vein.

THE SQUASH BUG (*Anasa tristis*). This species is the best known member of this large family of bugs. The adult is a robust bug ½ to ⅔ inch in length and about ¼ inch wide (Figure 84). Its general color is dark brown, produced by a yellow background densely covered by black punctuations. The nymphal stages are grayish, except the first instar, which is green and black.

The insect attacks squashes, pumpkins, and other cucurbits. Infested leaves assume a grayish cast, wilt, and die. If the infestation is heavy, the entire plant may be killed. Following the death of the plant, clusters of the bugs may be found sucking the juices of the fruit. Most injury occurs in the latter part of the season when nymphs are numerous.

The squash bug overwinters in the adult stage under crop residues, piles of boards and trash, in buildings, and other available shelter. It emerges late in the spring. When the plants have emerged and are growing, the adults begin feeding and egg laying. Eggs are usually laid in rows on the underside of the leaves between large veins. When plants are heavily infested, eggs may be laid on the upper surface of leaves and other places as well. The eggs are oval, brown, and about ¹⁄₁₆ inch in length. About 24 eggs are laid in an average cluster. A female will lay a total of several hundred eggs before she dies. Eggs hatch in 1–2 weeks. Maturity is reached by passing through 5 nymphal instars and the egg to adult development ranges from 45 to 60 days. The number of generations annually varies from 1 to 3.

The squash bug is difficult to control. The destruction of crop residues and elimination of hibernation quarters are essential practices in controlling the pest. Hand picking when the bugs first appear may be practical when only a few plants are involved. Chemical control has not proved very satisfactory. Applications of carbaryl afford a measure of control. Parathion is recommended for use on commercial crops.

THE LEAF-FOOTED BUG (*Leptoglossus phyllopus*). This insect is commonly a pest of peas, beans, potatoes, tomatoes, pecans, and other plants. It feeds upon the fruit and tender growth. The fruit of the peach, tomato, and others may be disfigured and gnarled by the feeding of this species, and the attacks upon ripening fruit may result in rotting. Peas and beans are injured the most when the

Figure 84. The squash bug (*Anasa tristis*). A. Eggs. B. Adult. (From USDA.)

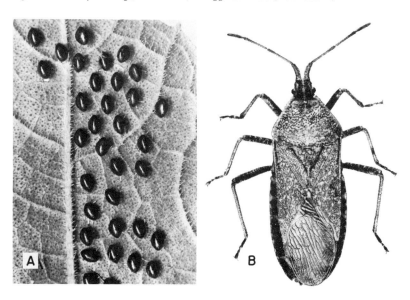

insect punctures the seed in the pod and sucks out the plant juices. Injury to the nuts of pecans is identical with that produced by stinkbugs.

The leaf-footed plant bug is brown, oblong, and about ⅘ inch in length (Figure 85). A white band extends across the front wings. The hind tibiae are dilated or leaflike, a characteristic that has suggested the common name of the insect.

The insect overwinters as an adult in almost any sheltered place. The adults emerge in the spring and feed on a rather wide range of host plants. Fifteen to 35 eggs are laid in a cluster and in definite rows, and are usually placed on the smooth surface of twigs of host plants. Two generations annually have been observed in warm climates. Cleanup measures to eliminate hibernation quarters and alternate host plants, and dusting or spraying with carbaryl are recommended control measures.

THE BOXELDER BUG (*Leptocoris trivittatus*). This bug often becomes a nuisance about homes in the fall and during warm winter days, when it may collect in large numbers upon tree trunks and porches or find its way into dwellings. It overwinters as an adult in homes or other dry protected places. These bugs are dark brown with three longitudinal red lines on the thorax and with the veins of the hemelytra red. They are somewhat narrow and about ½ inch long (Figure 86). This insect feeds principally on boxelder but it may also attack a number of other plants. The presence of the

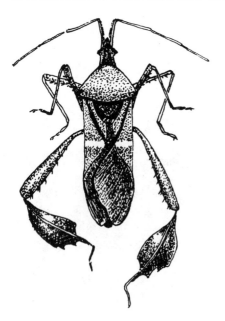

Figure 85. The leaf-footed plant bug (*Leptoglossus phyllopus*).

insects in dwellings is a nuisance only, as they do not injure man or any of his household belongings in any way.

Boxelder bugs may be controlled with chlordane sprays. Liberal applications of the spray should be made, particularly on tree trunks and other places where concentrations of the bugs occur.

Family Lygaeidae (The Chinch Bug Family)
Members of the chinch bug family have both beaks and antennae 4-segmented; ocelli are usually present and the membrane of the hemelytra has 4 or 5 simple veins which arise from a transverse basal vein. This is a large family of small bugs including more than 1500 species of which more than 200 occur in North America. All are phytophagous and several are important pests.

THE CHINCH BUG (*Blissus leucopterus*). This insect ranges in distribution from Central America northward to southern Canada, and is a pest of much importance in the Middle West. Host plants are corn, wheat, oats, barley, grain sorghums, and other members of the grass family.

This is a small insect not more than ⅙ or ⅕ inch in length, but its smallness belies its capacity for injury, as enormous numbers more than compensate for size. The body is black. The front wings are white with a black spot near the middle of each outer margin.

The chinch bug overwinters as adults in any available cover. Clumps of grass are commonly selected as places of hibernation; however, it may be found in corn shocks, hedgerows, woodlands,

Figure 86. The boxelder bug (*Leptocoris trivittatus*). (Prepared by the Clemson University Cooperative Extension Service's Entomology-Plant Pathology and Agricultural Communications Sections, Federal Extension Service Cooperating.)

stubble, and other places during the winter. In the spring the adults emerge from hibernation and fly to fields of small grain. Eggs are deposited behind the sheaths of the lower leaves and on the roots of the plants if the soil is loose. Each female lays 200 or more eggs during a period of 3 or 4 weeks. The eggs are small, cylindrical, and yellow. They hatch in 1–2 weeks into reddish nymphs which are characterized by a light band across the back. The adult stage is reached in 30–40 days after passing through 5 nymphal instars (Figure 87). The chinch bug usually has 2 generations annually, but in the Southwest at least a partial third generation occurs.

In the southernmost parts of the United States the chinch bug may fly directly from hibernation quarters to corn (Figure 88). Also, in parts of Oklahoma and Texas the first generation may be completed on small grain by the time these crops mature, and the migration to corn and grain sorghums is then accomplished by flight and not by crawling. In the Middle West small grains mature and are harvested before the first generation of the chinch bug is completed and the insect usually crawls to the cornfields.

Wet weather is the most important control factor for the chinch bug. Heavy beating rains destroy many of the insects at the time the eggs hatch. Wet cloudy weather also fosters outbreaks of the chinch bug fungus (*Beauveria globulifera*). The combination of these factors will usually eliminate serious infestations of the insect.

Chinch bugs avoid shade and prefer sunshine. Planting cowpeas or soybeans among corn to shade the base of the plants creates conditions unfavorable for the bugs and will help reduce injury. Varieties of grain sorghums and corn are being developed which show some resistance to chinch bug attack. Rotation of crops so that fields of corn are not adjacent to wheat, oats, or

Figure 87. Nymphs and adults of the chinch bug (*Blissus leucopterus*). (From Agricultural Research Service, USDA.)

Figure 88. A heavy infestation of chinch bugs on a cornstalk. (From USDA.)

barley is advisable. The burning of overwintering quarters is a worthwhile practice when the insects are found chiefly in bunch grass. The value of this practice is questionable in other areas.

When chinch bugs are migrating from small grain fields to corn by crawling, the construction of a barrier around the margin of the field which they are leaving is an effective method of control. A very satisfactory barrier may be made by spraying dieldrin in strips about 4 rods wide between the fields of small grains and corn or sorghum. To prevent the bugs from going around the barrier, short strips should be sprayed across each end. These need to be 8–10 rods long and 2 rods wide. The spray should be applied a few days prior to migration of the bugs. The time of application may be estimated by observing the stage of maturity or ripening of the small grain upon which the insects are feeding. The spraying of chinch bugs on infested crops is effective but more expensive. Carbaryl and toxaphene along with other insecticides are recommended.

The hairy chinch bug (*Blissus leucopterus hirtus*) is predominantly a short-winged form and lacks the migratory habit of the common chinch bug. Sometimes it is a pest of lawns and greens in the northeastern states. The use of fertilizers, watering, and frequent cutting helps the grass withstand injury. Chlordane and other recommended insecticides provide control of the species.

The southern chinch bug (*Blissus insularis*) is a pest of importance to St. Augustine lawns in the South. It also attacks crosses of St. Augustine grass. The adults have a black body with white wings folded over the back. Upon hatching, the nymphs are yellow but soon turn red with a light colored band across the abdomen. The damage is first observed as small yellow or brown discolored areas which gradually increase in size. The injury may be confused with a disease condition or a physiological disorder. The infestation can only be diagnosed by careful examination and finding of the bugs. Carbophenothion (Trithion), diazinon, or ethion sprays are recommended.

The false chinch bug (*Nysius ericae*) feeds on grain sorghums, potatoes, grapes, cruciferous plants, cotton, and many other plants. Only occasionally is it an important pest of any crop. Superficially the insect resembles the chinch bug; its color is more uniform and ranges from grayish to fuscous. When control measures are advisable, applications of malathion are recommended.

Family Pyrrhocoridae (Stainers or Red Bugs)

Most members of the family Pyrrhocoridae are found in tropical and subtropical countries. About 25 species occur in the South and Southwest. These bugs are rather large, elongate-oval in outline, stout in form, and marked with contrasting colors. Both antennae and beak are four-segmented, no cuneus is present on the hemelytron, and ocelli are absent. The insects are plant feeders and gregarious in habit.

In tropical regions cotton stainers (*Dysdercus* spp.) are major cotton pests, but in the United States their injury to the crop is of little importance. Damage is caused by puncturing of the bolls, which may then be destroyed or the lint stained to a yellowish or brownish color. The staining is produced by exudations of punctured seeds.

The biology of the insects is not fully known. In addition to cotton, oranges, cockleburs, eggplants, numbers of other plants serve as hosts. Eggs are laid in the soil or trash. The life cycle seems to be similar to that of stinkbugs (*Pentatomidae*). The best known species in the United States are the cotton stainer (*Dysdercus suturellus*), the southwestern cotton stainer (*Dysdercus albidiventris*), and the bordered plant bug (*Euryophthalmus succinctus*). Sprays or dusts of endrin are recommended if control measures are needed.

Family Tingidae (Lace Bugs)

The lace bugs are readily recognized by the reticulated and lace-like structure of the hemelytra; this characteristic is usually accompanied by lateral expansions of the pronotum of similar markings (Figure 89). Members of this small family of bugs feed on the sap of plants and occur on the under surface of leaves. Infested leaves may be recognized by the light stippled effect of

Figure 89. A lace bug (*Corythucha*). (From USDA.)

the dorsal surface Trees, shrubs, cotton, and many other plants are attacked. Eggs are deposited in plant tissue and are usually covered by a secretion which hardens and forms conical projections on the surface. Nymphs are usually darker and have little resemblance to the adults.

About 100 species of lace bugs are known to occur in North America. The sycamore lace bug (*Corythucha ciliata*) is a common form. Eggs are laid in the ribs of the underside of leaves. Seven to 9 weeks are required for a life cycle. Two or more generations are produced each season. The adult is the overwintering stage. The oak lace bug (*Corythucha arcuata*) is another common species. Its life history is similar to that of the sycamore lace bug, except the winter is passed either in the egg or adult stage. The elm lace bug (*Corythucha ulmi*), the cotton lace bug (*Corythucha gossypii*), and the hawthorn lace bug (*Corythucha cydoniae*) are other common members of the family. Should control measures be necessary, sprays of nicotine sulfate, lindane, malathion, and dimethoate are recommended.

Family Miridae (Plant Bugs or Leaf Bugs)
The Miridae are a large family of small to medium sized bugs. The most distinctive family characteristics are found on the hemelytra. The cuneus is present and one or two cells are found at the base of the membrane. Other characteristics are the four-segmented beak and the absence of ocelli. Most of the species feed on plant juices; however, some are predaceous on other insects.

A wide variety of plants are fed upon by these insects, which cause several types of injury. Fruit trees, vegetables, alfalfa, cotton, weeds of various kinds, and grasses are typical host plants. Both fruit and vegetative buds are injured or destroyed by the feeding activities of plant bugs. Fruit may be attacked, and become malformed and of reduced value. Flowers and seeds are subject to attack and may be destroyed. Plant bugs may increase rapidly to large numbers, and major damage to crops may be done.

THE TARNISHED PLANT BUG (*Lygus lineolaris*). This insect is a well known pest throughout the United States. The adult is brown and mottled with yellow, black, and red. It is about ¼ inch in length and less than half as broad (Figure 90A). The nymphs are green.

Injury to leaves, stems, fruit and growth buds, flowers, seeds, and developing fruit is caused by the feeding of the insect. The adult overwinters in trash and other available shelter. In the spring eggs are laid in the tissues of various herbaceous weeds, vege-

Figure 90. A. The tarnished plant bug (*Lygus lineolaris*). B. The rapid plant bug (*Adelphocoris rapidus*). (From Illinois Natural History Survey.)

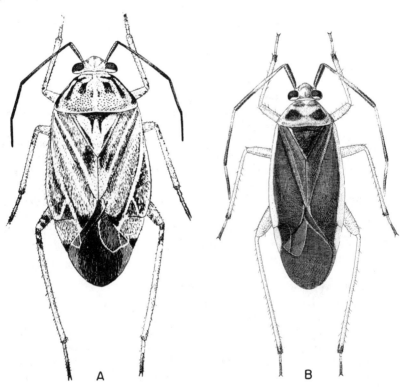

A   B

tables, and other plants. Eggs hatch in 1–2 weeks and 2–3 weeks later the adult emerges from the fifth developmental instar. Thus a generation may be completed in 3–5 weeks. Five generations may occur during a season.

Elimination of favorable overwintering quarters and the destruction of weeds will help to reduce the numbers of this insect. Dieldrin and parathion are among the compounds recommended for use in control of this pest.

Two species related to the tarnished plant bug and commonly known as lygus bugs, *Lygus elisus* and *L. hesperus*, are important pests of alfalfa and cotton in the West and Southwest. These bugs are slightly smaller and somewhat lighter in color. The biology of the two species is similar to that of the tarnished plant bug. The rapid plant bug (*Adelphocoris rapidus*) (Figure 90B) is often associated with the lygus bugs, to which it is similar in both biology and type of injury.

These plant bugs are serious pests of alfalfa, particularly when it is grown for a seed crop. Buds are destroyed, flowers drop, and seeds shrivel and turn brown when they are fed upon by the insects. The effect of these attacks also is evident in the vegetative growth. Stems branch excessively, and frequently the leaves become distorted, smaller, and more numerous. Malathion sprays are recommended for use in the late bud stage of alfalfa. If control measures are needed during the blooming period, toxaphene is recommended because this insecticide is less toxic to honeybees, which are needed for pollination.

When alfalfa and weeds are cut or have become unsuitable as hosts, the plant bugs migrate to cotton fields. Feeding on this crop causes squares, blooms, and young bolls to drop. Malformations of the plants also result. Carbaryl, parathion, or methyl parathion are recommended in control of the pest.

THE COTTON FLEAHOPPER (*Psallus seriatus*). The cotton fleahopper (Figure 91) is an important pest of cotton, particularly in the southern part of the Cotton Belt. The adult is obovate in outline, pale green, and about ⅐ inch in length. The insect may be recognized by four black marks near the tips of the front wings and small dark spots on the body surface, legs, and antennae. The nymphs are green.

The fleahopper injures cotton by puncturing and feeding on the terminal buds and newly formed squares with its piercing-sucking mouthparts. The young squares are shed, which often results in tall, whiplike plant growth without the formation of fruiting branches. Injury to the terminal buds often produces abnormal plant growth.

The cotton fleahopper diapauses in the egg stage in the stems of its host plants, particularly goat weeds (*Croton* spp.). The eggs hatch in the spring, and the nymphs feed on available weeds such as evening primrose (*Oenothera* spp.) and horsemint (*Monarda*

Figure 91. A. The cotton fleahopper (*Psallus seriatus*). B. Eggs of the cotton flea-hopper in the bark of a goatweed (*Croton capitata*). (From Texas Agricultural Experiment Station.)

spp.). When a scarcity of suitable host plants occurs, the winged forms may migrate to cotton fields. Later in the season when the weeds, particularly goat weeds, become more attractive than the cotton plant, a reverse migration to the weeds occurs.

The egg stage averages 8 days. Upon hatching the nymphs progress through 5 instars and attain the adult stage in about 11 days. Three days after maturity the females begin egg laying. An entire life cycle may be completed in 22 days. Theoretically at least, 7 or 8 generations may be completed in one season.

The cotton fleahopper is not a difficult insect to control. When cotton has reached the fruiting stage, it should be examined at weekly intervals for fleahoppers. When 15 to 35 fleahoppers per 100 plant terminals are found, control measures should be employed. A number of insecticides may be used either as sprays or as dusts in control of this pest. Some of the commonly used compounds are carbaryl and trichlorfon (Dylox).

THE GARDEN FLEAHOPPER (*Halticus bracteatus*). These small blackish insects (Figure 92) resemble plant lice, and their type of injury is quite similar. They attack peas, beans, cabbage, tomatoes, and numbers of other plants; and suck sap from the leaves and stems. Winter is passed as adults. Eggs are laid in punctures made by the mouthparts in the stems and leaves of the hosts. The nymphs are green and develop rapidly to the adult stage. Two types of females develop: a long-winged and a short-winged form. The jumping habits and the hosts of the species have probably suggested the common name. As many as five generations in one season have been recorded. Carbaryl and malathion have been recommended as control measures. Destruction of weeds which serve as hosts is recommended, because this practice will aid in prevention of the buildup of populations of the pest.

Family Phymatidae (Ambush Bugs)
The front legs of members of the Phymatidae provide the most striking marks of identification (Figure 93). The femur is short, thickened, and at least one-half as broad as long. The tibia is small and curved. The two form an efficient organ for grasping the prey, for they fit closely together and both are armed with teeth. Antennae are knobbed and in *Phymata* each fits in a groove under the lateral margin of the pronotum.

Figure 92. The garden fleahopper (*Halticus bracteatus*). A. Male. B. Short-winged female. (From Illinois Natural History Survey.)

A   B

Figure 93. An ambush bug (*Phymata pennsylvanica*). (Courtesy of C. O. Mohr.)

Phymata erosa is the most common representative of this group of predaceous insects in the United States. It is yellowish green and ⅓ to ½ inch in length. The bug hides in flowers and feeds on the insect visitors. Among its victims may be such relatively large insects as bees, wasps, and butterflies.

Family Nabidae (Damsel Bugs)
Bugs of the Nabidae are rather small with the body somewhat narrowed anteriorly. The front tibia is armed on the inner face with a double row of short spines and is capable of closing tightly on the femur to form a grasping organ. Damsel bugs are predaceous and feed on such insects as aphids and caterpillars. Some species have both long- and short-winged forms. Most common species of this small group of insects belong to the genus *Nabis* of which *N. ferus* is the best known. The bug is yellowish brown and about ⅓ inch long. It hides among foliage or in flowers and captures the insects upon which it subsists.

Family Reduviidae (Assassin Bugs)
The assassin bugs are medium to large in size, diverse in form, and some are of contrasting colors. The beak is three-segmented, arises from the tip of the head, and when at rest it lies in a cross striated groove between the front coxae. These bugs are predaceous. They feed upon diverse groups of insects and in a few cases on man and large animals. Chagas' disease, an important disease of man, is transmitted by assassin bugs. This disease is found from Mexico southward through South America.

The genus *Triatoma* includes a number of species of which *T. sanguisuga* (Figure 94A) is probably the best known. It passes under the common names of cone-nose, big bedbug, and Mexican bedbug. The insect may enter homes, and its bite is quite severe.

It is occasionally found in poultry houses and feeds on the blood of poultry as does the fowl tick (*Argus persicus*).

The "kissing bug" (*Reduvius personatus*) is one of the more common species of the family. It is found in dwellings and commonly feeds on bedbugs, flies, and other insects. The insect occasionally bites man. The nymphs cover themselves with particles of lint to camouflage their presence.

Melanolestes picipes is often attracted to lights in the home. The insect is to be avoided as it may inflict painful bites if handled carelessly. This species is black and occurs outdoors where it feeds on insects of various kinds.

Probably the most striking representative of the family is the wheel bug (*Arilus cristatus*). It was given the name because of the presence of a crested pronotum, notched along the median line. The insect is quite large and the general color is gray. It is predaceous on other insects. When molested this insect defends itself by inflicting a painful bite.

Family Anthocoridae (Flower Bugs or Minute Pirate Bugs)
The members of this family of small predaceous bugs, unlike most Hemiptera, have hemelytra provided with a well developed embolium. The species are small and are usually black with white markings. They feed on insect eggs, newly hatched larvae, nymphs, spider mites, thrips, and other small forms.

Figure 94. Assassin bugs. A. The blood sucking cone-nose (*Triatoma sanguisuga*). (From Department of Entomology, Texas A&M University.) B. *Zelus bilobus*, a beneficial predator. (Prepared by the Clemson University Cooperative Extension Service's Entomology-Plant Pathology and Agricultural Communications Sections, Federal Extension Service Cooperating.)

Orius insidiosus is the best known species (Figure 95). It is an important predator in the fields and gardens where it feeds on a rather wide variety of small insect life. The adults are about ¹⁄₁₂ inch long and black. The corium of the hemelytra is yellowish white and is marked by a large triangular black spot at the tip; the membrane is white. The insect bears a superficial resemblance to the chinch bug. The tiny nymphs are yellowish. Adults overwinter in trash. Eggs are deposited in plant tissues. Several generations are completed each season.

Family Cimicidae (Bedbugs)

Bedbugs are wingless parasites that feed on the blood of mammals and birds. Wings are absent, but vestigial front wings are usually present. The body is decidedly flattened dorsoventrally so that the bugs may readily hide in cracks and crevices. The beak is three-segmented, and ocelli are absent. About 30 species have been described and of these, 8 are found in North America.

The common bedbug (*Cimex lectularius*), is an old and unwelcome guest of man (Figure 96). It is reddish brown, ovate, about ¹⁄₅ inch long, and possesses a distinctive odor. The insect is nocturnal and is known to feed only at night. Besides man, other common hosts are rats, mice, and poultry. Chicken houses and coops may become infested as with the fowl tick.

The bedbug is capable of living for a year without food. It may crawl from one apartment to another or to another house in close proximity. Incipient infestations are usually established by bringing the insect into the home in clothing, handbags, and other articles.

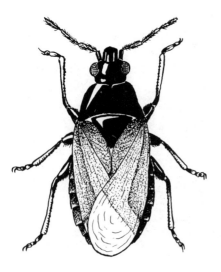

Figure 95. A flower bug (*Orius insidiosus*).

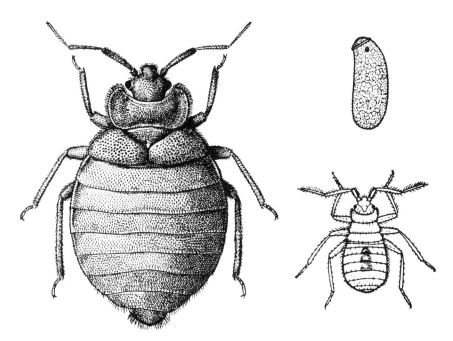

Figure 96. The bedbug (*Cimex lectularius*); adult male, nymph, and egg (not all of the same magnification). (From J. Smart, *Insects of Medical Importance*, after McKinney-Hughes and Johnson. Copyright 1943. Used by permission of British Museum of Natural History, London.)

The bedbug reproduces rapidly. A female lays 200–500 eggs during a period of 2–3 months. When conditions are favorable, a life cycle can be completed in 6–8 weeks. Three or 4 generations in a year are possible.

Since the bedbug is a common parasite of man, it has been carefully studied as a possible vector of human disease, but it has been found to be an important vector of no disease.

A number of remedies have been employed in bedbug control, but their use has now been superseded by the newer chlorinated hydrocarbon insecticides. The bed, together with the springs and mattress, should be thoroughly sprayed with household sprays. The cracks and crevices of the woodwork of the room should also be treated. Chlordane and lindane are efficient in bedbug control, but the recommended precautions must be taken.

A counterpart of the common bedbug is the tropical bedbug (*Cimex hemipterous*). Whereas the common bedbug is a cosmopolitan form, the tropical bedbug is confined more or less to tropical regions. It is common in India and Africa, is also found in Jamaica and Brazil, and is even reported in the United States.

The poultry bug (*Haematosiphon inodorus*) infests poultry houses in Mexico and the southwestern part of the United States. *Oeciacus vicarius* infests the nests of swallows, and *Cimexopsis nyctalis* feeds on chimney swifts.

Several families of Hemiptera are aquatic or semiaquatic in habit. With the exception of most water boatmen (Corixidae), all are predaceous forms. These aquatic families are of little economic importance and only a few of the more common and more interesting families will be mentioned here.

Family Corixidae (Water Boatmen)

Water boatmen (Figure 97A) are found particularly in fresh water where an abundance of vegetation grows. They are oval and flattened dorsally. The hind legs are long, flattened, and fringed with bristles, and are adapted for swimming. These insects can remain submerged even in impure water for a while by enveloping most of the body surface with a bubble of air. Air is also collected in a depression underneath the wings.

Water boatmen feed in ooze at the bottom of streams and

Figure 97. A. A water boatman (*Arctocorixa alternata*). B. A backswimmer (*Notonecta undulata*).

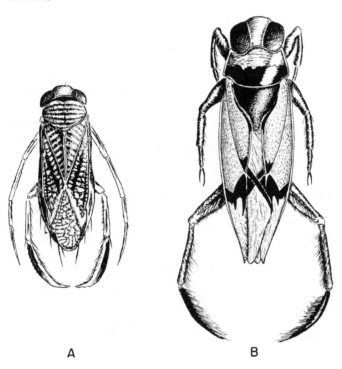

A   B

ponds, on algae and diatoms—a few forms feed on small animal life. Eggs are laid on stems of submerged plants. One species, at least, deposits its eggs on the body and appendages of crayfishes. Dispersion is by flight, and members of the family are often attracted to lights in large numbers.

Family Notonectidae (Backswimmers)
The backswimmers are easily recognized by the peculiar habit of swimming on the back and by the long oarlike legs (Figure 97B). The back of the insect is keel shaped like the bottom of a boat, which results in the body being relatively thickened. These insects may leave the water by flight, as do the water boatmen.

Backswimmers are predaceous and feed on small animal life such as insects, crustaceans, and newly hatched fish. Members of the family are relatively small insects but have a powerful beak and may inflict painful bites when carelessly handled.

Family Gerridae (Water Striders)
Water striders, known as Jesus bugs in some communities, are small, elongate, and long-legged insects (Figure 98A). They are

Figure 98. A. A water strider (*Gerris nyctalis*). B. A water scorpion (*Ranatra fusca*).

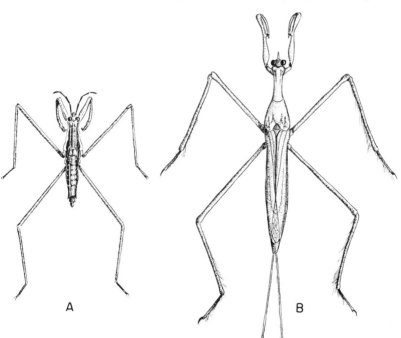

commonly seen running around or resting on the surface of ponds and other bodies of still water. They feed on dead insects and others they may catch. Both winged and wingless insects of the same species exist.

The genus *Halobates* consists of species that live on the surface of seas. These are the only truly saltwater inhabiting insects. They are most common in the calms of tropical regions.

Family Nepidae (Water Scorpions)

Water scorpions can be recognized by the long respiratory tube on the end of the abdomen (Figure 98B). The tube is formed by the two cerci which are grooved on the inner face and applied closely together. This respiratory apparatus permits the bugs to feed on the bottom of shallow pools and obtain air from the surface. The insects are predaceous and the front legs are modified for grasping the prey. Although aquatic in habitat, the second and third pairs of legs are modified for walking and not for swimming. The body of members of the family may be almost linear, as in the genus *Ranatra,* and oval in other genera. The species of Ranatra resemble walking sticks somewhat in appearance. Eggs are embedded in aquatic plants. Wings are fully developed but the insects seldom fly. The ability to inflict painful bites when handled probably suggested the common name.

Figure 99. A giant water bug (*Lethocerus americanus*). (From Department of Entomology, Texas A&M University.)

Family Belostomatidae (Giant Water Bugs)
This family includes some of the largest insects of the order. A tropical species is about 4 inches in length. They are most commonly found in bodies of shallow water which contain an abundance of plant life. Members of this group are brown, broad, and flat, with the front legs fitted for grasping prey (Figure 99).

Giant water bugs feed on insects, tadpoles, snails, and small fish. They will inflict painful bites when handled. These insects fly at night; they are often seen around lights and are known as electric light bugs in some sections of the country. Females of certain species deposit their eggs on the back of the males, where they remain until hatched.

CHAPTER 11
ORDER HOMOPTERA[1]

APHIDS, SCALE INSECTS, LEAFHOPPERS, AND OTHERS

Chief characteristics of the order are:

1. When present, 2 pairs of wings (male scale insects excepted) of the same texture throughout and when at rest usually held rooflike over the body. Many wingless forms occur.
2. Mouthparts (not always present) of piercing-sucking type, arising from the underside of the head near the prothorax.
3. Gradual metamorphosis excepting male scale insects and whiteflies.
4. Excretion of honeydew common to many members of the order.

The order Homoptera is comprised of a heterogeneous group of insects. They range in size from minute forms to individuals 2 or more inches long. Many members are wingless. When wings are present, they are of uniform thickness throughout, though in some species the front pair may be subcoriaceous in texture. The wings are held sloping over the body, like the roof of a house, when not in use. The male scale insect has only one pair of wings in contrast to the two pairs of other winged members of the order (Figure 100).

Mouthparts are for piercing and sucking, as are those found in the Hemiptera. In contrast with the mouthparts of the Hemiptera, which arise near the front of the underside of the head, they arise far to the rear near the prothorax. In those members that do not partake of food in the adult stage, e.g., the male of scale insects, mouthparts may be absent.

Metamorphosis is gradual as with the true bugs. However, the whiteflies (*Aleyrodidae*) and males of scales (*Coccidae*) have a quiescent stage prior to the emergence of the adults, comparable to the pupa in complete metamorphosis. Metamorphosis of these members is not gradual nor may their development be considered

[1] *Homos*, same; *pteron*, wing.

Figure 100. A common cicada (*Tibicen pruinosa*). (Courtesy of C. O. Mohr.)

wholly holometabolous, but probably intermediate between the two types.

Many members of the Homoptera excrete a sweet substance known as honeydew. This material drops on the leaves, stems, bark, and fruit of the plants where it dries. When the insects occur in abundance, honeydew may be excreted so copiously that the foliage may drip with it. A sooty mold grows in this medium, producing a blackened appearance. Ants and honeybees feed on honeydew avidly. Some most interesting biological relationships have developed between ants and aphids where the ants protect and care for the aphids to secure the honeydew they excrete.

Family Cicadidae (Cicadas or Harvest Flies)

These insects are probably better known in the United States as locusts than by any other name. This is a misnomer. The term locusts, correctly used, refers to migratory species of grasshoppers. The name was given them by early settlers in the eastern states when they observed swarms of the periodical cicada (*Magicicada septendecim*). These swarms of cicadas or harvest flies reminded them of locusts (grasshoppers) of the Old World.

The harvest flies and the shrill notes of their males are a part of summer and its long sultry days. A person with a trained ear and acute hearing may differentiate the various species by their songs. Sound is produced by complicated vibratory organs located at the base of the abdomen on the ventral side of the body.

Harvest flies are generally large with a large blunt head and a subconical body; however, some species are rather small. Eyes are prominent and are located on the outer angles of the head. The three ocelli are prominent and are triangularly arranged between the eyes.

The only discernible injury produced by cicadas is the oviposition punctures of the females in twigs of shade, forest, and fruit trees. Serious damage to fruit trees may be done by the periodical cicada. Twigs and sometimes small trees are killed. Eggs deposited in these punctures hatch and the nymphs drop to the ground.

They enter the soil and feed on the sap of roots of trees. The length of a life cycle is 1, 2, or more years, depending upon the species and the climate. The periodical cicada (*Magicicada septendecim*) has a life cycle requiring 17 years for development in the northeastern states. A race of this species develops in 13 years in the South. Its range extends westward to Kansas and Nebraska. Specimens have been taken on rare occasions in east and northeast Texas. The species is black with reddish legs, wing veins, and eyes; and about 1 inch in length. A blackish W is discernible near the apex of the forewings. The appearance of a brood of these insects with the W on the front wings was thought to presage war by superstitious people of the Southeast.

Family Cercopidae (Spittlebugs)

A white frothy mass of material is often observed on weeds, grass, and shrubs during the summer months. Within this mass may be found the nymph of a spittlebug. It lives here until the adult stage is reached. This froth is formed by a fluid voided from the anus of the nymph in which is mixed a mucilaginous substance excreted by hypodermal glands and into which air bubbles are incorporated. The purpose of the frothy covering is to provide a moist environment and to protect the insect from its enemies. The adults are dark and small. These insects usually hibernate in the egg stage and produce only one generation annually.

The meadow spittlebug (*Philaenus spumarius*) (Figure 101) is

Figure 101. The meadow spittlebug (*Philaenus spumarius*). (From Ohio Agricultural Experiment Station.)

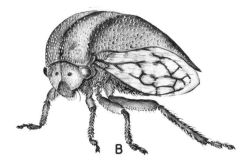

Figure 102. A. The buffalo tree-hopper (*Stictocephala bubalus*). (From USDA.) B. The three-cornered alfalfa hopper (*Spissistilus festinus*). (From Texas Agricultural Experiment Station.)

the common representative in the eastern part of the country. Its common hosts are a wide variety of meadow and garden plants, and weeds. Heavy infestations seriously affect the yield of hay crops. Satisfactory control of the insect is obtained by spraying with methoxychlor.

Family Membracidae (Treehoppers)
The pronotum of treehoppers extends posteriorly over the abdomen and in some species completely covers the wings. The presence of lateral and vertical prolongations of the pronotum often results in giving many species an odd appearance. These insects are sometimes referred to as the clowns of the insect world.

Treehoppers are found on trees, shrubs, grasses, and other plants. Their food is the juices of plants; however, most species never become sufficiently abundant to become pests of economic importance. The buffalo treehopper (*Stictocephala bubalus*) (Figure 102A) is the best known and most widely distributed member of the family. It becomes a pest of nursery stock and young fruit trees through injury produced by numerous egg punctures in the stems of young plants. Injury through feeding of the nymphs and adults is negligible. The insect is about ⅓ inch long, green or yellow with short stout horns on the pronotum.

The three cornered alfalfa hopper (*Spissistilus festinus*) (Figure 102B) is often an important pest of alfalfa. Injury is produced by the insect girdling the stems with its feeding punctures. The insect also attacks other legumes, weeds, and fruit trees. It is about ⅕ inch in length, bright green in general color and without pronotal horns. Winter is passed in the adult stage. Four or five generations may develop annually in warm climates. Malathion and carbaryl are recommended in the control of this pest.

Family Cicadellidae (Leafhoppers and Sharpshooters)
The Cicadellidae is a large family of small elongate insects. The most characteristic feature of the family is the double row of spines on the hind tibiae. As the name leafhopper implies, these insects are alacritous hoppers. Both nymphs and adults have the habit of running sidewise. Leafhoppers are usually about ¼ inch in length and of variable colors, with some species very beautifully marked. They may become extremely abundant and do considerable damage to a wide variety of field crops, fruits, shrubs, and other plants. Their feeding not only injures the plant, but transmits plant diseases. Leafhoppers produce from one to four generations annually. Some of the more common species diapause as adults; others overwinter in the egg or nymphal stages; while in the Gulf Coast states reproduction of some forms may continue throughout the winter with a migration of the winged forms northward in the spring.

Probably more than 1000 species of leafhoppers occur in North America. Although a number are of economic importance, only a few can be mentioned here. The potato leafhopper (*Empoasca fabae*) (Figure 103A) is one of the most common and best known pests of this family. It is small green leafhopper, wedge shaped, and about ⅛ inch long. A row of six rounded light spots is found along the anterior margin of the pronotum. The insect attacks potatoes, beans, alfalfa, apple trees, peanuts, and other plants. A disorder known as tipburn or hopperburn is produced on potatoes. The cause of this trouble has not been fully explained. Stunting, crinkling, and curling of the leaves are characteristic injuries on beans and apples. Alfalfa leaves turn yellow when the plants are attacked. A diseased condition known as "peanut pouts" is caused by infestations of the insect on peanuts. The potato leafhoppers apparently do not winter in the North in any stage and migrate from the Gulf states, where they breed throughout the year. The use of toxaphene, malathion, and methoxychlor are satisfactory for control.

THE GRAPE LEAFHOPPER (*Erythroneura comes* and others). This insect is a widespread and consistent pest of grapes. It also attacks

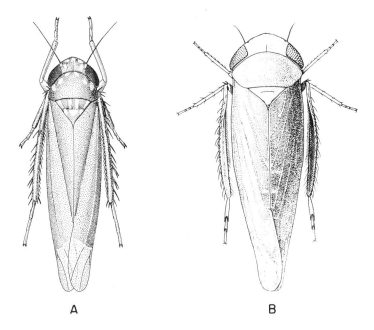

A   B

Figure 103. A. The potato leafhopper (*Empoasca fabae*). (From Illinois Natural History Survey.) B. The beet leafhopper (*Circulifer tenellus*). (From Utah Agricultural Experiment Station.)

Virginia creeper, apple, and other plants. The foliage of infested plants assumes a grayish cast and later the leaves become shriveled and brown. Both quantity and quality of the fruit are affected. When infested plants are examined, countless numbers of the pale yellow insects with red or black markings are found. The pest diapauses as an adult in fallen leaves and other trash. Only one generation of the insect annually may be developed in its northern range while there may be three in the southern states.

Destruction of leaves, grass, and other trash around vineyards will eliminate many of the overwintering adults of the grape leafhopper. Such insecticides as malathion are recommended for control.

THE BEET LEAFHOPPER (*Circulifer tenellus*). This leafhopper (Figure 103B) is the vector of a virus disease of sugar beets known as "curly top." It is a serious disease of the crop, and it has caused the abandonment of the growing of sugar beets in some localities. The insect is also a vector of tomato yellows. The small yellowish-green insect overwinters on Russian thistle, wild mustard, and other plants from which the first generation may migrate to beet fields hundreds of miles away. There may be several generations annually. Parathion and carbaryl will control the insect but it is difficult to prevent transmission of the disease. Varieties of sugar beets with a measure of resistance to the leafhopper have been developed. Destruction of winter host plants has met with success in some sections.

Several species of leafhoppers, called sharpshooters (Figure 104), are commonly found on the cotton plant. The most important is a large dark form (*Homalodisca triquetra*) which is also found on okra, various weeds, and trees. Damage caused by the feeding of these insects on cotton has been shown to be minor.

Family Chermidae (Jumping Plant Lice)

The jumping plant lice are quite small; they are less than ⅛ inch in length. They have some resemblance to winged aphids, but they appear more like extremely small harvest flies. They are very active insects, readily jumping or taking flight when disturbed. These insects subsist on plant juices and some species cause the formation of galls.

One of the best known gall forming species is the hackberry nipple gall (*Pachypsylla celtidismamma*). Unsightly galls are formed

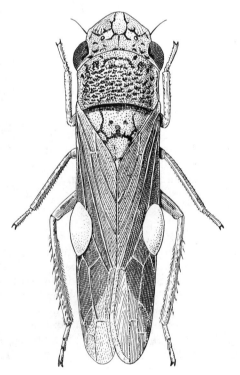

Figure 104. A sharpshooter (leafhopper) (*Oncometopia undata*). (From Illinois Natural History Survey.)

on the leaves and heavy infestations cause the leaves to drop early. Spraying with nicotine sulfate or oils early in the season as the galls are beginning to form is suggested as a control measure.

The pear psylla (*Psylla pyricola*) is the most important economic form of this group. It is widespread in the East and it is also an important pest of the pear in the Northwest. Leaves turn brown and are often shed; and, when the trees are heavily infested, the fruit drops prematurely or is of inferior quality. The pear psylla winters as an adult in sheltered places, such as under the bark of trees. There are three to five generations annually. The insect is difficult to control and several treatments such as dormant spray oil and summer sprays of toxaphene, malathion, and parathion are recommended.

Family Aphididae (Plant Lice or Aphids)

Plant lice or aphids are among the more important groups of insects from an economic viewpoint. Growers of nearly all plants will have aphid problems at times. Their life histories with the involved life cycles and relationships of many species are intriguing and of much interest.

Aphids are small, delicate, and more or less pear-shaped insects, the largest species are not more than ¼ inch in length (Figure 105). Both winged and wingless individuals are found, with the latter the predominant form. Antennae and legs are generally long. Most aphids have a pair of tubes, known as cornicles, projecting upward and backward from the dorsal surface of the abdomen. They secrete a waxlike substance. It was formerly thought honeydew was excreted by them, but it is now known that this substance is excreted from the anus. Aphids excrete honeydew copiously. This falls on the leaves, twigs, and fruit. A number of insects, particularly ants, feed upon this sweet substance, and a sooty mold grows in it. In most instances no biological relationship exists between ants and aphids, but in others definite relationships have developed. The best known of these relationships is between the cornfield ant (*Lasius alienus americanus*) and the cornroot aphid (*Aphis ' maidiradicis*). These aphids are dependent on the ants for care and protection, and in turn the ants are repaid for their services in honeydew as food.

Much variation is found in the biology of aphids. However, there are certain general biological facts that may be applied to the group as a whole. Aphids usually reproduce parthenogenetically (asexual reproduction) and by giving birth to living young (ovoviviparous reproduction). With some exceptions, males and eggs of aphids are unknown in the southern states. In the North, aphids reproduce in the spring and summer as they do in the warmer climates; but with most species a generation of true sexual forms, males and females, appears in the fall. These forms mate and the females lay black, shining, overwintering eggs which hatch

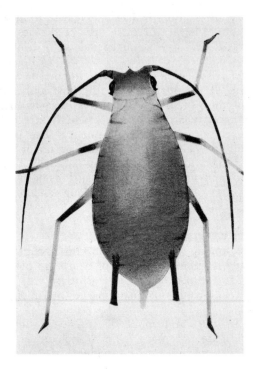

Figure 105. Adult stem mother of the English grain aphid (*Macrosiphum avenae*). Note the paired tubes, cornicles, on the end of the abdomen. (From Department of Entomology, Texas A&M University, Courtesy of Dr. J. G. Thomas.)

the next spring. Conversely, certain species of aphids in the tropics may lay eggs to carry the species over the hot dry season.

Most aphids are wingless; winged forms are relatively scarce. In general, only wingless individuals are found when the food supply is adequate and no overcrowding occurs. With deterioration of the host plants or overcrowding, the tendency is for the development of winged forms which migrate to other plants. It is true that certain species have a series of wingless generations followed by a winged generation which migrates to another host, but such species are in the minority. Species of aphids are usually rather restricted in their host plants, feeding on a group of more or less related plants. Some species have alternate hosts on which they are found at different seasons.

Aphids have the highest reproductive potential of any insect. For example, under greenhouse conditions the cotton aphid (*Aphis gossypii*) may complete a maximum of 51 generations in a year, with each adult producing about 85 young. In the Gulf Coast region, the turnip aphid (*Hyadaphis pseudobrassicae*) may produce a maximum of 35–46 generations annually with each adult reproducing 50–100 young. Under the above conditions all of these aphids are females. These examples probably represent those known forms with the highest reproductive rate—aphids as a group normally may not increase so rapidly. But, under conditions favorable for the insects, any species may be considered as a potential pest.

Aphids are normally held in check by natural factors. The more important of these are adverse weather conditions such as low temperatures and beating rains, fungus diseases, and insect predators and parasites. The most beneficial insect enemies are lady beetles, syrphus fly larvae, aphis lions, and small wasplike braconid parasites of the subfamily *Aphidiinae*.

Crops most susceptible to aphid injury should be carefully checked during those periods when infestations most commonly occur; or else, because of the rapid rate of reproduction, major damage may result before control measures can be used. A number of insecticides will control aphids, but the one selected for use depends upon the crop and circumstances. Parathion, diazinon, and malathion are among those most commonly used.

THE COTTON APHID (*Aphis gossypii*). The cotton aphid is of worldwide distribution. It attacks cotton and melons wherever they are grown (Figure 106). In addition, it seriously injures other cucurbits, okra, and citrus. Cowpeas, beans, beets, eggplants, strawberries, and many weeds also serve as hosts.

The cotton aphid injures plants by sucking sap from the stems

Figure 106. A colony of cotton aphids (*Aphis gossypii*) on a cantaloupe leaf. (From Department of Entomology, Texas A&M University.)

and foliage, and by the excretion of honeydew. Another type of injury to cotton is caused by honeydew falling on open bolls, lowering the grade of the lint.

Light and dark phases of the cotton aphid are found, with the latter the predominant form. The light phase is yellowish green; the dark phase is black, brown, or dark green. There are no distinct broods of the cotton aphid. The length of a life cycle depends upon weather conditions. Sexual maturity is reached in 4–10 days. The reproductive period is about 3 weeks and the average length of life of an adult is approximately a month. A maximum of 51 generations may be completed in 1 year with each female producing about 85 young under greenhouse conditions.

Several insecticides will effectively control the cotton aphid which they are properly applied. Malathion and parathion are recommended for use on truck crops. Demeton, methyl parathion, and parathion are in common use to keep the pest in check on cotton.

THE TURNIP APHID (*Hyadaphis pseudobrassicae*). The turnip aphid (Figure 107) is probably the most destructive insect attacking turnips, mustard, and radishes in the warmer climates. This widely distributed insect is rarely observed during the summer months in the southern states. It appears in the fall on cruciferous plants with the advent of cool weather. Reproduction is rapid and damag-

Figure 107. The turnip aphid (*Hyadaphis pseudobrassicae*). (From Department of Entomology, Texas A&M University.)

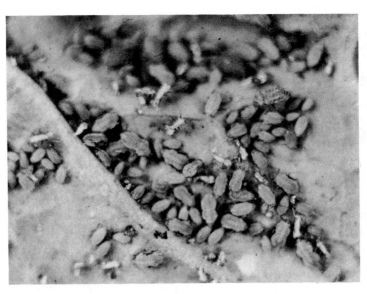

ing numbers of the insect are reached soon if the pest is not checked by cold weather or other factors. In late spring the insect tends to disappear with the multiplication of its natural enemies or the deterioration of the host plants.

The turnip aphid is about ¹⁄₁₆ of an inch in length and colored light to dark green. Wingless and winged forms may be present on plants, with the former predominant. Sexual maturity is reached in 10–12 days and the reproductive period extends over a period of 20–30 days. Reproduction is rapid with a maximum of 35–46 generations and 50–100 offspring produced by each female.

A number of parasitic and predaceous insects prey upon the turnip aphid. In warm, moist weather fungus diseases may almost eradicate it. Although these factors are very helpful, insecticidal control is necessary for the successful production of crops. Malathion, parathion, and other synthetic organic compounds are also efficient in the control of the pest, but precautionary measures must be carefully observed to prevent harmful residues.

THE CABBAGE APHID (*Brevicoryne brassicae*). The cabbage aphid and the turnip aphid are quite similar in general appearance and were not recognized as different species for many years. The two species may be most readily separated by the appearance of the colonies. Colonies of the cabbage aphid are covered by a conspicuous waxy bloom which is absent in the turnip aphid. The cabbage aphid attacks the same group of plants as the latter species, but it is more frequently found on cabbage, collards, and rape.

The number of generations and the rate of reproduction appear to be similar to that of the turnip aphid; however, the cabbage aphid is somewhat more difficult to control. Thorough and timely applications of dusts or sprays containing malathion, parathion, or diazinon are recommended in control of the insect. Crop residues should be destroyed as an aid in preventing subsequent infestations.

THE GREENBUG (*Schizaphis graminum*). This aphid is one of the most destructive pests of wheat and other small grains in the Southwest. This old-world insect was introduced into the United States many years ago. It is now found in most parts of the United States and Canada. Most damage is done in the grain-growing states west of the Mississippi River, particularly in Kansas, Oklahoma, Texas, and Nebraska.

The favorite host plants of the greenbug are wheat, oats, and barley, but the insect will also attack corn, rice, sorghum, and other cultivated plants of the grass family, and many native grasses.

Outbreaks do not occur every year due to a complex of weather and other natural control factors. When widespread outbreaks of the insect occur, enormous losses may result.

First indications of the presence of the greenbug in late fall, winter, or early spring are spots of bare ground bordered by yellow dying plants in the grain field. If conditions are favorable for the insect, these spots enlarge and entire fields may be destroyed in the spring.

The most critical period in the seasonal history of the insect is during the summer months. Cool, wet summer months provide adequate host plants. When small grain is growing in the fall, winged forms migrate to the grain fields. Reproduction continues at temperatures as low as 40° F. Warm, dry winter weather is favorable for the insect's multiplication. The most important natural enemy of the greenbug is the small hymenopteron parasite, *Lysiphlebus testaceipes*. This parasite is not active at temperatures below 65° F. Late, cool spring months may hold it in check but permit the greenbug to reproduce in great numbers and destroy large areas of wheat and oats. Thus, cool, wet summers, mild, dry winter months, and cool springs favor outbreaks; whereas hot, dry summer months, cold, winter weather, and early springs tend to prevent infestations.

The pale green wingless females are about 1/16 inch in length. They have a dark green stripe down the back and have black tarsi (feet). The winged females may be recognized by the discoidal vein of the forewing with but one branch.

North of the thirty-fifth parallel the pest overwinters in the egg stage. In warmer climates the insects breed continuously throughout the year and eggs are never laid. Each female gives birth to 50 or 60 young on an average. There may be 20 or more generations annually.

Greenbug infestations do not occur sufficiently often to warrant regular control programs. The destruction of volunteer grain, especially oats, during the summer months is recommended, as this practice tends to minimize chances of infestations of fall-planted grain. The grazing of infested fields to obtain some benefit out of the crop and later plowing it under and planting other crops is sometimes advisable. Crops growing in dry soil are more severely injured than those grown under moist conditions.

Parathion, demeton, and methyl parathion are recommended for control of the greenbug. These sprays should be applied when the temperature is not lower than 50° F. All recommended precautions must be taken in the applications of these compounds.

The English grain aphid (*Macrosiphum avenae*) may be associated with the greenbug in the grain fields. Infestations of this insect tend to be more widespread over the fields and usually are not confined to spots. The English grain aphid may be distinguished from the greenbug in the winged forms by the presence of two branches in the discoidal vein instead of only one as is found in the front wings of the latter species. The biology of this insect is similar to that of the greenbug. Should the natural enemies fail to control the pest, insecticidal control as recommended for the greenbug may be employed.

THE PEA APHID (*Acyrthosiphon pisum*). The pea aphid is a green, long-legged insect infesting field and garden peas, vetch, clover, alfalfa, and other leguminous plants. When plants are heavily infested, their white cast skins may litter the ground. These insects cause the plants to wilt, and bronze-colored patches appear throughout the field. Flower heads of vetch and other crops are attacked and the seed crops may be destroyed or greatly reduced.

The pea aphid overwinters in the northern states either in the egg stage or as ovoviviparous females, and further south reproduction continues throughout the year. Each ovoviviparous female gives birth to 50–100 young. Seven to 20 or more generations may occur within the course of a year.

The pea aphid is held in check by adverse weather conditions, parasites, predators, and fungus diseases. When conditions are favorable, it increases in large numbers.

In control of this pest several insecticides may be employed. Rotenone and malathion may be used, particularly in home gardens. In commercial plantings demeton sprays, and parathion sprays and dusts are recommended. Parathion is frequently used also in protection of seed crops of vetch. The two latter compounds should be applied only by trained operators.

THE BLACK PECAN APHID (*Tinocallis caryaefoliae*). This aphid may produce serious defoliation of pecan trees, with the subsequent reduction of the crop of nuts. Infestations most generally occur following sprays for the control of the pecan nut casebearer and the use of Bordeaux mixture. The insect feeds on the foliage and produces bright yellow spots somewhat rectangular in shape. These areas turn brown and if a number of feeding spots are present, the leaflets may drop prematurely.

The mature insect is about $\frac{1}{16}$ inch in length, and dark green with a series of prominent black humps on the back and sides of the body. The insect is quite agile and jumps when disturbed. Winter is passed as small black eggs deposited in the crevices of the bark. Normally about 15 generations occur during the year, with each ovoviviparous female producing 50–100 living young.

Satisfactory control is rather difficult; however, sprays of malathion and parathion provide adequate control if properly applied.

THE WOOLLY APPLE APHID (*Eriosoma lanigerum*). The woolly apple aphid is of worldwide distribution and is a pest of the apple wherever the fruit is grown. The presence of the aphid is indicated by white cottony masses which conceal clusters of the purplish insects. The trunks, branches, foliage, and roots of the apple, mountain ash, pear, quince, and elm are attacked. In the northern states winter is passed in the egg stage, chiefly on the elm. Clusters or rosettes of leaves of the elms in the spring are caused by the feeding of the insects. A winged generation later migrates from the elm to the apple and other trees; however, the insect lives entirely on the apple trees in most of the western states. Chief injury to the apple trees results from the feeding of the aphids on the roots. For control, a number of products are recommended, such as malathion and diazinon. Those practices which tend to keep the trees in vigorous condition, such as fertilization and cultivation, will be of aid in lessening the damage produced by these insects.

THE GRAPE PHYLLOXERA (*Phylloxera vitifoliae*). Species of Phylloxera differ from common plant lice in that both parthenogenetic females and sexually perfect females lay eggs.

The best known and most destructive of all the species of Phylloxera is the grape phylloxera (Figure 108). This insect is a native of the middle and eastern United States, feeding on the native varieties of grapes of these regions. Grapes here have developed partial immunity to their attacks.

The grape phylloxera was introduced into France about 1860 and destroyed nearly one-third of the vineyards of this country before control measures were found. The insect was discovered in California about the same time it was found in France. It is a serious pest here of the European or vinifera varieties of grapes.

The biology of this insect is rather involved as there are several distinct forms, and both roots and leaves are involved in the injury produced. Hibernation is either as nymphs on the roots or as eggs on the canes. Overwintered eggs hatch in the spring into

A   B

Figure 108. The grape phylloxera (*Phylloxera vitifoliae*). A. a, galls on grape roots; b, enlarged gall with louse feeding; c, adult louse; d, cast skin of nymph. B. Root of grape vine showing louse with eggs. (From USDA.)

Figure 109. Galls of phylloxera on pecan twig. (From Texas Agricultural Experiment Station.)

nymphs which produce small galls in which a number of young are produced. After several generations on the leaves, some of the insects drop to the ground, burrow into the soil, reach the roots and produce galls upon them, causing serious injury to the vinifera varieties. Toward the end of the season winged migrants leave the soil and find their way to the vines. The migrants produce a generation of true sexual forms which mate, and each female deposits an egg on the bark of the 2-year-old wood. The root-infesting form of the phylloxera is rare in the East, but this is the only form found on the Pacific Coast.

The most effective control is grafting susceptible European varieties of grapes on resistant rootstock of the middle and eastern sections of the United States. Most of the grapes sold by nurseries are grafted on resistant rootstock. In those parts of Europe and California where European rootstock is used, the insect is controlled by fumigating the soil with carbon disulfide and by flooding the vineyards at certain periods of the year.

Several species of the phylloxera attack the pecan, hickory, and walnut. One of the most destructive is the pecan phylloxera (*Phylloxera devastatrix*). The insect attacks the current year's growth and produces galls on leaves (Figure 109). Severe infestations result in heavy defoliation of the trees. The small insects appear in the early spring and begin to feed on the unfolding buds. The effects of the feeding cause the growth of the gall which soon envelops the insect. Within this gall large numbers of young are produced. Later the gall splits and releases the insects.

Sprays containing BHC, lindane, or malathion are suggested for control of the pecan phylloxera. They should be thoroughly applied as delayed dormant sprays, or until buds show 1–2 inches of growth in the springtime.

Family Aleyrodidae (Whiteflies)

The adults of Aleyrodidae are small, four-winged insects about 3 mm in length. Superficially they bear a resemblance to tiny moths. They are covered with a waxy powder which is usually white. In contrast to the appearance of the adults, the larvae are small, flattened, oval bodies which resemble early stages of soft scales. Metamorphosis of whiteflies approaches the holometabolous type. Eggs hatch into larvae or crawlers which attach themselves to the underside of leaves (Figure 110). With the first molt the larvae lose their legs and antennae. Following two additional molts, the insects enter a pupal or transformation stage from which the winged adults soon emerge. Whiteflies are tropical or

Figure 110. Whitefly larvae and eggs on the underside of a gardenia leaf.

subtropical insects. The injury they produce is similar to that of scale insects and aphids. They suck quantities of sap from the plants and also excrete honeydew copiously. The sooty mold which grows in the honeydew produces a black unsightly appearance on the leaves of infested plants.

THE CITRUS WHITEFLY (*Dialeurodes citri*). The citrus whitefly attacks citrus, gardenia, crepe myrtle, chinaberry, privet, and many other plants. It is an important pest of citrus in Florida and other Gulf states. In its range of distribution all stages of whiteflies may be found throughout the year; however, there is little development during cold weather.

The small, pale yellow and oval eggs of the citrus whitefly are laid on the underside of the leaves to which they are attached by tiny stalks. Under Florida conditions three main generations occur annually.

White summer-oil emulsion sprays thoroughly applied to the underside of the leaves of hardy plants will control this pest. In case of heavy infestations, applications of at least two sprays annually are recommended. Spraying with parathion is a satisfactory control measure, but this insecticide cannot be used around homes because of its toxicity. When numbers of adults are present on gardenias, the application of malathion dust will destroy many, reducing subsequent infestations.

THE CITRUS BLACKFLY (*Aleurocanthus woglumi*). This is an important pest of citrus. It also attacks mango, coffee, and a large number of other plants which serve as secondary hosts. Injury is through feeding on the sap of the plants and the excretion of honeydew.

The citrus blackfly is a native of the Orient. It is now found in Cuba, the West Indies, Central America, Mexico, and in other parts of the world. The minute yellowish eggs have a spine arising from the truncate end which anchors the egg to the underside of the leaf. The larvae are black, oval, convex, and armed with spines. The small four-winged adults are grayish black. Four generations of the insect are thought to occur annually in Mexico. Each female lays about 100 eggs. In heavy infestations large numbers of eggs may be deposited on a single leaf.

A parasite, *Eretmocerus serius*, and a predator, *Catana clauseni*, together with several other natural enemies, control the pest in most countries where it is found. Oil sprays or parathion are recommended for the control of the blackfly. Rotenone in a light-medium oil spray appears quite promising in the control of the pest.

THE GREENHOUSE WHITEFLY (*Trialeurodes vaporariorum*). This common pest of greenhouses is found throughout the country. When conditions are favorable, outdoor plants are also attacked. It feeds on hibiscus, coleus, begonia, tomato, cucumber, and many other plants. The white adults are less than 2 mm in length. Each female lays about 100 yellowish eggs on leaves. The eggs are often deposited in a ring. The larvae are small, oval, flattened, and light green. They resemble small soft scale insects. The length of the larval stage is about 1 month. Several overlapping generations are produced in the course of a year.

Several sprays are recommended in the control of the greenhouse whitefly. Regardless of the spray employed, it must be thoroughly applied, especially to the underside of the leaves. Applications of nicotine sulfate and soap solutions at weekly intervals for 2 or 3 weeks are recommended. White oil emulsion sprays may be used on hardy shrubs. However, applications of this spray at short intervals are not advisable as injury to the plant may result. The use of parathion aerosols are the most successful means of control of whiteflies in a greenhouse.

Family Coccidae (Scale Insects and Mealybugs)

The Coccidae are unusual inasmuch as they are so modified in appearance that they do not resemble ordinary insects, with the exception of the adult males, which are winged. They are usually quite small and inconspicuous, and most of them are found on the leaves, stems, and fruit, but some species infest the roots of plants. A majority of the species remain immotile at least for a part of their life cycle and they may be transported alive long distances on nursery stock.

More than 2000 species of scale insects are known. Some of the most important pests of fruit trees, shade trees, shrubs, and plants in greenhouses are found in this group of insects.

The products of certain species have a commercial value. Shellac is a product of the secretions of the lac scale (*Laccifer lacca*). This scale insect is found in India and some neighboring countries. It feeds chiefly on trees belonging to the Malvaceae and Leguminosae families. Chinese wax is a product of *Ericerus pela*. It is used in the manufacture of candles. Dyes made from the bodies of a cactus scale (*Coccus cacti*) and *Kermes ilicis*, found on oaks, were once rather important.

In scale insects the male has complete metamorphosis while the metamorphosis of the female is gradual. The males begin their development much as the females, but pupate at the end of the developmental period. From the pupae emerge small two-winged flies without mouthparts—the males do not feed in the adult stage. The females remain wingless throughout life and most of them are immotile on the host plants. All species have their bodies covered with a waxy or resinous secretion, a thickened integument, or a waxy scale. Mealybugs and soft scales excrete honeydew.

The biology of scale insects has not been studied adequately except in the more important species, and taxonomy of the family is difficult. Scale insects may be placed for general study into three 'groups: (1) the mealybugs, (2) the soft scales, and (3) the armored scales. Only a few species can be considered for study here.

THE MEALYBUGS. The mealybugs are the least degenerate of all the Coccidae. Legs and the power of locomotion are retained throughout life (Figure 111). The bodies have remained distinctly segmented and the eyes and antennae have not been lost during their development. The bodies are covered with a waxy powder which may extend from the sides of the body in cottony threads or plates. Injury is caused in feeding on the sap, and the excretion of honeydew in which a sooty mold grows. Mealybugs generally lay eggs, but in some cases, as with the long-tailed mealybug (*Pseudococcus adonidum*), living young are produced. Eggs are laid in conspicuous saclike masses of a cottony material secreted by the females.

THE CITRUS MEALYBUG (*Planococcus citri*). This is the most common species; it attacks greenhouse plants and in warmer climates it is a pest of importance on a large number of hosts—citrus, ornamental, and flowering plants.

Cottony masses of the insects may be found on twigs, foliage, fruit, and under loose bark of the host plants. A female may lay 300–600 eggs. The length of the egg stage is a week or longer. The nymphs develop through three instars, each instar being

Figure 111. Mealybugs showing winged males. (From Department of Entomology, Texas A&M University.)

somewhat more than 2 weeks in duration during warm weather. At the end of the third instar, the males pupate; from the pupa a two-winged adult later emerges. There are two or three generations annually of this insect; winter may be passed in all stages, but chiefly as eggs.

THE LONG-TAILED MEALYBUG (*Pseudococcus adonidum*). The long-tailed mealybug is another widely distributed species. The insect has very long anal filaments, as its common name implies. This pest is common in greenhouses and also outdoors in warm climates. It attacks a wide range of plants as does the citrus mealybug. This species gives birth to living young, the average number of offspring being about 200.

Mealybugs are very difficult insects to control. Fortunately in the citrus groves of California, biological control with introduced hymenopterous parasites and lady beetles has been very effective; and at the present time other control measures are not usually necessary.

A measure of control of mealybugs on ornamentals and other plants may be obtained by syringing with water, employing as much pressure as the plants will stand without causing injury to them. A spray containing white oil emulsion and nicotine sulfate, repeated in 2 weeks, will provide fair control. The most effective control in greenhouses is the use of parathion aerosols. All precautionary measures must be taken when parathion is used as this insecticide is highly toxic to human beings. Applications of malathion are also recommended.

THE COTTONY-CUSHION SCALE (*Icerya purchasi*). This insect (Figure 112) is not a true mealybug, but it is more closely related to this group than to the soft scales. It is an important pest of citrus and a wide variety of other plants. At one time it was considered a serious threat to the citrus industry of California. The pest was brought into California in 1868 or 1869 on *Acacia* from Australia. The insect is not a pest in its native home, and investigation showed it was held in check there by a lady beetle, *Rodolia (Vedalia) cardinalis*. The importation of this lady beetle to California led to its control in this country. This was the first successful introduction of a beneficial insect into a country to control an insect pest. Similar successes have since been attained in the control of other insect pests. Both larvae and adults of the vedalia lady beetle feed upon the pest. The extensive use of insecticides recently has reduced the populations of the predator in some localities. With the resulting increase in infestations of the pest, control with parathion or malathion may become necessary.

The cotton-cushion scale is one of the larger coccids. The insect is brown, red, or yellow-orange and is about 6–8 mm in length, the egg sac not included. The egg sac is large, elongate, white, and fluted. The most characteristic feature of the insect is the

Figure 112. The cottony-cushion scale (*Icerya purchasi*) on *Pittosporum*. (From Department of Entomology, Texas A&M University.)

fluted egg sac. Within the egg sac may be found 600–800 eggs. Several generations occur during the year.

THE SOFT SCALES. Soft scales are rather large (Figure 113). Their bodies are soft in the nymphal instars; but in the adult females the exoskeleton on the back becomes thickened, tough, and often quite convex. Antennae and legs are not lost during development, and the insects are capable of limited locomotion, but the adult females appear to remain quite sessile. When wax is secreted, it is usually for the formation of an egg sac at the rear end of the body. The soft scales, as do the mealybugs, excrete honeydew.

THE EUROPEAN FRUIT LECANIUM (*Lecanium corni*). Several species of soft scales of economic importance belong to the genus *Lecanium* (Figure 114). One of the most common is the European fruit lecanium. It commonly attacks plum, pecan, peach, apple, apricot, pear, grape, and a host of other plants. The scale varies considerably in shape, size, and color. Typical specimens are brown, nearly hemispherical in shape, and 3–5 mm in length. Winter is passed in the nymphal stage. The insect grows rapidly when the weather becomes warm. After maturity in the spring the females lay a great number of eggs which fill the cavity beneath the scale. More than 2000 eggs may be deposited. Only one generation is produced annually.

Figure 113. A common soft scale, the cottony maple scale (*Pulvinaria innumerabilis*). (From Texas Agricultural Experiment Station.)

Figure 114. A soft scale (*Lecanium* sp.). (From Texas Agricultural Experiment Station.)

The terrapin scale (*Lecanium nigrofasciatum*) is another well known and widely distributed member of this genus. The scale is usually dark brown, semihemispherical with somewhat crinkled margins of the body, and 3–4 mm in length. It attacks peach, plum, apple, and many other common fruits, shrubs, and shade trees. Winter is spent as fertilized females. They reproduce ovoviviparously and begin giving birth to young in the spring. Only one generation annually is produced. Lecanium scales may be controlled with malathion or parathion sprays.

THE HEMISPHERICAL SCALE (*Saissetia coffeae*). This soft scale may become a serious pest in greenhouses; it also attacks avocado, citrus, and other plants. It is hemispherical, shiny brown, and about 3 mm in length. The insect usually reproduces parthenogenetically. Males are rare. Five hundred to 1000 eggs are produced. There are usually two generations annually. Spraying with either parathion or malathion, or a combination of the two, is recommended for control of this scale.

THE BLACK SCALE (*Saissetia oleae*). The black scale is widely distributed and it is an important pest, especially of citrus. The insect attacks a wide variety of other plants such as apple, plum, pear, fig, grape, and greenhouse plants. More damage is produced by the excretion of honeydew on the fruit and leaves than by the feeding of the insect.

The black scale is dark brown to black, about 5 mm in length, and has a letter H on its back formed by ridges. The females deposit about 2000 eggs each. These hatch and the young nymphs usually settle on the leaves and other new growth. While they are partly grown, most of the scales migrate to the branches and twigs. Males are rare, and reproduction is usually by parthenogenesis. One or two generations are produced annually.

In citrus groves the black scale is controlled with oil emulsion sprays. Parathion and malathion sprays are also recommended.

THE ARMORED SCALES. The armored scales constitute the most important group of scale insects. Some of the most injurious pests of fruit trees, shade trees, and ornamentals are armored scales. The bodies have undergone greater modifications than other scales. In general, the scales are smaller; they may be circular, elongate, or threadlike. Females are active only after hatching. When the crawlers once settle on the host plant, no further movement occurs. With the first molt legs are lost and antennae reduced.

In armored scales, the small insect is hidden by a protective covering. This scaly covering is separate from the body of the insect and it consists of secreted wax within which is incorporated the exuviae (cast skins) of the molts. Another striking characteristic of armored scales is the fusion of the last four abdominal segments into a structure known as the *pygidium*. Identification of armored scales is largely by structures located on the pygidium. Armored scales do not excrete honeydew as do the mealybugs and soft scales.

THE SAN JOSE SCALE (*Quadraspidiotus perniciosus*). The San Jose scale is the most widely known and one of the most destructive of all armored scales (Figure 115). The native home of the insect is believed to be China and it was introduced into California about 1870, whence it soon spread throughout the country. The insect is also quite widespread throughout other parts of the world.

Figure 115. The San Jose scale (*Quadraspidiotus perniciosus*). (From the Department of Entomology, Texas A&M University.)

Peaches, plums, apples, pears, apricots, and many other plants are attacked by the San Jose scale. All parts of the trees except the roots may become infested. Great numbers of deciduous fruit trees die annually from attacks of the pest. The fully grown scales are circular, about ⅟₁₆ inch in diameter, and gray. They have a dark, central elevation, the exuviae, surrounded by a yellowish ring. The immature scales are black with a gray spot in the center. This spot is ringed by a black depression which is bordered by gray. Heavily infested limbs assume a gray appearance produced by the overlapping scales.

Winter is usually passed in the nymphal stage; however, in the southern states some reproduction may occur throughout the season unless the weather is unusually cold.

The San Jose scale reproduces ovoviviparously. Each female produces about 400 young. The crawling young disperse over the trees. When a suitable place is found, an insect inserts its mouthparts into the tissues of the bark and does not move again. Five to six weeks later a new generation is begun. The number of generations annually may be from two in the North to six or more in the southern states.

During the crawler stage the insects may be blown over the orchard by the wind, or carried on the feet of birds or bodies of beetles and other insects. Most infestations have arisen from infested nursery stock.

A number of natural enemies prey upon the San Jose scale but its rate of reproduction is so great that it still may increase to damaging numbers. A number of small hymenopterous parasites and lady beetles are the most important natural enemies. The twice-stabbed lady beetle (*Chilocorus stigma*) is the most common lady beetle predator. Either lubricating oil sprays or lime-sulfur will control the San Jose scale, provided the spray is thoroughly applied. The sprays should be applied during the dormant season. Malathion and parathion are also recommended in the control of the San Jose scale.

THE WHITE PEACH SCALE (*Pseudaulacaspis pentagona*). This insect is often referred to as the West Indian peach scale. It is sometimes injurious to peaches, cherries, privet, and other plants. The mature females are circular, about ¹⁄₁₀ inch in diameter, and dirty white with brown or yellow exuviae located slightly away from the center of the scale (Figure 116A). The males occur in clusters and are usually found at the base of the branches. These are white and elongate in outline. This insect winters as mature females. Four or five generations may occur annually in warm climates.

Lime-sulfur applied as a dormant spray on deciduous trees controls the white peach scale. Lubricating oil emulsion sprays will also control the pest. Parathion sprays have shown promising results in controlling the insect.

THE OBSCURE SCALE (*Melanaspis obscura*). This species is an important pest of pecans. The scale also attacks hickory, oak, and other trees. Chief injury resulting from attacks of the insect is the killing of smaller branches and weakening the trees, which results

Figure 116. A. The white peach scale (*Pseudaulacaspis pentagona*) on mulberry. B. The euonymus scale (*Unaspis euonymi*). (From Texas Agricultural Experiment Station.)

in lower yields of nuts. This dark gray scale resembles closely the bark of its host plants. The female scale is ⅒ to ⅛ inch in diameter with a black concentric exuviae. The insect winters in the nymphal stage and eggs are produced in the spring. Only one generation occurs annually. Spraying the trees in the dormant season with lubricating oil emulsion sprays will control the scale but it must be thoroughly applied.

THE CALIFORNIA RED SCALE (*Aonidiella aurantii*). The California red scale ranks as possibly the most important pest of citrus. In addition to citrus, the insect attacks acacia, fig, willow, rose, grape, and other plants. Injury results from the sucking of sap and also the probable injection of a toxic substance through the mouthparts into the tree. It attacks fruit, stems, leaves, branches, and the trunk of the tree. The female scale is reddish brown, circular, flat, and about ¹⁄₁₂ inch in diameter. The exuviae are located in the center and are darker colored.

Each female gives birth to about 150 young. The young emerge and crawl around on the host plant until a suitable place is found. Mouthparts then are inserted and feeding is begun. The developmental period is usually 10–12 weeks. The females produce young over a period of about 2 months. Males are present; there is no parthenogenesis. A maximum of 4 generations has been recorded in 1 year but the average is less.

Spraying with suitable oils has been a standard control measure for this pest for many years. Parathion and malathion may be used.

THE FLORIDA RED SCALE (*Chrysomphalus aonidum*). This important pest of citrus also attacks palm, oleander, holly, ivy, poinsettia, and a number of other plants. In comparison with the California red scale, this scale is slightly larger, convex, and dark reddish brown. The centrally located exuviae are lighter than the remainder of the body. The scale appears to be adapted to conditions of higher humidity than the California red scale. Therefore, it is not a pest of any consequence in California, but it is important in Florida and other Gulf states.

The life history of the Florida red scale is approximately the same as that of the California red scale except that eggs are laid. The Florida red scale is controlled with oil sprays. Parathion sprays are also quite effective. They are recommended for use particularly during the latter part of the summer.

THE PURPLE SCALE (*Lepidosaphes beckii*). This is the most important scale insect pest of citrus trees in Florida and the Gulf Coast. It is also a pest of importance in California. Although feeding primarily on citrus, this insect also attacks such plants as avocado, eucalyptus, and fig.

The female scale is oyster-shell shaped, about ⅛ inch long, and brown. The female deposits 40–50 eggs underneath the scale covering and it then dies. Upon hatching, the crawlers or nymphs emerge and seek the shady part of the trees where they settle in a suitable place. Two to four generations may occur during the year. The same recommendations are given for the control of the purple scale as for the California red scale.

CHAPTER 12

ORDERS COLEOPTERA AND STREPSIPTERA

ORDER COLEOPTERA[1]
BEETLES

Characteristics of the Coleoptera are:

1. Wings (rarely absent) 2 pairs; front pair (*elytra*) greatly thickened and hornlike, and when at rest meet in a straight line down the back; hind wings membranous and protected by the front pair.
2. Chewing mouthparts.
3. Complete metamorphosis.
4. Bodies usually quite stout.

The Coleoptera, beetles, comprise the largest order of insects. More than a quarter of a million species have been described. Of this huge number, nearly ⅒ are known to occur in North America north of Mexico. Most species of beetles are plant feeders, and there are many important pests of a wide variety of plants in this order. However, some beetles are predaceous and others live as scavengers. Most beetles are terrestrial, but some are aquatic or semiaquatic.

The most distinctive morphological characteristic of beetles is the structure of the first pair of wings, which are horny veinless sheaths (*elytra*); when the insect is not in flight these are folded to form a straight line down the back (Figure 117). Only the earwigs (Dermaptera) have similar front wings, but they may be distinguished from the beetles by a pair of forcepslike appendages on the end of the body. Only the membranous hind wings of beetles are used in flight. When not in use they are folded underneath the front pair.

Beetles are generally stout bodied. Their exoskeletons are usually thick and strong. Both larvae and adults possess chewing mouthparts which are strongly developed. Some families of beetles have the head prolonged into a snout which may be longer than

---

[1] *Coleos*, sheath; *pteron*, wing.

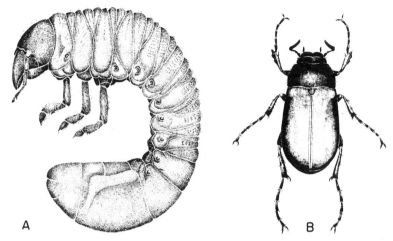

Figure 117. A May beetle (*Phyllophaga*). A. Larva. B. Adult. (From Department of Entomology, Texas A&M University.)

the entire body. On the end of the snout functional chewing mouthparts are found. This long snout enables the insects to feed on the inner tissues of plants and make deep holes for the deposition of eggs.

Larvae of beetles are commonly known as grubs. They usually have three pairs of thoracic legs; snout beetle grubs are legless. The head is distinct and ordinarily dark in color. The thorax and abdomen usually bear conspicuous spiracles. Pupae are of the exarate type, which means that the appendages are free. Generally both larvae and adults have the same hosts and feeding habits; however, exceptions may be found. In many species of blister beetles the adults feed on the foliage of plants, while the larvae are beneficial since they feed on grasshopper eggs in the soil.

Family Carabidae (Ground Beetles)
The Carabidae is a large family comprising more than 2500 species in this country alone. Most members of this family are beneficial, preying on other insects in both the larval and adult stages. A few are harmful, but only rarely does their feeding produce economic damage.

Ground beetles are commonly found running on the ground in search of prey or hiding under stones, logs, and rubbish. Most of them feed at night. Their bodies are somewhat flattened; they have long legs, and are usually dark in color (Figure 118A). Some, however, are colored blue, brown, or green. The elytra of most species are marked with rows of longitudinal ridges and punctuations. The larvae, which are seldom seen, are elongate, have sharp mandibles,

Figure 118. A. A ground beetle (*Calosoma scrutator*). B. Larva of a ground beetle feeding on a cutworm. (From USDA.)

and usually bear a pair of bristlelike appendages on the end of the abdomen (Figure 118B).

The most common ground beetles belong to the genus *Harpalus*. A number of species, the adults of which are dark colored, are found in this genus. *Calosoma scrutator* is perhaps the most striking native species. It is a large beetle measuring more than 1 inch in length. Its elytra are violet or green and are bordered with reddish brown. The body is green, gold, blue, and copper.

The bombardier beetles (*Brachinus*) are interesting in their unusual means of self-defense. At the posterior end of the abdomen are glands that secrete a fluid which, when discharged, changes into a smokelike gas. This substance has an irritating effect on tender skin. The fluid is ejected with such force that an audible sound is produced, like that made by a tiny popgun. When pursued, the bombardier beetle shoots its astonished attacker in the face and then escapes behind the smoke screen. These beetles are commonly found under rotten logs and in similar environments. They have black or bluish-black wing covers and their bodies are reddish brown.

Family Cicindelidae (Tiger Beetles)
Tiger beetles (Figure 119) are commonly found along country roads, dusty pathways, and sandy shores of ponds and streams.

When approached, they readily take flight and then alight several yards ahead of and usually facing the observer. Most tiger beetles are strikingly colored. They are usually blue, bronze, or green and are spotted or marked with yellow or white. Some are dark gray or grayish white. Their beautiful colors and remarkable color patterns have made these insects collectors' favorites.

Tiger beetles are smaller, more cylindrical, and more brightly colored than ground beetles. Like the latter, both larvae and adults are predaceous on other insects. Most of them are diurnal; however, species of certain genera, such as *Tetracha*, feed at night.

The ugly, hump-backed larvae of tiger beetles live in cylindrical vertical tunnels in the soil. They place themselves at the opening of their tunnels to await the passing of their prey, which they seize with their powerful mandibles and readily devour. Children often thrust straws in their burrows, which the larvae grasp. The children attempt to jerk them out, and sometimes succeed. The larvae are sometimes called doddlebugs, but doodlebugs or ant lions are the larvae of a neuropteroid insect which, as adults, superficially resemble damselflies.

Family Dytiscidae (Predaceous Diving Beetles)

Predaceous diving beetles abound in pools, lakes, and streams. They are shining dark in color, and oval and flattened in outline (Figure 120). They may be distinguished from the water scavenger beetles by their threadlike antennae. The hind legs are long and

Figure 119. Tiger beetles. A. *Cicindela purpurea.* B. *Cicindela sexguttata.* (Courtesy of L. S. Dillon.)

Figure 120. A predaceous diving beetle (*Dytiscus verticalis*). (Courtesy of L. S. Dillon.)

fitted for swimming. Some of the largest species may approach 1½ inches in length. Both larvae and adults are predaceous, feeding on insects as well as other small animal life in the water, including small fish.

The larvae are rapacious creatures, a characteristic that has won them the name of water tigers. They are elongate and spindle shaped with a pair of needle-sharp, sicklelike mandibles. They seize their prey, secrete enzymes into the body cavity of the victim, and then suck out the body contents through channels in the mandibles.

Family Hydrophilidae (Water Scavenger Beetles)

Members of the Hydrophilidae resemble the carnivorous diving beetles but they may be distinguished from them by their club-shaped antennae. They are elongate, oval in shape, and some are as much as 2 inches in length. These insects are commonly found in quiet bodies of water. Their food consists mainly of decaying plant and animal material, but they feed also on living animals and plants.

Family Gyrinidae (Whirligig Beetles)

Whirligig beetles, "apple bugs" or "mellow bugs," are as familiar to a country boy in the South as the sun-flecked swimming pool. These insects are usually seen in groups gyrating, or resting on the surface of still pools. They are agile and difficult to capture.

When captured, they may secrete a milky fluid which has the odor of overripe apples. Whirligig beetles are bluish black, oval, and somewhat flattened (Figure 121). The compound eyes are divided by the front margin of the head so that the insects appear to have four eyes instead of two. The pair on the underside of the head looks into the water and the upper pair into the air. Both the larvae, which develop in the water, and the adults are predaceous on small insects. The adults have well developed wings and readily fly from one body of water to another. The North American fauna include three genera of this family, *Dineutes*, *Gyretes*, and *Gyrinus*.

Family Staphylinidae (Rove Beetles)

Rove beetles are small elongate insects with short wing covers (Figure 122). The largest species are hardly more than ½ inch in length. They run rapidly, and when disturbed lift up the end of the abdomen in a menacing way as if they were preparing to sting their adversary. Thousands of species of this group are known. They are chiefly associated with decaying plant and animal material and are commonly found around manure piles and similar places. The larvae, which are found in the same environment as the adults, resemble those of the ground beetles. A number of species are predaceous; others live with ants and termites in their colonies. As a whole, the family is considered beneficial.

Family Lampyridae (Fireflies)

The twinkling light of fireflies (Figure 123) is first seen in the warm spring evenings. As dusk deepens into darkness, the number of flashes increases. This continues well into the night. These

Figure 121. A whirligig beetle (*Dineutes horni*). (Courtesy of L. S. Dillon.)

Figure 122. A rove beetle (*Philonthus fusciformis*). (Courtesy of L. S. Dillon.)

Figure 123. A firefly (*Photinus pyralis*). (Courtesy of L. S. Dillon.)

are signals of courtship, and it seems each species has its own code.

The light-producing organs are located on the underside of the abdomen. The light, which is yellow, blue or green, is not continuous but is produced in flashes. This luminescence is produced by the oxidation of a substance known as luciferin in the presence of an enzyme, luciferase. Light production appears to be controlled by the nervous system. Larvae and pupae also produce light but it is continuous. The larvae and the wingless females of certain species are known as glowworms.

Larvae and adults are nocturnal and prey on small, soft-bodied animals. Many adults, however, probably do not feed. The larvae do not devour their food but inject predigestive enzymes into the body of the victim and suck out the partly digested body contents through grooves in the curved mandibles.

The soldier beetles (Figure 124) belong to a closely related family, *Cantharidae*. These insects are active during the day and feed on pollen of flowers. They do not emit light. *Chauliognathus pennsylvanicus* is a common species often seen on flowers. This is a yellow beetle with a dark area on the thorax and on the apical half of each elytron.

Family Silphidae (Carrion Beetles)
Often a dead rat or bird is found in the process of being buried by an insect which burrows underneath and pushes the soil up

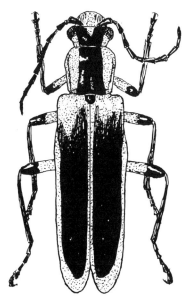

Figure 124. A soldier beetle (*Chauliognathus marginatus*). (Courtesy of L. S. Dillon.)

around it. This is the work of certain species of carrion beetles of the genus *Necrophorus* (Figure 125). Eggs are laid and the larvae develop in the decaying flesh. Carrion beetles are elongate, ranging from ½ to 1½ inches in length. Most of them feed on dead animal matter. However, some live in colonies of ants; others subsist on fungi; and certain species are plant feeders. The family is considered beneficial.

Family Meloidae (Blister Beetles)

The blister beetle family is a comparatively small group, represented in the North American fauna by about 300 species. Blister beetles are of medium size and their bodies are cylindrical and relatively soft. Their wing covers are soft and flexible. The prothorax is narrower than the wing covers. The head is narrowed into a neck where it joins the prothorax. Adults of blister beetles feed on plants, and several species are pests of potatoes, tomatoes, eggplants, beans, peas, melons, spinach, carrots, chard, and other cultivated crops. Larvae of many species of blister beetles are beneficial since they feed on grasshopper eggs.

Blister beetles have been given this name because their bodies contain a substance, cantharidin, which has been used as a vesicant. The compound also has properties as a diuretic and a stimulant to the reproductive organs. Cantharidin is obtained chiefly from the dried bodies of a European species (*Lytta vesicatoria*), which is commonly known as the Spanishfly.

Blister beetles have a rather unusual life cycle in that the larvae appear in a different form after each molt (Figure 126). This type

Figure 125. A carrion beetle (*Necrophorus orbicollis*). (Courtesy of L. S. Dillon.)

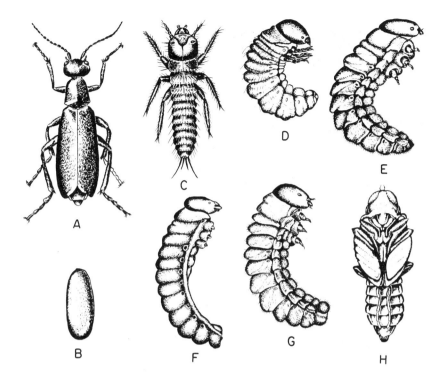

Figure 126. Stages in the development of the immaculate blister beetle (*Macrobosis immaculata*). A. Adult. B. Egg. C. First larval stage (triungulin). D. Second larval stage (caraboid). E. Third larval stage (scarabaeoid). F. Pseudopupa or coarctate stage. G. Last larval stage. H. Pupa. (After Gilbertson, from South Dakota State College Agricultural Experiment Station.)

of development is known as hypermetamorphosis. Females lay 50–300 eggs in cavities prepared in the ground. The eggs hatch into active and very agile larvae known as triungulins. The triungulins search for pods of grasshopper eggs. When an egg pod is found, the larva immediately begins feeding. Shortly afterward, it molts into a second stage, the caraboid. The caraboid molts and emerges as a scarabaeoid larva. These are summer stages. The scarabaeoid stage changes in molting to a pseudopupa or coarctate stage. This is the overwintering stage. In the spring the coarctate larva molts into an active stage which prepares a cell in which it soon pupates. The adult emerges about 2 weeks later. Some species may remain in the soil for 1–2 years in the coarctate stage. Normally, there is one generation annually, but in the South some species are known to have a partial second generation.

The larvae of some species develop in the nests of solitary bees. In these species, the triungulin climbs a plant and waits on the

Figure 127. The margined blister beetle (*Epicauta pestifera*). (Prepared by the Clemson University Cooperative Extension Service's Entomology-Plant Pathology and Agricultural Communications Sections, Federal Extension Service Cooperating.)

flowers for a visiting bee. It clings to the bee and is carried to the bee's nest. There it remains in the cell and eats the eggs and the stores provided for the bee larva.

Blister beetles are often called "old-fashioned potato bugs" as they were pests of the potato before the Colorado potato beetle invaded the East. Blister beetles often appear suddenly in fields of tomatoes, potatoes, and other crops in swarms traveling like armyworms.

Some of the more important species are the three-striped blister beetle (*Epicauta lemniscata*), the striped blister beetle (*Epicauta vittata*), the black blister beetle (*Epicauta pennsylvanica*), the spotted blister beetle (*Epicauta maculata*), and the margined blister beetle (*Epicauta pestifera*) (Figure 127).

Blister beetles are usually found first in a small part of the field, and it may not be necessary to apply insecticides to the entire crop. Carbaryl or toxaphene is recommended for their control. The insecticides should be applied directly upon the beetles as much as possible.

Family Dermestidae (Dermestids)

Dermestids are small, oval, plump beetles. They can be differentiated from beetles with related habits by the wing covers which completely cover the abdomen. The adults are dull colored and are usually marked with brown, reddish, or white scales. The adults of common species feed on the pollen of plants. The larvae are hairy or bristly grubs about ¼ inch long. They feed on woolens, furs, feathers, bristles, silk, meat, waxes, insect specimens, and many other animal and plant products.

THE LARDER BEETLE (*Dermestes lardarius*). The larder beetle is a common pest of pantries, kitchens, and other places where meat, cheese, and similar products are stored. The adult is about ¼ inch long and black with a broad yellowish band across the wing covers near the base. The larva is brown and is clothed with long black hairs. It attacks meats, cheese, waxes, and similar oily materials. Eggs are laid directly on the food. The life cycle is completed in about 7 weeks.

Cleanliness and close checking of those food materials that are fed upon by this pest should be practiced. Infestations should be eliminated in their incipiency. Meats in cold storage will not become infested. Infestations in cured meat may be eliminated by dipping in hot water and trimming away the infested parts. Hides and skins may be protected by dusting or spraying them with chlordane or related compounds.

CARPET BEETLES. The larvae of four species of carpet beetles are pests of importance on rugs, upholstery, furniture, padding, clothing, curtains, and other articles. The two most common and most destructive species are the common carpet beetle (*Anthrenus scrophulariae*) (Figure 128) and the black carpet beetle (*Attagenus megatoma*) (Figure 129).

The common carpet beetle is about ⅛ inch long, and its color consists of mottled black and white with markings of red along the middle of the back. Adults are often found on window screens. Eggs are laid on the food material of the larvae. Fully grown larvae are brownish plump grubs clothed with black hairs. Injury consists of irregular holes eaten into fabrics, or slits in the carpets along cracks in the floors (Figure 130). The length of a life cycle is from 3 months to a year, depending upon temperatures and food supply.

The black carpet beetle is small, black, and about ⅛ inch in length. Its larva is reddish brown, slender, and bears a tuft of long reddish hairs on the tip of the abdomen. The life cycle of the black carpet beetle may extend from 8 months to more than a year. Adults feed particularly on the pollen of *Spiraea*.

Good housekeeping helps to prevent carpet beetles from becoming established in homes. Old clothing, blankets, and draperies should be discarded, fumigated in tight boxes or chests, or sprayed with chlordane or other approved household sprays. Lint and dust should not be allowed to accumulate. Such materials as rugs and blankets should be periodically cleaned and sunned.

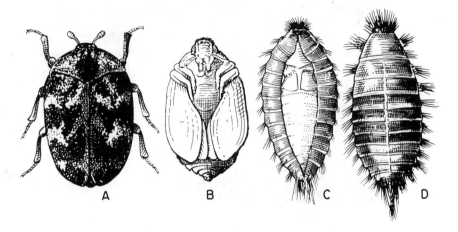

Figure 128. The common carpet beetle (*Anthrenus scrophulariae*). A. Adult. B. Pupa. C. Pupa within larval skin. D. Larva. (From USDA.)

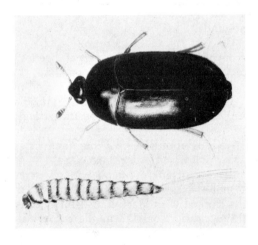

Figure 129. The black carpet beetle (*Attagenus megatoma*). A. Larva. B. Adult. (From USDA.)

Should infestations develop, thorough spraying with chlordane or other household sprays is recommended. Upholstered furniture may be sent to companies to be mothproofed if it is badly infested. Cedar chests may prevent infestations through the repellent action of the cedar oil in the wood, but will not kill the insects. Cedar lined closets are helpful in preventing infestations, but should not be depended upon entirely.

Family Buprestidae (The Flatheaded Borers)
The adults of the flatheaded borers are stout, broad, and hard bodied. They are generally dark with a metallic luster, but some

Figure 130. Carpet beetle larvae feeding on a carpet. (From USDA.)

are brightly colored. The larvae are legless grubs, with the thorax broadly flattened. They lie with the abdomen inclined to one side in shallow flat burrows mostly underneath the bark in the cambium and the sapwood of trees. The adults are quite active and fly readily. They prefer sunlight and are usually found on the sunny side of the trunks of trees and the larger limbs. A life cycle is generally completed in a year. Devitalized, dying, and dead trees are usually attacked. Healthy trees are not generally subject to injury by these borers, because the sap repels them.

THE FLATHEADED APPLE TREE BORER (*Chrysobothris femorata*). This widely distributed insect (Figure 131) is an important pest of fruit, shade, and forest trees. It kills many trees and shrubs each year. Indications of the presence of this insect are brown sawdust pushed out of cracks in the bark, dead areas of bark, exudation of sap, and the broad shallow burrows in the cambium. The fully grown larva or borer is about 1 inch long with the characteristic yellowish-white color and flattened thorax. The adult beetle is about ½ inch long, dark grayish brown with a metallic sheen, and with slight depressions on the wing covers.

The insect overwinters as a larva. Pupation occurs in the spring, and the adult emerges a few weeks later. Eggs are laid during late spring and summer usually on unhealthy trees in crevices of the bark or in injured spots. One generation develops each year.

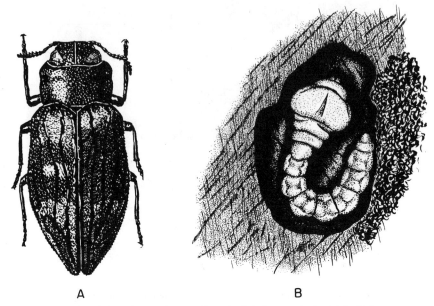

A   B

Figure 131. Flatheaded apple tree borer (*Chrysobothris femorata*). A. Adult. B. Larva. (From USDA.)

Maintaining trees in a vigorous growing condition is important in preventing infestations of the flatheaded apple tree borer. Trees grown in the proper soil tend to be more thrifty and less subject to attack by this insect. Approved horticultural practices entailing proper cultivation, fertilization, and maintenance of soil moisture should be followed. Low heading of trees to provide more adequate shading of the trunks reduces egg laying as the females prefer to oviposit in the sun. All prunings should be burned. The trunks of recently transplanted trees should be wrapped with heavy paper or burlap. These wrappings should remain through the second season. The borers may be removed with a knife and the wounds painted with a tree paint. Spraying the trunks and larger branches with BHC or lindane helps to prevent attacks.

Other important species of flatheaded borers are the bronze birch borer (*Agrilus anxius*), Pacific flatheaded borer (*Chrysobothris mali*), and the flatheaded cherry tree borer (*Dicerca divericata*). Their biologies and habits are similar to those of the flatheaded apple tree borer.

Family Elateridae (Click Beetles)

Click beetles are elongate, robust insects, somewhat tapered at each end, and usually brownish in color. They are so named because they can suddenly snap their bodies when they are on their backs, and throw themselves in the air with an audible clicking sound in an effort to land on their feet. Because of this habit they are also called skipjacks or snapping bugs. More than 500 species of click beetles are known in North America. The larvae are known as wireworms because of their body characteristics. They are long, cylindrical, distinctly segmented, and usually yellow or brown. The terminal segment of the abdomen usually bears structural characteristics which are of value in identification of the insects. In most species the larvae are found in the soil, but some live in rotten wood, moss, under bark of trees, and in other environments. The life cycles of click beetles are extremely variable. Some species complete a life cycle in 1 year; others require 5 or 6 years. Winter is passed either in the larval or the adult stage.

The eyed elater (*Alaus oculatus*) (Figure 132) probably has attracted more interest than any other click beetle. It is a large insect about 1½ inches in length, black and dotted with white. Its most striking characteristic is the presence of two large velvety black eyelike spots on the pronotum. The larvae live in decaying wood and are predaceous on other insects.

In the southernmost part of the United States and in the tropics are found species of *Pyrophorus* which bear yellowish "eyespots" near each rear corner of the pronotum. These spots intermittently emit greenish yellow light at night. The larva are also said to be luminous; they are predaceous on white grubs.

A number of species of wireworms (Figure 133) are injurious to cultivated crops. Seeds of such crops as peas, beans, and corn are destroyed by the larvae. Tubers of potatoes and the roots of

Figure 132. The eyed elater (*Alaus oculatus*). (Courtesy of L. S. Dillon.)

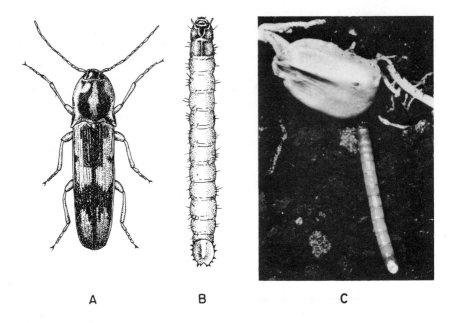

A   B   C

Figure 133. The southern corn wireworm (*Monocrepidius vespertinus*). A. Adult. B. Larva. (From Agricultural Research Service, USDA.) C. Wireworm feeding on sprouting corn. (Prepared by the Clemson University Cooperative Extension Service's Entomology-Plant Pathology and Agricultural Communications Sections, Federal Extension Service Cooperating.)

tomatoes, watermelons, cotton, corn, turnips, and onions may suffer injury. Cultural practices designed to control wireworms should be suitable for the crops affected. If a field is known to be infested with wireworms and is to be planted to a susceptible crop, it should be plowed during summer and thoroughly cultivated until cold weather to eliminate as many of the insects in the soil as possible. Then for a period of 2 years, crops that are not seriously attacked, such as clover, should be grown before the planting of the susceptible crop. If the infested land is poorly drained, drainage will be of great aid in eliminating the infestation. Flooding the land in irrigated districts during warm weather is also beneficial. In some cases early planting, fertilizing, and intensive cultivation will produce early and vigorous crops which will not be seriously injured by the pests.

Soil applications of chlordane have been found to control certain species of wireworms. The insecticide should be disced into the soil to a depth of 6–9 inches. Chlordane, dieldrin, aldrin, and other insecticides have been recommended also. Seed treatments with dieldrin, lindane, or heptachlor will afford protection to stands of young grain.

When valuable crops are grown on infested land, the soil may be fumigated. D-D mixture (dichloropropane and dichloropropylene) and ethylene dibromide are efficient fumigants. Equipment is available for the application of these compounds to the soil. Small garden plots may be treated by pouring the desired amount of the product in holes 6 inches deep made at intervals of 12 inches. Crops should not be planted for 2 or 3 weeks following treatment of the soil.

Family Coccinellidae (Ladybird Beetles or Ladybeetles)
Ladybird beetles are semihemispherical insects and look very much like split peas. They are tan, black, or red, and spotted or marked with contrasting colors of red, yellow, or white. They are rather small, varying in length from ⅟₁₆ to ¼ inch. Ladybird beetles often are confused with leaf beetles from which they may be distinguished by the presence of three distinct segments in the hind tarsi, while the latter have four apparent segments. The larvae are elongate, tapering posteriorly. Their general color is dark with bright markings and their bodies are covered with spines. The larvae are sometimes mistaken for aphis lions (lacewing fly larvae) but they lack the large sicklelike jaws of the latter.

With few exceptions, both adults and larvae are beneficial. They are predaceous on aphids, scale insects, spider mites, eggs of a number of insects, and small larvae of many pests, such as the corn earworm and the cotton leafworm. Some conception of the beneficial results obtained from the predatory activities of ladybird beetles may be derived from the fact that larvae have been observed to devour 11 to 25 aphids; and adults 16–56 aphids daily.

Ladybird beetles diapause as adults, often in numbers, in places affording protection and reasonably dry conditions. Their eggs are yellow and are laid on end in clusters. When a larva has completed its development, it attaches itself to some part of the plant upon which it has been feeding or to some nearby object and pupates. It pupates within the slit larval skin or works this skin downward to the end of the abdomen. In a common representative species a female lays 200–500 eggs. The length of a life cycle varies with the species and temperature, but it usually is 3–4 weeks in duration. Since ladybird beetles reproduce rapidly and have voracious habits, they are among the most beneficial of all insects.

The convergent ladybird beetle (*Hippodamia convergens*), (Figure 134) is the most common North American species. It is so named because of two converging light marks on the pronotum. The body color is tan with the elytra spotted with black. This is a large species, measuring about ¼ inch in length. In mountainous regions of the far West the adults often collect in huge numbers for hibernation in protected places.

The genus *Scymnus* includes a number of small black or brown

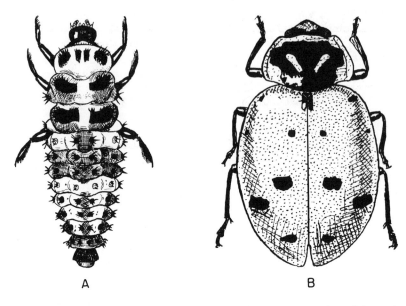

A   B

Figure 134. *Hippodamia convergens*, the convergent ladybird beetle and larva. A. Larva. B. Adult. (Courtesy of L. S. Dillon.)

species, measuring about ½₂ inch in length. The larvae are usually clothed with a waxy secretion and they are often mistaken for mealybugs by the novice. Other common native species are the twicestabbed ladybird beetle (*Chilocorus stigma*), the spotted ladybird beetle (*Coleomegilla fuscilabris*), and the nine-spotted ladybird beetle (*Coccinella novemnotata*) (Figure 135).

A number of species have been imported to prey on introduced pests. The best known of these introductions is the vedalia ladybird beetle (*Rodolia cardinalis*), which was brought from Australia to control the cottony-cushion scale (*Icerya purchasi*).

Another introduced ladybird beetle, the mealybug destroyer (*Cryptolaemus montrouzieri*), has been quite successful in controlling mealybugs in California, where it is well established. It has also been reared in insectaries in large numbers and liberated in the citrus groves.

All ladybird beetles are beneficial, with the exception of a small number of species in the genus *Epilachna* which are phytophagous in habit. The best known and most destructive pest in this genus is the Mexican bean beetle (*Epilachna varivestis*) (Figure 136). It is an important pest of snap and lima beans. It will on occasion attack cowpeas, soybeans, and other legumes. The larvae and adults feed on the underside of the leaves, skeletonizing them and giving them a lacelike appearance.

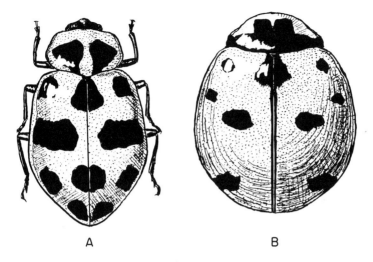

A   B

Figure 135. Two common ladybird beetles. A. *Coleomegilla fuscilabris*. B. *Coccinella novemnotata*. (Courtesy of L. S. Dillon.)

Figure 136. The Mexican bean beetle (*Epilachna varivestis*). (From USDA.)

Adults of the Mexican bean beetle are ¼ to ⅓ inch in length, oval, brown or yellow, with 16 black spots on the wing covers. The full-grown larvae are oval, ⅓ inch in length, and are covered with branching spines tipped in black. Winters are spent as adults in trash or rubbish. After feeding on the young beans in the spring, the adults begin egg deposition. Each female deposits about 500 yellow eggs in batches of 40 or 50 on the underside of the leaves. A generation may be completed in about 1 month. Malathion, methoxychlor, or rotenone thoroughly applied as a dust or spray will control the pest if the applications are made at 10-day intervals. Crop residues should be destroyed following harvest.

The Mexican bean beetle is an old pest in Mexico, New Mexico, Arizona, Utah, Wyoming, Colorado, and western Texas. Only in comparatively recent times has it been found east of the Mississippi River. It is now present throughout this area with the possible exception of Wisconsin.

The squash beetle (*Epilachna borealis*) is another ladybird beetle which is a pest of plants. It attacks squashes, pumpkins, melons, and other cucurbits. The adults are yellow and are spotted with black. The larvae are covered with branching spines. They feed on the leaves of the host plants. The biology of this insect is similar to that of the Mexican bean beetle, as are the control measures.

Family Tenebrionidae (Darkling Beetles)

Darkling beetles comprise a large family of Coleoptera, with more than a thousand species in North America. They vary much in size but most of them are uniformly dark in color, superficially resembling ground beetles (Figure 137). They may be distinguished from the latter by the presence of four segments instead of five in the hind tarsi. They are found chiefly in the West and South-

Figure 137. A common darkling beetle. (From Texas Agricultural Experiment Station.)

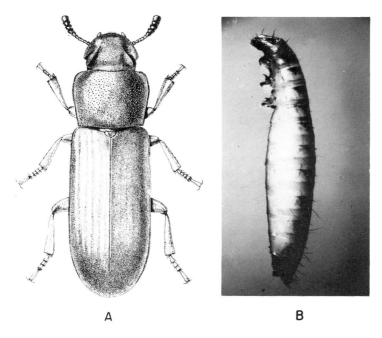

A   B

Figure 138. The confused flour beetle (*Tribolium confusum*). A. Adult. B. Larva. (From USDA.)

west. Food consists mostly of vegetable matter, but a few species are predaceous.

The confused flour beetle (*Tribolium confusum*) (Figure 138) is a common pest of such food products as flour, grains, beans, dried fruit, nuts, chocolate, and pepper. The adults are reddish brown and are about ⅐ of an inch in length. They are often found in large numbers in grain elevators, mills, groceries, and other places where food products are stored.

The confused flour beetle is long lived, adults often living for a year or more. During this period, the female may lay 400–500 eggs. The brownish white larvae feed on the same food products as the adults. In warm weather the developmental period may be as short as a month, but the time is usually longer. Several generations occur during a 12-month period. A closely related but less common species is the red flour beetle (*Tribolium castaneum*).

Infested places should be cleaned and badly infested residues destroyed. Painting or spraying the woodwork and walls with methoxychlor will aid in preventing infestations. Infested material may be fumigated with an ethylene dichloride–carbon tetrachloride mixture, methyl bromide, or other fumigant.

Mealworms (*Tenebrio* spp.) often become pests around grain

bins and other places, particularly in dark and damp environments (Figure 139). They prefer to feed on farinaceous products that are in a poor or decaying condition. The two common mealworms are the yellow mealworm (*Tenebrio molitor*) and the dark mealworm (*T. obscurus*). The adults are black beetles about 1 inch in length. The larvae resemble wireworms since they are brown or yellowish, smooth, and distinctly segmented. There is usually one generation annually.

Another related pest of grain is the cadelle (*Tenebroides mauritanicus*) (Figure 140). It is not a darkling beetle but belongs to a related family, Ostomidae. The cadelle is black, elongate, flattened, and about ⅓ inch long. The adults have the habit of cutting bolting cloth and making holes in sacks and cartons, even though these materials are not used as food.

The full-grown cadelle larvae are about ¾ inch in length with dark heads, dark spots on the thorax, and a pair of hooks on the end of the abdomen. Both adults and larvae make burrows in the woodwork of grain bins. Here they may remain for long periods until new grain is available. Although primarily grain feeders, larvae and adults may prey on other grain-infesting insects. The cadelle is long lived, having been known to live for nearly 2 years. Females lay about 1000 eggs each. Development from egg to adult may occupy as little as 2½ months, but the time is often greatly prolonged. Control measures recommended for flour beetles are suggested for mealworms and the cadelle.

The plains false wireworm (*Eleodes opaca*) and related species are occasionally pests of importance in the dry regions of the West and Southwest. Wheat primarily, but also oats, maize, cotton, corn, native grasses, and other plants are attacked. The chief injury consists of larval feeding on germinating seed and roots. The adults are general feeders and are usually considered harmless, although they may seriously injure young cotton plants.

Figure 139. Mealworm (*Tenebrio* spp.) feeding. (Prepared by the Clemson University Cooperative Extension Service's Entomology-Plant Pathology and Agricultural Communications Sections, Federal Extension Service Cooperating.)

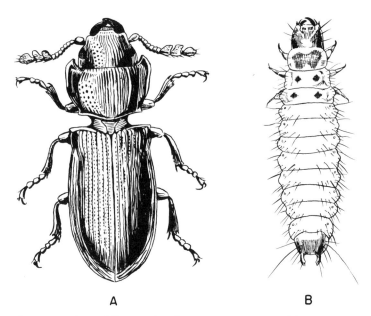

Figure 140. The cadelle (*Tenebroides mauritanicus*). A. Adult. B. Larva. (From the University of California, Division of Agricultural Sciences.)

The larvae are brown or yellowish and have the general appearance of wireworms, but differ in the possession of longer antennae and legs. Adults are dark colored with ridged, granulate, or smooth wing covers, which characteristic depends upon the species. They are less than 1 inch in length.

Diapause is either in the adult or partly grown larval stage. In the spring, eggs are laid in the soil. When conditions are favorable, larvae hatched from these eggs mature in about 4 months. Two to 3 weeks after pupation in the soil the adults emerge. Later in the season there is another period of egg laying. Larvae developing from these eggs diapause in a partly grown stage.

The growing of corn or other less susceptible crops for 2 years or longer between crops of wheat is the most effective cultural control. Seed treatment with aldrin, lindane, or other approved toxicants provides satisfactory control of the larvae.

POWDER POST BEETLES. Powder post beetles often seriously damage lumber, floors, furniture, frames of houses, and books. They make long cylindrical tunnels through these materials, and heavy infestations often reduce them to mere shells. The pests are infrequently seen and their presence is usually first indicated by the small exit holes made by the adults and tiny piles of sawdust on the floor.

Powder post beetles constitute a heterogeneous group of beetles belonging to several families, *Lyctidae, Bostrichidae, Anobiidae,* and *Ptinidae.* The most destructive forms are members of the genus *Lyctus* (Figure 141) and the furniture beetle (*Anobium punctatum*). These are small dark-colored stout insects, usually about ⅕ inch in length. Exit holes made by the adults may not be more than ¹⁄₁₆ inch in diameter. Usually there is one generation annually of these insects. Under natural conditions the winter is spent in the larval stage.

As *Lyctus* beetles attack only sapwood of hardwoods, the use of only heartwood will eliminate them. Painting or varnishing all surfaces will fill the pores of the wood and prevent egg laying. Kiln drying the lumber is effective in destroying the borers but this treatment does not prevent reinfestation. Treatment of floors, furniture, and other woodwork with pentachlorophenol in a petroleum solvent is highly recommended. Painting furniture and woodwork with a solution of chlordane is also recommended. Fumigation of lumber and furniture with methyl bromide is suggested.

Some adults of the Bostrichidae have the mischievous habit of boring through solid objects. In the West, one species, *Scobicia declivis,* bores through the lead sheathings of aerial telephone cables, causing short circuits. Some of the beetles of this family have been known to tunnel through wine barrels and wooden water tanks.

Figure 141. The southern lyctus beetle (*Lyctus planicollis*). (From USDA.)

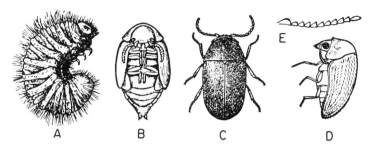

Figure 142. The cigarette beetle (*Lasioderma serricorne*). A. Larva. B. Pupa. C. Adult. D. Lateral view of adult. E. Antenna. (From USDA.)

The most interesting of the Anobiidae is the deathwatch beetle (*Zestobium rufovillosum*). This beetle is the chief source of the superstition that a ticking sound presages the death of some member of the family. The ticking noise so often heard in the walls of old houses during the silent hours of night is probably produced in the most part by this insect and a closely related species. The sound, which is believed to be a sex call, is produced by the insect striking its head or mandibles against the walls of its tunnel in the wood.

The well known cigarette beetle (Figure 142) is another representative of the family Anobiidae. Some of its food materials are stored food products, tobacco, drugs, pepper, raisins, ginger, and upholstered furniture. This insect is an ancient pest of man and it has shown no respect for royalty or dignity, as indicated by evidences of its presence in the tomb of King Tut. As many as three generations may occur annually in the United States. Control of the cigarette beetle should begin with thoroughly cleaning warehouses and other places before new products are stored. Infested materials may be fumigated with commercial fumigants. The use of approved space and residual sprays in enclosures is recommended. Infested upholstered furniture may also be sprayed.

Family Scarabaeidae (Scarabs or Lamellicorn Beetles)

The scarabs are short, robust beetles of variable size. They are most readily recognized by the lamellate club of the antennae which is formed by three or more flattened terminal segments capable of close apposition. The family is large, with more than 1000 North American species. It may be divided into two groups based on habits, the scavengers or tumblebugs (Figure 143), and the leaf chafers.

The scavengers are of slight importance; however, their habits attract attention. Common species of these beetles, often in pairs, form a ball of dung which is rolled over the ground for some

Figure 143. A tumblebug (*Canthon viridia*). (Courtesy of L. S. Dillon.)

distance and then buried. An egg is laid on the organic matter, and the grub feeds on this decomposing food material. The best known of the scavenger beetles is the sacred scarab of Egypt (*Scarabaeus sacer*).

Most species of scarabaeids belong to the group known as the leaf chafers. These beetles are so named because the adults commonly feed on the foliage of trees; however, some feed on pollen, flowers, and fruits of various plants. Larvae, commonly known as white grubs, are chiefly found in grasslands feeding on the roots of many plants; others develop in decaying organic material. They have fleshy, curved bodies with brown heads and well developed legs.

MAY BEETLES OR JUNE BUGS. The May beetles or June bugs are the most common leaf chafers and their larvae are among the most destructive of soil pests. Most species belong to the genus *Phyllophaga*. The adults are brownish, stout in form, and are rather large, measuring about ¾ inch in length. About 150 species are recorded from the United States. They are nocturnal and are strongly attracted to lights, around which they fly clumsily with a loud buzzing sound. Emergence of the adults of some species may occur as early as March and April in the South, although their appearance is later for the country as a whole. The adults feed on the foliage of a number of trees, such as hickory, birch, elm, ash, and persimmon, which occasionally may be defoliated. With the approach of dawn, the insects return to the soil or debris in which they conceal themselves during the daylight hours.

Each female lays 150–200 eggs in the soil. Permanent pastures and lawns are the favorite places for oviposition. Cleanly cultivated row crops and clean stands of legume, such as clover and alfalfa, are the least preferred places for egg deposition. Eggs hatch into white grubs which feed upon the roots of grain crops, other grasses, strawberries, onions, potatoes, and numerous other plants. The larvae are much more injurious than the adults.

The length of the life cycle of May beetles depends upon the climate and species. Some species complete a life cycle in 1 year, and 4 years may be required for other species in colder climates. The 2-year life cycle is the most common in the southern states and the 3-year life cycle is the rule in the North. Both larvae and adults are found in the soil during the winter months. In the South common species such as *Phyllophaga crassissima* and *P. calceata* oviposit in April. The larvae feed on grass and other plant roots during this season and overwinter as larvae. It is during the second year that most damage is done to plant roots by the larvae. In the fall of the second season, pupation occurs. The adult emerges from the pupal stage but remains in the pupal cell in the ground until the next spring before emergence, thus completing a 2-year life cycle.

Crops susceptible to white grub attacks, such as corn, small grains, and potatoes, should not be planted on land likely to be infested, but should follow such crops as legumes and cotton. Thorough discing of fields in late summer or fall will not eliminate the pests, but many larvae and pupae will be destroyed.

Chlordane and heptachlor are effective insecticides in the control of white grubs in the soil. Should adult beetles threaten serious injury to the foliage of trees, they may be protected by sprays of carbaryl or methoxychlor.

THE GREEN JUNE BEETLE (*Cotinis nitida*). The adults of this insect are often pests of foliage and fruits of various plants. The larvae may do serious injury to the roots of grasses, vegetables, and ornamental plants. They also feed on decaying organic matter.

The adults are rather large, about 1 inch in length, flattened, green, and with the body margined with yellow or bronze (Figure 144). They fly during the daylight hours. The larvae are robust dirty-white grubs. They have the peculiar habit of crawling on their backs.

Winter is passed in the larval stage, which completes its development in the spring and then pupates. The adults emerge, feed, and the females lay eggs in soil rich in vegetable matter during the summer. There is one generation annually.

Soil applications of lindane have given fair control of the grubs. The insecticides recommended in the control of the common white grubs are also suggested for use. Bait pails containing malt extract, benzoate of soda, and water have been suggested to reduce infestations when ripe fruits are attacked by the adults.

THE ROSE CHAFER (*Macrodactylus subspinosus*). This insect is distributed over the eastern United States as far south as Virginia

Figure 144. The green June beetle (*Cotinis nitida*). (Prepared by the Clemson University Cooperative Extension Service's Entomology - Plant Pathology and Agricultural Communications Sections, Federal Extension Service Cooperating.)

and westward to Texas and Colorado. It is particularly abundant in localities with sandy soils. The adults feed on foliage, flowers, or fruit of many plants such as grapes, peaches, and roses. They are tan colored beetles with long legs and about ⅓ inch in length (Figure 145). The larvae, which resemble small May beetle grubs, live in the soil and feed on grass roots. There is one generation annually, the winter being passed in the larval stage. The insects are poisonous to poultry when eaten. The adults are controlled by sprays of carbaryl or methoxychlor.

THE JAPANESE BEETLE (*Popillia japonica*). The japanese beetle, a serious pest of many plants, was imported into New Jersey in about 1916 on the roots of nursery stock from Japan. The adults feed on the fruit and skeletonize the foliage of many plants. Roots of grasses and other plants are destroyed by the feeding larvae. This pest is found in most states east of the Mississippi River with the exception of those along the Gulf of Mexico. It is well established in New Jersey and neighboring states.

The adults are about ⅜ inch long, and broadly oval with brownish elytra (Figure 146). The head and thorax are greenish bronze. There are two prominent white spots and also several smaller ones near the end of the abdomen. The larvae are similar in appearance to common white grubs, but they are much smaller.

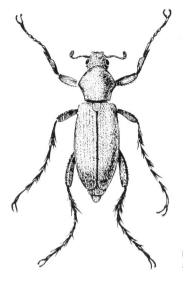

Figure 145. The rose chafer (*Macrodactylus subspinosus*). (From USDA.)

Figure 146. The japanese beetle (*Popillia japonica*). (Prepared by the Clemson University Cooperative Extension Service's Entomology-Plant Pathology and Agricultural Communications Sections, Federal Extension Service Cooperating.)

Larvae complete their development in early summer and the adults appear in large numbers in July and August. The adults live for 30–40 days, depositing eggs in small clusters in the soil. Winter is passed as larvae in the soil. Normally, there is one generation annually, but larvae in cold wet soil may develop more slowly and the adults may not appear until the second season.

Carbaryl or methoxychlor sprays will control the adults feeding on foliage and fruits. Several applications of the spray may be necessary. Treating the soil with chlordane or dieldrin is recommended for the control of the larvae. These compounds will remain in the soil and provide adequate protection against the grubs for several years. Inoculation of the soil with spores of the milky disease (*Bacillus popillae*) is also being employed for control of the larvae.

Rhinoceros beetles are the largest known Coleoptera. These beetles are so named because males of the best known species bear a horn on the head. One or more horns may be present on the thorax also (Figures 147 and 148). One of the largest species is a greenish-gray form, *Dynastes tityrus*. Adults of the genus *Strategus* are black and somewhat smaller than *Dynastes*. The larvae of both genera which are found in the southern states develop in rotten wood and other decaying vegetative material.

Family Cerambycidae (Roundheaded or Longhorned Borers)

The roundheaded or longhorned borers constitute a large family of beetles, with more than 1000 species represented in North America. As a whole, the adults are rather large, some of them being several inches in length. They are usually elongate and rather cylindrical in shape, and are often strikingly marked. Antennae are at least as long as the combined length of the head and thorax, and in many cases are much longer than the entire body.

The larvae are wood borers. They are white or yellow, thin skinned, and more or less cylindrical in outline. Small thoracic legs are present on some species. The straight, cylindrical body is in sharp contrast with the curved body outline and flattened thorax of the flatheaded borers, family *Buprestidae*.

Roundheaded borers attack primarily dead or dying and devitalized timbers. However, some forms, such as the locust borer and the roundheaded apple tree borer, feed on healthy trees. Most damage to shade and forest trees occurs when droughts, defolia-

Figure 147. A rhinoceros beetle from the tropics.

Figure 148. A stag beetle or pinching bug (*Lucanus elaphus*). (Courtesy of L. S. Dillon.)

tion, or diseases have devitalized and made them susceptible to attack. Based on these facts, the best control of roundheaded wood borers on shade and other valuable trees is to keep trees as healthy and vigorous as possible through fertilization, watering, pruning out dead and dying limbs, and other cultural practices.

THE BANDED HICKORY BORER (*Cerasphorus cinctus*). This wood borer is one of the common borers in the southern, eastern, and central states. The larvae (Figure 149A) feed upon dead and dying hickory, pecan, oak, and other hardwoods. The adult (Figure 149B) is brown with a grayish pubescence; the elytra are crossed by a yellowish band near the base. In warm climates, a generation is completed in 1 year. Two years are required for a life cycle in colder climates. Long tunnels are made under the bark and through the wood. Rustic furniture and log cabins also may become infested by this borer.

As this borer attacks only dying or dead wood, it cannot be considered an important pest of shade and forest trees. The larvae appear to be completing a job of destruction started by other agencies. Should rustic woodwork become infested with the borers, spraying or painting it with a solution of pentachlorophenol is recommended.

THE ROUNDHEADED APPLE TREE BORER (*Saperda candida*). The roundheaded apple tree borer is probably the best known of the ceram-

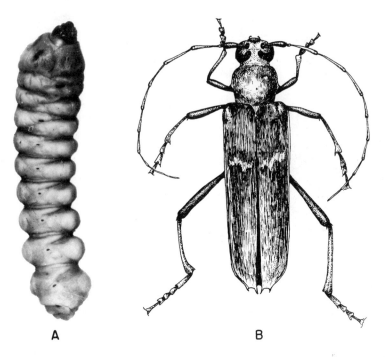

Figure 149. The banded hickory borer (*Cerastophorus cinctus*). A. Larva. B. Adult. (Larva from USDA.)

bycids. It is commonly found in most parts of the country. The insect attacks healthy trees and is a particularly important pest of apple trees. In addition to the apple, it feeds on pear, serviceberry, haw, mountain ash, and others. The grubs burrow through the inner bark, sapwood, and also into the heartwood.

The adult is somewhat less than an inch in length, and velvety brown with two white stripes extending dorsally along the entire length of the body (Figure 150). The full-grown grubs are more than an inch in length. Two or more years are required for a life cycle.

The roundheaded apple tree borer is difficult to control. The grubs may be removed with a knife in a few trees. This should be done in late summer or early fall and repeated in the spring. Lead arsenate sprays, prepared with wettable powders and applied when the adults are active, will kill many of them.

THE LOCUST BORER (*Megacyllene robiniae*). This destructive pest is a dark, robust beetle of medium size, strikingly marked with transverse yellow bands (Figure 151). Adults emerge and are found feeding on the pollen of goldenrod in the fall when this plant is in

Figure 150. The roundheaded apple tree borer (*Saperda candida*).

Figure 151. The locust borer. A. Larva. B. Adult. (From USDA.)

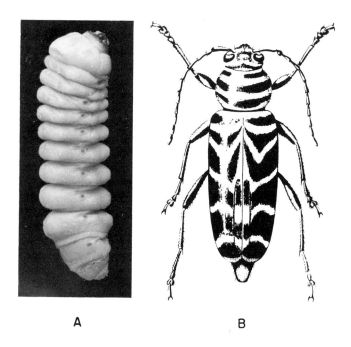

A   B

full bloom. Eggs are laid in the fall underneath bark scales of locust trees. These soon hatch and the young larvae tunnel into the corky bark where they overwinter. The next spring the grubs resume activity and tunnel through both the sapwood and heartwood. Pupation occurs in the burrows during middle or late summer and the adults emerge when goldenrod begins to bloom. There is one generation annually.

The locust borer is difficult to control. Dense stands are attacked less severely than sparse plantings. Rapidly growing trees are less susceptible to injury than trees in poor condition. Interplantings are damaged less than pure stands of locust trees. Severe pruning of heavily infested trees produces a dense growth and a shaded condition which discourages attacks by this insect. The spraying of trunks of shade trees before growth begins in the spring with lead arsenate and malathion may aid in the control of the pest.

THE TWIG GIRDLER (*Oncideres cingulata*). The twig girdler is widely distributed and may do considerable damage when it is abundant (Figure 152). A related form, *O. texana,* is found in the Southwest. Hickory, pecan, persimmon, elm, and other trees are attacked. Adults emerge in late summer or fall and girdle the branches with

Figure 152. Twigs severed from a single pecan tree by twig girdlers (*Oncideres cingulata*). (From Florida Agricultural Experiment Station.)

their powerful mandibles. Eggs are deposited in the girdled twigs, which provide conditions suitable for the development of the larvae. The branches are almost completely severed, leaving intact only a few strands of heartwood. Later, the branches drop, falling to the ground or lodging in the trees. Winter is passed in the larval stage. One generation develops annually. Severe injury may be caused, especially to nursery stock, by the girdling of the terminal branches. The insect may be controlled, particularly in nurseries, by gathering and burning the severed branches during late fall and winter, provided there are no infested woodlands nearby. Azinphosmethyl and parathion sprays applied when adults are active in late summer and fall will destroy many of them. These are highly toxic compounds which should not be used around homes and should be applied by trained operators only.

Family Chrysomelidae (Leaf Beetles)

More than 1000 species of the chrysomelidae are known to occur in North America. Leaf beetles are rather small, the Colorado potato beetle being one of the largest forms. Their bodies are rather short and more or less oval in shape with antennae of normal length. Color patterns of the adults are variable, but many common species are yellow with black markings. Both larvae and adults are foliage feeders, with the exception of the larvae of some species which attack the roots of plants. Eggs are yellowish, usually elongate, and are deposited on the food plants or in the soil. The larvae are usually short and grublike, but some are elongate. Most chrysomelids diapause in the adult stage.

THE COLORADO POTATO BEETLE (*Leptinotarsa decemlineata*). The Colorado potato beetle is one of the best known of all American insects. It is a pest of the potato throughout most of the United States and eastern Canada, and it has been exported to Europe.

This insect is primarily a pest of the potato, but it also attacks tomatoes, eggplants, Jimson weeds, and other solanaceous plants. Both larvae and adults feed on the leaves and terminal growths of the plants. The Colorado potato beetle is an example of a native insect that was of no economic importance until the pioneer farmers brought to it a new food supply in the potato. The insect was first observed about 1823 on the eastern slopes of the Rocky Mountains feeding on a native weed known as the buffalo bur (*Solanum rostratum*). When the potato was planted in this area and became available as food, the beetle spread rapidly eastward over the United States. Entire crops were often destroyed, for no efficient control of the pest was known until the efficacy of paris green as a stomach poison was discovered about 1865.

The adults are about ⅜ inch in length, oval, and yellow with ten longitudinal black stripes on the wing covers (Figure 153). The insect overwinters in the soil as an adult. The adults emerge in the spring after potatoes are growing, and begin feeding and deposit-

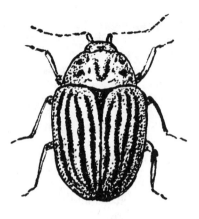

Figure 153. The Colorado potato beetle (*Leptinotarsa decemlineata*).

ing yellowish eggs in clusters on the underside of the leaves. Each female lays an average of 500 eggs during a period of about 5 weeks. These eggs hatch in a week or less into soft, brick-red, humpbacked larvae or grubs. Following a feeding period of 2 or 3 weeks, the grubs enter the ground for pupation. The adult beetles emerge from the pupal stage 1 or 2 weeks later. There may be as many as three generations annually in the insect's southern range.

Although the Colorado potato beetle once was a formidable pest, both larvae and adults are now easily controlled by the use of modern insecticides. Carbaryl and other insecticides are recommended for its control.

THE STRIPED CUCUMBER BEETLE (*Acalymma vittata*). The striped cucumber beetle is a very important pest of cucurbits east of the Rocky Mountains. The insect feeds on the plants throughout their growing season. The leaves, tender terminals, blossoms, and stems are fed upon; and, particularly in the fall, rinds of the fruits are attacked. The larvae attack the roots and underground portions of the stems of the plants. The adult is the vector of the bacterial wilt disease of cucurbits. This insect and the spotted cucumber beetle (*Diabrotica undecimpunctata howardi*) are the only known vectors of this important disease. They not only carry the disease from plant to plant, but the disease organisms live over the winter in their digestive tracts. The striped cucumber beetle is also a vector of the cucurbit mosaic disease.

Although the larvae are restricted to cucurbits, the adults also attack corn, beans, peas, and the flowers of many other plants.

The adults are about ⅕ inch long with three black stripes extending the length of the yellow wing covers (Figure 154). The elytra are minutely punctate. The larvae are white, elongate, and about ⅓ inch long when full grown.

Unmated adults overwinter in protected places near fields where cucurbits were grown the previous season. They emerge in the spring, and egg deposition begins when their host plants are available. Eggs are deposited in the soil, and the larvae feed on the stems and roots of plants until completion of their development; pupation is in the soil. A life cycle varies from 4 to 8 weeks, depending upon the climate. The number of generations varies from 1 in the North to 4 in the southern range of the insect.

The striped cucumber beetle may be controlled by dusting or spraying the plants with methoxychlor. Dusts or sprays of carbaryl are also recommended. The first application of insecticide should be made when the first beetles are seen and further applications should be made as needed. Planting an excess of seed and thinning to a stand later is advisable.

A closely related species, the western striped cucumber beetle (*Acalymma trivittata*), is found on the Pacific Coast. The biology of this species is similar to the striped cucumber beetle and control measures are the same.

The banded cucumber beetle (*Diabrotica balteata*) is another species associated with the striped cucumber beetle in its southern range. The adult is yellowish green with three transverse green bands across the wing covers. This insect is more general in its feeding habits than the striped cucumber beetle, attacking a num-

Figure 154. Striped cucumber beetles (*Acalymma vittata*) feeding. (Prepared by the Clemson University Cooperative Extension Service's Entomology-Plant Pathology and Agricultural Communications Sections, Federal Extension Service Cooperating.)

ber of crops other than cucurbits. It may be controlled by the same measures as recommended for the striped cucumber beetle.

THE SOUTHERN CORN ROOTWORM OR SPOTTED CUCUMBER BEETLE (*Diabrotica undecimpunctata howardi*). This pest is widely distributed through the United States east of the Rocky Mountains and its range extends into Canada and Mexico. It is probably more destructive than the striped cucumber beetle and other species of *Diabrotica*. The insect is most injurious to corn; however, it also attacks cucurbits, oats, wheat, rice, rye, sorghums, alfalfa, beans, and many other plants. The adults are general feeders, and are frequently found feeding on flowers of many plants. The silks of corn are attacked, but damage to the foliage is slight. Injury to cucurbits is the same as that caused by the striped cucumber beetle. The insect is also a disseminator of the bacterial wilt disease of these plants. The larvae feed on the roots of corn and drill into the stems, often destroying the stand of young corn, which necessitates replanting. More mature plants are attacked in the North where the roots are eaten and the stalks may fall over. Injury is most severe to corn in years of heavy rainfall or the season following. Infestations are also greatest in lowland areas when corn is planted after a legume crop.

The adult is a familiar insect; it is about ¼ inch long and yellowish green with black spots on the wing covers (Figure 155A). The larva is ½ to ¾ inch long when full grown, yellowish white, wrinkled, with the head and the last abdominal segment brownish in color (Figure 155B).

Winter is passed as an adult in protected places. In the extreme South the insect may be more or less active throughout the season. It is possible that reinfestation in the North may occur from flights of the adults from the southern states. This is one of the first insects to appear in late winter or early spring. Eggs are laid in the soil around the base of the host plants. The number of generations varies from one in the North to four in the South.

Delaying planting until the first generation of larvae has ceased feeding is recommended in some sections. However, weather conditions and other insects make it impractical to delay planting in many areas. Crop rotation is of no value in controlling the insect. The application of insecticidal granules such as chlordane, aldrin, and lindane, to furrows just before planting has given promising results. Seed treatments with dieldrin and lindane have also proved effective in control of this pest. Control of the insects on cucurbits is the same as for the striped cucumber beetle. West of the Rocky Mountains, the above species is replaced by the western spotted cucumber beetle (*Diabrotica undecimpunctata*). The biology of this form is similar to that of the preceding species. The larvae are commonly found attacking the roots of corn, alfalfa, peas, and other plants. The native hosts are probably roots of grasses and weeds.

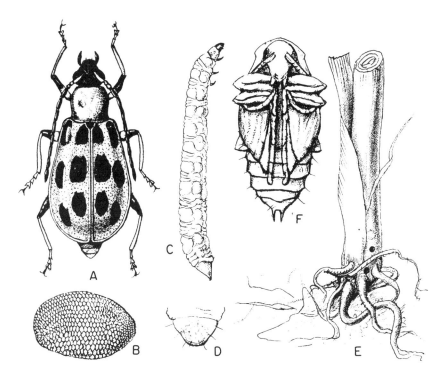

Figure 155. The southern corn rootworm (*Diabrotica undecimpunctata howardi*). A. Adult. B. Egg. C. Larva. D. Anal segment of larva. E. Injury by larva at base of cornstalk. F. Pupa. (From USDA.)

THE NORTHERN CORN ROOTWORM (*Diabrotica longicornis*). The northern corn rootworm (Figure 156) has practically the same distribution as the southern corn rootworm, but it is best known as a pest of corn in the Upper Mississippi Valley. The larvae of this insect attack the roots of the corn, which results in stunted plants which may fall during wind and rainstorms. The full-grown larvae are about ½ inch in length, and white with brownish-yellow heads. It is believed that the larvae develop only on the roots of corn. The adults are about ⅕ of an inch long and are yellowish green. They feed on the silks and the pollen of the tassels, as well as the pollen of a number of other plants.

This insect passes the winter in the egg stage in the ground. Eggs hatch in the spring, the larvae feed on the corn roots, and pupate in the soil. The adults emerge during the summer months. Eggs for the next generation are laid in the cornfields in early fall. There is only one generation annually.

A closely related form, the western corn rootworm (*D. virgifera*), occurs principally in Colorado, New Mexico, Arizona, and Texas. It has a similar biology and causes the same injury.

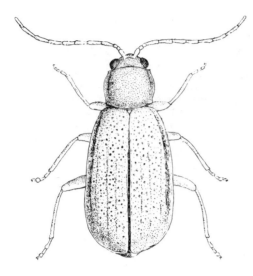

Figure 156. The northern corn rootworm (*Diabrotica longicornis*). (From Illinois Natural History Survey.)

Since the insect is known to develop only on corn and overwinters in cornfields in the egg stage, crop rotation will control it. Insecticidal control as recommended for the southern corn rootworm will afford effective control.

FLEA BEETLES. Flea beetles comprise a rather large group of small insects with enlarged hind femora which enable them to leap when disturbed. They injure plants chiefly by eating numerous small holes in the leaves, causing them to appear as if they have been perforated with small shot. Plants may be so heavily attacked that they die. These holes afford a means of entrance for plant disease organisms such as bacterial wilt of corn and early blight of potato. The larvae of some species feed on the roots, while others are foliage feeders. Both larvae and adults usually feed on one host or a group of related plants, but some are general feeders.

Some of the more common species are the pale-striped flea beetle (*Systena blanda*) (Figure 157A), the striped flea beetle (*Phyllotreta striolata*), the grape flea beetle (*Altica chalybea*), the sweet-potato flea beetle (*Chaetocnema confinis*), the spinach flea beetle (*Disonycha xanthomelas*), the potato flea beetle (*Epitrix cucumeris*) and the tobacco flea beetle (*Epitrix hirtipenni*) (Figure 157B). Flea beetles are oval and vary from $\frac{1}{16}$ to $\frac{1}{5}$ of an inch in length. They are bluish black to yellowish brown in color, and are frequently marked with yellow or red.

Life histories of flea beetles vary with the species. Generally they overwinter as adults in trash, leaves, grass, or rubbish. Adults emerge in the spring and attack weeds or other plants until cultivated plants are available. Frequently they seriously injure seedlings in seedbeds and young transplanted plants. Eggs are laid on the plants or in the soil near the base of the plants. These eggs hatch into tiny whitish elongate larvae which, when fully grown, are from ⅛ to ⅓ inch in length. The larvae usually pupate in the soil. There are one or more generations annually. Carbaryl and methoxychlor should provide adequate control. Young plants may be protected by covering the seedbeds with tobacco cloth. Destruction of weeds in and around gardens and fields of truck crops is important as the insects often feed and reproduce on these plants.

THE ELM LEAF BEETLE (*Galerucella xanthomelaena*). This pest, introduced from Europe, is confined chiefly to the eastern states. Both larvae and adults feed on the foliage of the elm. Adults are about ¼ inch long and greenish or yellowish colored with an indistinct black band along the margin of each wing cover. The insect overwinters as an adult in whatever protected places are available. Adults emerge in the spring and begin feeding and ovipositing on the young leaves shortly after they appear. Two or more generations occur annually. Effective control may be obtained by spraying the trees with carbaryl or toxaphene.

TORTOISE BEETLES. These are interesting insects and many species are very beautiful with their green, golden, or iridescent colors. The bodies are convex above, with the margin of the wing covers and prothorax expanded and forming an oval outline suggestive of the shape of the tortoise. The larvae have spines around the

Figure 157. A. The pale-striped flea beetle (*Systena blanda*). (From Virginia Agricultural Experiment Station.) B. The tobacco flea beetle (*Epitrix hirtipennis*). (From USDA.)

A   B

margins of the body with the posterior pair about as long as the body. Cast skins and excrement collect on these posterior spines, causing the larvae to have the appearance of bits of animated dirt or filth.

Tortoise beetles feed mostly on sweet potatoes, bindweeds, and morning glories. Among the more important species are the argus tortoise beetle (*Chelymorpha cassidea*), striped tortoise beetle (*Cassida bivittata*), and the golden tortoise beetle (*Metriona bicolor*) (Figure 158). Adults overwinter in protected places, emerge late in the spring, feed, and oviposit on the foliage of the host plants. Should insecticide control measures be necessary, carbaryl may be employed.

Family Bruchidae (Pea and Bean Weevils)

The Bruchidae is a relatively small family of beetles which feed, as larvae, chiefly on seeds of leguminous plants. The adults are chunky beetles, usually ⅕ inch or less in length. The head is prolonged into a short quadrate beak. The wing covers are short, leaving the tip of the abdomen exposed.

THE BEAN WEEVIL (*Acanthoscelides obtectus*). The bean weevil is the most injurious insect pest of garden beans of all varieties in the United States. It is also an important pest in other countries. The adults are brownish gray or olive, about ⅛ inch long. Injury is caused by the small footless larvae which feed in the seeds, destroying them completely or rendering them unfit for food or planting. Beans are attacked both in the field and in storage. In the field, eggs are laid in cracks in the pods or in holes gnawed by the females, but not on the outside of the pods as occurs with some other species. In storage, eggs are laid either on the beans or on the sides of the container.

This pest is quite prolific, each female laying an average of

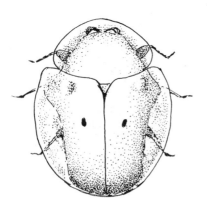

Figure 158. The golden tortoise beetle (*Metriona bicolor*).

85 eggs. A generation is produced in 3 weeks or longer, depending on locality and season. A number of generations may be produced annually. Breeding may continue throughout the winter if the weather is sufficiently warm and food is available.

The bean weevil may be controlled in stored beans by fumigation or heating. Ethylene dichloride mixture is a safe and efficient fumigant for farm use. If beans are heated for 3 or 4 hours to a temperature of 135° F, all stages of the weevils will be killed. Beans intended for planting purposes may be protected from the depredations of weevils by mixing with diatomaceous earths. Plant residues should be fed to livestock, plowed under, or burned to destroy overwintering weevils.

THE COWPEA WEEVIL (*Callosobruchus maculatus*). The cowpea weevil is an important pest of cowpeas both in the field and in storage (Figure 159) throughout the South where the crop is grown. Damage is caused by the fleshy, grublike larvae feeding in the seed. The adults are ⅛ to ⅕ inch long and dark colored with four pale brown spots on the wing covers (Figure 160A). All varieties of cowpeas are attacked. It appears doubtful that the species can reproduce on any other host. Most damage occurs in storage; eggs are glued to the peas, and are laid on the pods, at least to some extent, in the fields.

Under favorable conditions a life cycle from egg to adult is

Figure 159. Cowpeas showing eggs and exit holes of the cowpea weevil (*Callosobruchus maculatus*). (From Texas Agricultural Experiment Station.)

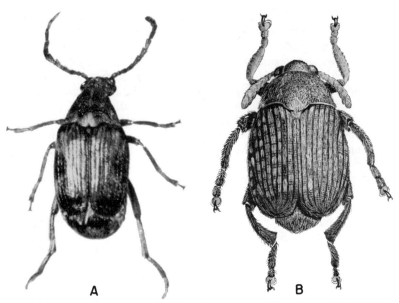

Figure 160. A. The cowpea weevil (*Callosobruchus maculatus*). (From USDA.) B. The vetch bruchid (*Bruchus brachialis*). (From Texas Agricultural Experiment Station.)

complete in less than 3 weeks, with each female laying an average of more than 100 eggs. In warm climates reproduction continues throughout the winter with as many as 9 generations occurring annually.

To protect cowpeas in storage, the bins should first be cleaned and the surfaces sprayed with malathion or methoxychlor. Then fumigation with the ethylene dichloride mixture as needed is advised.

THE PEA WEEVIL (*Bruchus pisorum*). The pea weevil is a pest of garden and field peas of the genus *Pisum* only. This insect does not attack cowpeas and beans as is commonly believed. Injury occurs when the larvae feed on the contents of the seeds. Heavily infested peas are reduced to mere husks. The round exit holes of adults are commonly observed. Only green peas are attacked; peas in storage are not attacked.

The adults are robust beetles about ⅕ inch in length, brownish and spotted with light and dark areas. The larvae are white chunky grubs with short legs. Adults diapause within the seeds or elsewhere in protected places. The beetles emerge in the spring when peas begin to bloom. They feed upon pollen and later lay eggs on the pods in all stages of development. The eggs hatch and each small larva bores into the pod and enters a pea in which it feeds and develops. Upon completion of larval growth, pupation occurs within the cavity of the seed. Normally, there is only one generation annually.

The application of malathion or methoxychlor when blooming starts is recommended for the control of the insect in the field. Other control measures are the same as for the bean weevil.

THE VETCH BRUCHID (*Bruchus brachialis*). The vetch bruchid is an important pest of vetch where the crop is grown for seed. As much as 50–90 percent of the seed may be destroyed. Such varieties as Hungarian and common vetch are not damaged, while purple vetch, smooth or hairy vetch are most heavily attacked.

Adults are about ⅛ inch long, black with wing covers marked with light-colored patches (Figure 160B). The larvae are yellowish, fleshy, and grublike. Biology of this weevil is similar to that of the pea weevil. The adults emerge from diapause in the spring and oviposit on the seed pods. The larvae hatching from the eggs bore through the seed pods and enter the seeds, feeding on the contents of the seed throughout larval development. Pupation occurs within the seed, and the adults emerge through a circular hole during the summer and seek hibernation quarters. Only one generation occurs annually. The insect does not develop in dry seeds.

Methyl parathion and toxaphene have been recommended for use and should be applied when the first pods have set. Weevils in the seeds may be killed by fumigation as for the bean weevil.

Family Curculionidae (Curculios, Weevils, or Snout Beetles)
The family Curculionidae is very large, more than 2000 species having been recorded from North America alone. The adults of this group are typified by the prolongation of the head into a distinct snout. This snout in some cases may be longer than the body and is quite generally curved (Figure 161). Chewing mouthparts are located at its tip. The snout enables the insects to feed on the

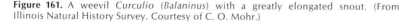

Figure 161. A weevil *Curculio* (*Balaninus*) with a greatly elongated snout. (From Illinois Natural History Survey. Courtesy of C. O. Mohr.)

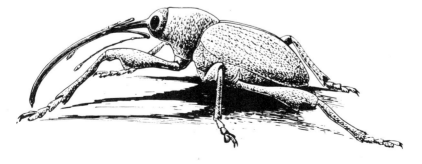

internal tissues of plants and provides places for egg deposition. Generally the larvae are internal plant feeders. As a rule these insects not only have specialized feeding habits, but also are quite specialized in their host plants. Each species has its particular plant or group of plants or plant products upon which it lives and reproduces. The larvae are light colored, fleshy, legless grubs.

THE BOLL WEEVIL (*Anthonomus grandis*). No insect has had a more profound influence on agriculture of the southern United States or has attained more notoriety than the boll weevil. The original home of the insect was in Mexico or Central America, where it fed on its wild host plants of those regions. Little is known of the pest prior to 1892 when it was found at Brownsville, Texas. From here it has spread over the entire Cotton Belt with the exception of California, Arizona, New Mexico, the western extension of the cotton belt of Texas, and possibly a few isolated areas along the northern edge of the cotton-growing belt.

The boll weevil is one of the most destructive of all agricultural pests. For all practical purposes, cotton is its only host. Both larvae and adults feed in and destroy the squares (flower buds) and later the bolls (developing fruit). The adult is generally grayish brown or dark yellowish brown in color (Figure 162C). The average length is about ¼ inch with a snout about one-third the length of the entire body. The most distinctive characteristic of the weevil is the presence of two spurs on the inner surface of the front femur. The larva is a white, wrinkled, fat, legless grub, found only in the squares or bolls (Figure 162A). It attains a length of ¼ to ⅓ inch.

The adult overwinters in a state of diapause in all types of shelter such as ground and gin trash, seed houses, Spanish moss, and under bark of trees. Those individuals that are best protected,

Figure 162. The boll weevil (*Anthonomus grandis*). A. Larva. B. Pupa. C. Adult. (From Agricultural Research Service, USDA.)

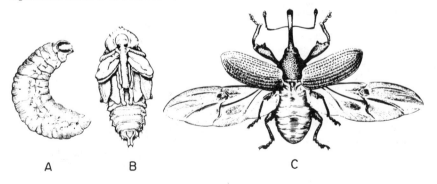

A   B   C

as in Spanish moss or in the deep recesses of woods, have the best chances for survival. Winter mortality is quite high as the average survival is only about 6 percent. Emergence begins in the spring when the mean air temperature reaches 64° F and may extend over several months. The first weevils to emerge from overwintering feed on the terminal portions of the young cotton plants. When squares become available, they puncture them and feed on the highly nutritious pollen sacs. Eggs are laid in punctures made by the females, one egg being deposited in each square as long as there is a sufficient supply. When the squares are punctured, they usually flare and later drop or else hang on the stalks where they wither and turn brown. Bolls are heavily attacked when squares are not available. Small bolls may drop, but large ones do not, although one or more locks (locules) may be destroyed. The length of life of adult weevils depends greatly upon conditions. During the summer months weevils live an average of 50 days, while some that diapause in the fall may live into the next summer.

Female boll weevils oviposit an average of about 100 eggs. These are laid over a period of about 1 month. The length of the egg stage may be as short as 1 day, but the average is about 3 days during the growing season. The larvae feed on the contents of the squares and bolls usually for a period of 7–12 days before the completion of growth and pupation. During this period two or three molts occur. The pupae are found within a pupal cell formed in the squares or bolls. The length of the pupal stage is 3–5 days. The adults emerge, and about a week later females begin oviposition. A life cycle may be completed in 3 weeks; however, the seasonal average length is somewhat longer. The average number of generations is 4–6 annually. With the approach of cold weather in the fall, weevils seek overwintering quarters.

Climate is the most important check on the boll weevil. Extremely cold weather in the winter may destroy most of the adults that are dormant. Hot, dry weather is also a powerful check, especially on immature forms. There are more than 50 insects and arachnids which attack the boll weevil. Often they destroy large percentages of the immature forms. Natural factors, however, are not sufficient to keep the weevil in check. Other available control measures must be employed also. Overwintering quarters within the field, such as weeds and debris along fence rows, ditch banks, and roadsides, should be eliminated. The use of quick maturing varieties of cotton and planting of the crop reasonably early aid in maturing the crop before the boll weevil population increases to large proportions. The destruction of cotton stalks as soon as the crop is harvested and as long before frost as possible eliminates late-season increases of weevils and forces the adults into a starvation period prior to the time of diapausing. This practice, when conducted on a community-wide basis, materially reduces the number of weevils to emerge the next season.

The boll weevil is difficult to control with insecticides because the adult is largely an internal feeder and the immature stages are found only in the squares and bolls. However, a number of insecticides will kill the adult if they are correctly applied. Recommendations for the control of the boll weevil and other cotton insects differ in various sections of the Cotton Belt. The cotton farmer should procure from his local agricultural authority current detailed recommendations for his state, and these should be carefully followed.

Except for early season control, applications of insecticides should begin when 15–25 percent of the squares are punctured. These applications should be repeated at intervals of 5 days until the weevil is controlled. In those sections where early season control is recommended, two or more applications of insecticides are made at weekly intervals beginning before any of the first squares are one-third grown, to prevent egg laying.

There is a choice of several insecticides and their combinations available for use in a boll weevil control program. The insecticides employed are dependent upon several factors, such as costs, and presence of resistant weevils or of other pests, such as bollworms, aphids, and spider mites. Among the more generally used poisons are carbaryl, toxaphene, methyl parathion, and azinphosmethyl.

THE RICE WEEVIL (*Sitophilus oryzae*). The rice weevil is believed to be the most destructive insect attacking stored grain. It is a small, reddish-brown weevil about 1/8 inch in length with the wing covers marked with four lighter reddish spots (Figure 163A). Corn, rice, wheat, maize, and other seed or seed products are attacked. Adults may feed upon flour, but larvae cannot develop on it unless the material is caked. The female chews a hole in each seed preparatory to egg deposition. Three hundred to 400 eggs may be laid during a period of 4 or 5 months by a single female. The eggs hatch into white legless grubs which feed upon the contents of the seed. The immature stages are never found outside of the seed. When conditions are most favorable, the adult stage may be reached in less than 4 weeks from the time the egg is laid. In Kansas, four or five generations occur each year. In the South grain is attacked in the field as soon as the kernels become hard, and development may continue throughout the winter. In colder climates the insect is primarily a pest of stored grain and seldom attacks grain in the field. The granary weevil (*Sitophilus granarius*) is closely related to the rice weevil in hosts, habits, and life history. It is quite similar in appearance to the rice weevil, but lacks the light reddish spots on the wing covers; also, the wing covers are fused together and the insect cannot fly (Figure 163B). This insect never attacks grain in the field and is strictly a pest of stored grain.

Most of the loss caused by grain weevils may be prevented by

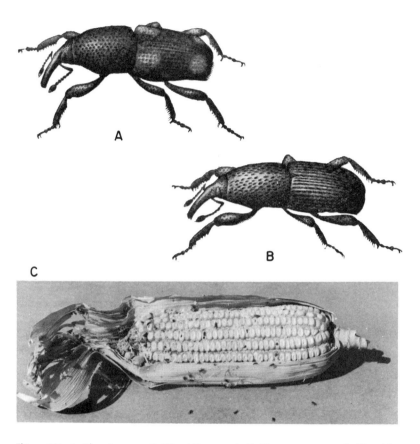

Figure 163. A. The rice weevil (*Sitophilus oryza*). B. The granary weevil (*Sitophilus granarius*). (From University of California, Division of Agricultural Science.) C. Ear of corn damaged by weevils. (From USDA.)

the use of proper control measures. Much of the infestation in fields may be prevented by fumigating or disposing of infested grain in storage before the crops begin to ripen. Bins should be thoroughly cleaned, and the surfaces sprayed with either methoxychlor or malathion before the new crop is stored. The moisture content of the grain should not be more than 12 percent. Malathion may be employed as a grain protectant. Several fumigants are effective in control of stored grain pests if properly used. Among the more commonly used are mixtures containing carbon tetrachloride and either ethylene dichloride or carbon disulfide. Rice in storage is fumigated with methyl bromide.

THE SWEET-POTATO WEEVIL (*Cylas formicarius elegantulus*). This is the most important insect pest of the sweet potato. The insect is widely distributed over the Gulf states; its native home is probably Asia.

Infested potatoes are honeycombed by the feeding of the grubs and their tortuous tunnels are filled with excrement. The grubs are legless, dirty white with yellowish brown heads, and about ¼ inch in length. Infested potatoes are bitter in taste and are unfit for human consumption. The larvae also feed in stems and roots.

The adult weevils are shiny snout bettles about ¼ inch in length and antlike in appearance (Figure 164). The head, wing covers, and abdomen are blue-black, while the thorax and legs are reddish brown. The adults feed on leaves, vines, sweet potatoes, and roots. In addition to sweet potatoes, the insect breeds to some extent in the roots of various species of morning glory.

Breeding is continuous during the year, with stored sweet potatoes being attacked throughout the winter. One overlapping generation follows another with a possibility of five or more annually. Under favorable conditions adults may live for several months.

Since flight is not important in the dissemination of the insect, most infestations begin through the use of infested slips or seed sweet potatoes. Quarantines are maintained to prevent the spread of the pest and to assist in eradication and control. In areas of light infestations, the insect may be eradicated if proper practices are followed. Only weevil-free slips or seed sweet potatoes should be used. Rotation and thorough cleanup of crop residues must be practiced. All infested sweet potatoes must be disposed of and storage places thoroughly sprayed.

In areas of general infestations, the same cultural control measures should be practiced. Also, stored sweet potatoes may be

Figure 164. The sweet-potato weevil (*Cylas formicarius elegantulus*).

Figure 165. The plum curculio (*Conotrachelus nenuphar*) and injury on section of fruit. (From Department of Entomology, Texas A&M University.)

dusted with methoxychlor at the rate of ⅕ ounce per crate. Excess residue must be removed before marketing or consumption.

Sweet potato slips or draws may be fumigated with methyl bromide. Three pounds of methyl bromide per 1000 cubic feet of space in a fumigation chamber with an exposure of 5 hours is recommended. Cured sweet potatoes may also be fumigated with methyl bromide. It is not advisable to hold sweet potatoes for long following fumigation.

THE PLUM CURCULIO (*Conotrachelus neuphar*). The plum curculio is a destructive pest of fruit, particularly plums, peaches, cherries, apricots, and apples. This native American insect is found east of the Rocky Mountains. The adult beetle is about ³⁄₁₆ inch long, dark brown, with mottlings of white and gray, and with four humps on its elytra (Figure 165). The larva is a whitish, crescent-shaped legless grub about ⅓ inch in length.

Injury produced by the curculio is in several forms. Much of the fruit may be destroyed by larval feeding on the pulpy tissues. Although it may not be destroyed, infested fruit is "wormy" and worthless. Feeding and egg-laying punctures of the adults cause knotted, gnarled, and misshapen fruit. The insect is also an important agency in the dissemination of brown rot of peaches.

Adults overwinter in leaves, bark, rubbish, grass, and other protected places. They emerge in the spring and feed first on buds, calyxes, and newly formed fruit. Females lay an average of less than 100 eggs. These are deposited in holes made by the snout through the skin of the fruit. After the egg is laid, the female cuts a crescent-shaped slit around it. This slit extends underneath the egg, leaving it in a flap of dead or dying tissues so that proliferating cells will not crush the egg or young larva. The eggs hatch in 2–12 days. In stone fruits, the young larvae tunnel to the center of the fruit and feed around the stone for 2 or 3 weeks. At the end of this time, the larvae leave the fruit and enter the ground to a depth of one to several inches. Here a pupal cell is formed and the insect transforms into the pupal stage. Thirty to 35 days after entering the soil, the adult emerges. The length of a life cycle from egg to adult is usually 50–55 days. In the North only one generation occurs annually, but in the South two full generations may develop in favorable seasons.

There are several orchard practices which aid in controlling the pest. Dropped and culled fruit should be gathered periodically and destroyed before the larvae have completed development and entered the soil for pupation. The ground underneath the spread of the trees should be disced at intervals to destroy the pupal cells. Most adults hibernate in the immediate environment of the orchards. The destruction of trash, leaves, and grass by burning or by other means will eliminate many of the overwintering insects.

In heavily infested areas, it is necessary to follow a definite spray schedule to control the pest satisfactorily. Spray schedules for various fruits differ, and schedules for the same fruits are not the same in different sections of the country. This necessitates obtaining correct spray information from the local or state agricultural authorities. Usually two or three well timed combination sprays when the curculios are most active in feeding and oviposition will control the pest. Dieldrin or parathion in combination with a fungicide provides satisfactory control if the spray is thoroughly applied.

THE PLUM GOUGER (*Anthonomus scutellaris*). The plum gouger is a pest primarily of native plums. Domestic plums, apricots, and prunes are also attacked. It is occasionally reported infesting peaches. Adults are reddish brown with yellowish head and thorax. They are about ¼ inch in length. Larvae are legless grubs found in the pit of the fruit. Adults, in feeding and ovipositing, make small holes in the fruit. Upon hatching, the grubs tunnel into the pits and feed upon the kernels. Pupation occurs within the pits and adults emerge in late summer. Only one generation is produced each season. Control measures for the plum curculio are also recommended for this pest.

THE PECAN WEEVIL (*Curculio caryae*). This insect is a pest of pecans in the southern states. Hickory nuts are also attacked. The adult is gray or light brown and its body is slightly less than ½ inch long. The snout of the female is somewhat longer than the body.

Adults usually emerge following rains during late summer (Figure 166). They feed first on the developing nuts, which causes them to drop. When the kernels develop in the earliest varieties, females begin to lay eggs in the nuts. Early maturing varieties suffer the greatest damage. Eggs hatch in a week, and the larvae feed upon the kernels for about a month. Larvae emerge from the nuts through holes about ⅛ inch in diameter. Larval emergence extends from September through December. The larvae enter the soil to a depth of 1–12 inches and earthen cells are formed. Here they diapause. Most of the population pupate the next season in late summer or late fall. Three weeks later the pupae transform into adults which in turn do not emerge from the soil until the following summer or fall, thus completing a life cycle in 2 years. Some of the larvae do not pupate and transform into adults until the second year, thus having a 3-year life cycle.

Figure 166. Schematic diagram of the life cycle of the pecan weevil (*Curculio caryae*). (From Department of Entomology, Texas A&M University. Courtesy of Dr. H. W. Van Cleave.)

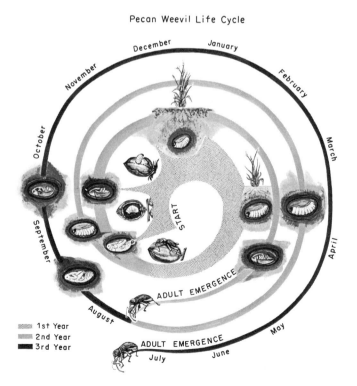

Pecan Weevil Life Cycle

In those sections where the insect is an important pest, checking for its presence should begin in early August. Control measures should begin in middle or late August. The trees should be thoroughly sprayed with carbaryl. If the infestation is severe, the spray should be repeated in 2 weeks. In orchards known to be infested, the nuts should be gathered as early as possible and placed in containers with tight bottoms or on tight floors so the emerging larvae cannot reach the soil and complete the life cycle.

Family Scolytidae (Bark Beetles)

Bark beetles are small to medium insects, measuring from 1 to 9 mm in length (Figure 167). They are usually cylindrical in form and brown to black in color. The posterior end of the body of many species ends abruptly as if cut off. The antennae are elbowed and clubbed on the end. Larvae are small, whitish, legless grubs.

Most bark beetles are wood borers, living principally under the bark or burrowing in hardwood. Patterns made by the tunnels of adults and larvae on bark and sapwood and burrows in the heartwood are quite characteristic, and a species often may be identified by these markings. Bark beetles spend almost their entire existence in their burrows. Adults usually leave their burrows only long enough to locate new hosts.

On the basis of tunneling habits and nature of food materials,

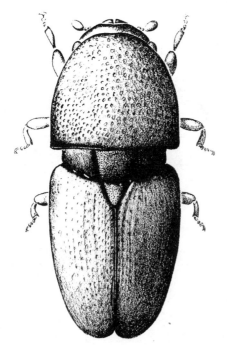

Figure 167. A bark beetle. (From Department of Entomology, Texas A&M University.)

bark beetles may be divided into three groups: (1) true scolytids which engrave the inner bark and sapwood; (2) wood-eating bark beetles which tunnel and feed on sapwood and heartwood; (3) ambrosia beetles, found in sapwood and which feed, as both larvae and adults, on ambrosia (fungi) which they invariably grow in their burrows.

Hosts of most bark beetles are forest trees; however, some attack fruit trees and herbaceous plants. Dead, dying, or devitalized timber is usually attacked; but some species attack trees that are healthy or only slightly devitalized.

Habits of bark beetles vary with the species. In general, an entrance gallery is made through the bark. Then it is either widened into an irregular cavity or one or more branching galleries are constructed, extending in diagonal, longitudinal, or transverse directions. Eggs are deposited in a mass in the irregular cavity or in one of several ways in the egg galleries, as in niches. Upon hatching, the larvae usually make separate tunnels at right angles to the egg gallery, but they may work together in a common chamber.

THE SHOTHOLE BORER (*Scolytus rugulosus*). This insect is a pest of importance of most deciduous fruit trees. Its presence is recognized by small holes in the bark. These holes are made by the adults when they emerge and later reenter the trees. Injury results from the feeding and tunneling of both larvae and adults between the bark and the cambium.

The adult beetle is a small, black beetle about ¹⁄₁₀ inch in length with the body quite blunt at each end. Adults emerge in the spring, mate, and the females search out new hosts for egg deposition. Usually healthy trees are not attacked if weak trees are available. Entrance holes are made in branches, usually near lenticels or projections. The females excavate galleries extending in directions parallel with the branches. Eggs are deposited on the sides of the galleries. These eggs hatch in a few days into white grubs which tunnel directly away from the parent gallery. Later, these larval tunnels turn in various directions. Larval maturity is reached in 6–8 weeks. Pupation occurs in the burrows, from which the adults emerge to mate and begin a new generation. The insect diapauses as larvae underneath the bark. One to four generations occur annually.

The most satisfactory method of preventing and overcoming attacks of the insect is keeping trees in the best possible condition. In healthy, vigorous trees the flow of sap tends to prevent larval development. Proper fertilization, watering, cultivation, and pruning practices should be followed. Diseased trees and limbs should be removed during the dormant season. All prunings should be gathered and burned.

THE SOUTHERN PINE BEETLE (*Dendroctonus frontalis*). The genus *Dendroctonus* contains several species of very destructive pests of coniferous trees. One of the most important is the southern pine beetle whose range extends from Pennsylvania to Florida and westward to Texas and Oklahoma. It infests and kills healthy pines when conditions are favorable, as well as devitalized and dying trees. Losses in the southern states due to this pest amount to millions of dollars. Usually the first indication of damage by this insect is the presence of dead or dying trees. The inner bark or wood surface will show S-shaped egg tunnels with short larval tunnels leading out from the sides (Figure 168). The middle and upper portion of the trunks of the trees are most commonly attacked. The adult beetles are about ⅛ inch long, brownish or black, and with the posterior end of the body smoothly rounded. The insect reproduces rapidly, completing a generation in 30–40 days under favorable conditions. There are as many as 5 generations annually. Winter is spent in all stages.

Epidemics of the southern pine beetle follow droughts or severe storms which have damaged timber, and large scale logging operations. Cutting timber in dry weather should be avoided. The removal of infested and weakened trees is recommended.

ORDER STREPSIPTERA[2]
STYLOPIDS OR TWISTED-WING PARASITES

Members of the order Strepsiptera are very small internal parasites, seldom observed even by entomologists. They are of little

[2] *Strepis*, turning; *pteron*, wing.

Figure 168. Winding galleries of the southern pine beetle (*Dendroctonus frontalis*). The larger galleries are made by larvae of the southern pine sawyer (*Monochamus titillator*). (From USDA.)

Figure 169. An adult male of a stylopid or twisted-wing parasite. (After E. O. Essig, *College Entomology.* Copyright 1942. Used by permission of The Macmillan Company.)

economic importance. Only about 300 species are known, yet they are widely distributed. Their morphology is so unusual that they comprise a separate and distinct order.

The order is characterized as follows:

1. Wings, present in the males only, 4 in number with the first pair reduced to paddlelike vestigial wings (elytra), and the second pair broad triangular, with reduced venation and fanlike folding.
2. Mouthparts in the male degenerate, in the female vestigial or wanting.
3. Metamorphosis complete.
4. Eyes stalked, antennae flabellate, and metathorax enlarged in the male. The female is wormlike with no legs, eyes, antennae, or wings.

Stylopids are endoparasites of certain Hymenoptera, Homoptera, Hemiptera, Orthoptera, and Thysanura. The largest males are not more than 3 mm in length (Figure 169). The presence of the parasites is indicated by small disclike or rounded and tuberculate objects extending between the abdominal segments of the host insect. The projected portions are the anterior ends of the parasites.

The biology of stylopids is imperfectly known and only an outline of their life activities can be given. The adult male is free living and can fly. It lives only a short time. Copulation is effected by the male through an opening between the extruded head and thorax of the female. The young larvae escape to the outside of the host and seek the immature stages of other hosts. When a new host is found, the larva burrows through the body wall and becomes an internal parasite. Upon molting, the larva becomes grublike and legless. Nourishment is thought to be taken from the body of the host by osmosis. Near the close of the larval stage the parasite works its anterior end out so that it extrudes between the abdominal segments of the host. The male pupates in a puparium formed by the last two larval skins. Escape of the adult male is effected by pushing off the operculum of the puparium. The female remains wormlike her entire life within the body of the host insect.

CHAPTER 13
ORDERS NEUROPTERA AND MECOPTERA

ORDER NEUROPTERA [1]
DOBSONFLIES, LACEWINGS, ANT LIONS, AND OTHERS

The Neuroptera are chiefly predaceous insects, and some species are highly beneficial. Members of the order may vary greatly in size and appearance but body structure is quite similar in all forms.

The chief characteristics of the group are:

1. Two pairs of large membranous wings, usually with many veins and cross veins, similar in size and texture, held rooflike over the body when at rest.
2. Mouthparts formed for chewing but modified into sucking organs in the larvae of several families.
3. Complete metamorphosis.
4. Cerci absent; tarsi with 5 segments.

This is not a large order of insects, there being only about 4000 known species. The biology of the group is quite variable. Most of the larvae are predaceous, but some are parasitic; no harmful species are known. Some species develop in water; most are found on land. Some of the larvae pupate in cells within the soil; most of them spin pupal cases out of a silk that is produced by the Malpighian tubes and spun from the anus. Mouthparts are for chewing, but in several families the mandibles and maxillae of the larvae are modified for sucking the body fluids of the prey. In these larvae the mandibles are long, curved, and fitted for grasping and piercing. Each mandible is ventrally furrowed, and the corresponding maxilla underneath has a dorsal groove. The two furrows form a tube extending from the tip of the combined mandible and maxilla to the mouth cavity. Larvae are long, somewhat flattened, and with well developed legs.

[1] *Neuron,* nerve; *pteron,* wing.

Family Sialidae (Dobsonflies, Alder Flies, and Fish Flies)

The best known insect of the Sialidae family is the dobsonfly or corydalus (*Corydalus cornutus*) (Figure 170), the larva of which is the dobson or hellgrammite. The adult is quite large, with a wing expanse of 4 or 5 inches. The males have strikingly long curved mandibles, which are relatively short in the females. The larvae are predaceous on aquatic insects and are found under stones and chunks of hard earth in swiftly flowing water. They have paired lateral filaments with a tuft of tracheal gills at the base of each on the first seven abdominal segments. The mature larvae are about 3 inches in length. Hellgrammites are prized for use as bait by many fishermen. When mature, the larvae leave the water and pupate underneath stones and other debris. About a month later the adults emerge. Soon after emergence, the females lay eggs in masses on limbs, stones, and other objects overhanging the water. Upon hatching, the larvae drop into the water. Adults live for only a short time. Two or 3 years are required for a life cycle.

Alder flies (*Sialis*) and fish flies (*Chauliodes*, *Neohermes*, and *Nigronia*) occur in about the same environment as dobsonflies. They are smaller and darker in color. Only 1 year is required for a life cycle of these insects.

A   B

Figure 170. Dobson flies (*Corydalus cornutus*). A. Male. B. Female.

Figure 171. A. A lacewing fly (*Chrysopa*). B. Larva feeding on a young bollworm. (From USDA. Courtesy of Dr. R. L. Ridgway.)

Family Chrysopidae (Lacewing Flies or Aphis Lions)

The lacewing flies (Figure 171) are well known insects. Their larvae, called aphis lions, are among the more important beneficial insects. They feed voraciously upon aphids, thrips, mites, young corn earworms, and other small, soft-bodied insects or eggs.

The adults are recognized by their usually greenish or yellowish green color, delicate lacelike wings, and in some species, shining golden eyes. They are rather delicate, soft-bodied insects and are less than 1 inch in length. Some species emit a disagreeable odor when handled or crushed, and for this reason are sometimes known as stinkflies.

The larvae have been named aphis lions because they prey chiefly upon aphids or plant lice. The aphis lions are elongate spindle-shaped (alligatorlike) larvae with long sicklelike mandibles. These characteristic mandibles readily distinguish them from lady beetle larvae, which they resemble. The larvae are very active in seeking their prey and obtain their food by puncturing the body of the victim and extracting the body fluids with their unusual mouthparts.

Among the more common species of lacewing flies are *Chrysopa oculata*, *Chrysopa carnea*, and *Chrysopa rufilabris*. Lacewing flies usually overwinter in their silken cocoons as prepupae. Some are reported to overwinter as adults. The adults emerge in the spring when the weather becomes sufficiently warm. Eggs are laid on silken stalks which project about ½ inch above the surface of the leaves or stems to which they are attached. It is thought the stalks protect the eggs from the natural enemies, particularly larvae of their own kind. Females probably lay an average of several hundred eggs each under natural conditions. Eggs hatch in about a week. At the end of the third instar, the larvae seek sheltered places on leaves or elsewhere and spin cocoons in which they pupate. The larval period averages between 2 and 3 weeks; the pupal period is of similar duration. The completion of a generation averages about 40 days; there may be 5 or 6 generations annually in warm climates.

Family Myrmeleontidae (Doodlebugs or Ant Lions)

Doodlebugs or ant lions are known by almost everyone, yet few realize they are the larvae of graceful gauzy-winged insects (Figure 172) which superficially resemble damselflies of the order Odonata. They may be readily distinguished from the latter by the antennae, which instead of being small and inconspicuous, are rather large and terminally enlarged. The jointlike structure, the nodus, on the front margin of the wings is also absent. Larvae are broad, spindle shaped, and somewhat flat. The head bears large and powerful mouthparts of the grasping-sucking type previously described. Principal food consists of ants. The larvae spin spherical silken cocoons in which they pupate.

Food is captured in various ways. Larvae of most species probably do not make pits to trap their prey but conceal themselves in sand or trash, and await the passing of an unwary insect,

Figure 172. A common doodlebug (Myrmeleontidae). (Prepared by the Clemson University Cooperative Extension Service's Entomology-Plant Pathology and Agricultural Communications Sections, Federal Extension Service Cooperating.)

or else actively search for their victims. The best known forms, however, construct conelike pits. They are members of the genera *Myrmeleon* and *Hesperoleon*. The pits are constructed in sandy soil in protected places, such as at the base of trees, and near or underneath buildings. The pits are 1–2 inches in diameter with a depth consistent with the nature of the soil. The ant lion lies concealed in the sand at the bottom of the pit and waits for an ant or other small insect to fall into the trap where it is quickly seized and drained of its body fluids. When an insect attempts to crawl out of the trap, the ant lion flips sand upon it, which usually sweeps the victim within reach of his powerful jaws. A doodlebug or ant lion constructs a number of pits during its life. As the larva grows, progressively larger pits are constructed; also, many pits are destroyed by rains, winds, and other agencies. The length of development of these insects is imperfectly known but indications are that about 2 years are required for a complete life cycle.

The family *Ascalaphidae* is closely related to the Myrmeleontidae. Members of this family may be readily distinguished from those of the latter by their long antennae. Adults have the habit of remaining motionless when at rest on a branch or stem. At this time the antennae are held parallel to the resting surface with the head depressed, abdomen elevated, and wings drooping. Both larvae and adults are predaceous. Larvae resemble doodlebugs, but are commonly larger. They do not construct pits but lie in ambush partly concealed on the ground and wait for the prey to come near enough to be seized. The ascalaphids, such as the myrmeleontids, are commonly found in regions of sandy soils.

Adult members of the family *Mantispidae* are very unusual in appearance. They resemble praying mantids with their elongate prothorax and front legs fitted for grasping prey. The adults are predaceous, but the insects are not numerous enough to be of much benefit as predators. Little is known of the biology of the group. As far as is known, the larvae feed on spider eggs and in wasp nests.

ORDER MECOPTERA [2]
SCORPION FLIES

Members of the order Mecoptera have the following characteristics:

1. Wings, rarely absent, 2 pairs, long, narrow, and net veined.
2. Mouthparts chewing, located at the end of an elongated deflexed beak.
3. Complete metamorphosis.
4. Larvae resemble caterpillars.

The ordinal name of this group of insects is derived from wing characteristics. The pincerlike organs, resembling the sting of a

[2] *Mecos*, length; *pteron*, wing.

Figure 173. A male scorpion fly (*Panorpa*).

scorpion, on the end of the abdomen of the males (Figure 173) of the most common forms have given rise to the common name. This is a small order, both in species and numbers, but its members are found in most parts of the world.

The most distinctive characteristic of the order is the elongation of the head on the underside, which forms a deflexed beak with chewing mouthparts at the tip. Wings are long and narrow with a number of cross veins. In one group, wings are lacking or vestigial. Antennae are long and slender; the tarsi are five-segmented.

Most scorpion flies belong to the genus *Panorpa*. The wings are marked with yellow and black. The adults, which appear in late summer and fall, are commonly found in moist places where there is a growth of rank vegetation. Larvae resemble caterpillars but have more abdominal legs. They live on the ground in rotten vegetative material or moss in wooded, damp environments. Both adults and larvae are scavengers, feeding on dead insects and other animal matter. The biology of these insects is imperfectly known.

Certain species are known as hanging flies. This name has been applied to them because they hang by their long legs from a supporting object when at rest. In flight they may be mistaken for crane flies. Adults catch their prey while in the resting position. When a small insect comes within reach, it is seized by the hind legs and transferred to the mouthparts where it is quickly devoured. Larvae of hanging flies are found in the same habitat as those of the genus *Panorpa* and have similar food habits.

CHAPTER 14
ORDERS TRICHOPTERA AND LEPIDOPTERA

ORDER TRICHOPTERA [1]
CADDISFLIES

Characteristics of the order may be summarized as follows:

1. Two pairs of membranous wings, usually covered with long hairs, and held rooflike over the body when at rest.
2. Mouthparts of the adults rudimentary, except the palpi.
3. Metamorphosis complete.
4. Larvae are aquatic (rare exceptions) and construct either cases or nets in which they live.

The order Trichoptera is rather small both in number of species and size of the individuals. Caddisflies (Figure 174) are moth-like in appearance, and most of them are somber in color. Their bodies are somewhat soft and clothed with long hairs. They are not strong fliers and are found most frequently in the vicinity of the aquatic environment of the larvae. They are nocturnal in habit. The wings are membranous, with the front pair longer and usually narrower than the hind pair. They are generally clothed with long hairs but sometimes are almost naked; in rare exceptions, scales are present. When the insects are at rest, the wings are held over the abdomen like the roof of a house. Antennae are long and bristlelike. Mouthparts are rudimentary with the exception of the palpi which are quite well developed. Legs are long and the tarsi have five segments.

Female caddisflies lay from several hundred to 1000 eggs either in the water or upon objects above its surface. They are usually laid in a gelatinous mass which absorbs water and swells. Often species may be identified by the form of the egg mass and the arrangement of eggs in the gelatinous matrix.

The larvae, known as caddisworms, resemble caterpillars but lack prolegs, except the anal pair. Thoracic legs are well devel-

---

[1] *Trichos*, hair; *pteron*, wing.

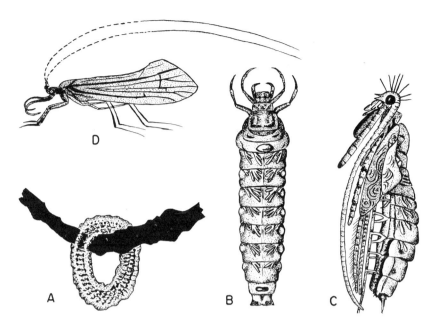

Figure 174. Developmental stages of typical caddisfly. A. Eggs of *Phryganea*. B. Larva. C. Pupa of *Halesus*. D. Adult of *Leptocerus*. (After S. W. Frost, *General Entomology*. Copyright 1942 by McGraw-Hill Book Co. Used with permission of McGraw-Hill Book Co.)

oped and mouthparts are for chewing. They respire by means of tracheal gills, blood gills, or a combination of both. Caddisworms feed upon both animal and vegetable materials; however, some are predominantly predaceous and feed on small insect larvae. Most caddisworms build portable cases in which they live, while others construct nets (Figure 175). Those larvae living in portable cases crawl partly out of the cases, which are dragged along wherever they go. Larvae of those species which construct nets to catch food live in tubes constructed of silk and debris. Cases differ in form and construction with the species. Silk is spun from the modified salivary glands through an opening in the labium, usually in a sheetlike mass. The cases of some species are constructed only of silk. Usually other materials, such as small pebbles, grains of sand, bits of leaves, or wood, are incorporated in the case and bound together with the silk. The cases are varied in shape, ranging in form from a straight tube to the coiled case of *Heliopsyche* which is quite like a snail shell. The interior of the case is lined with silk, which protects the soft abdomen of the larva.

The net-spinning species are found in swift water or along shores of lakes. The nets are funnellike and are held open by the

Figure 175. Caddisworm and its case. (From Illinois Natural History Survey.)

current. In the bottom of the funnel a strainer is constructed to capture food. The tube in which the larva lives opens into this strainer.

Mature caddisworms do not leave the water for pupation since the pupae are also aquatic. Pupae are of the exarate type with legs and wings free. Before the larva pupates, a cocoon is spun which, in the case-making forms, is simply made by lining the interior of the case with silk and closing the ends. The net-building forms spin special pupal cases of silk, sand, pebbles, or other materials. These cases are firmly cemented to stones or other objects in the swift water. Following pupation, the wings of those species that emerge from swift water expand instantly upon reaching the surface and the adults fly away immediately to prevent their being swept away by the current.

The complete life cycle of the caddisfly usually requires a year, most of which is spent in the larval stage. The egg stage is short; the length of the pupal stage is 2 or 3 weeks; and the adult lives for about a month. About 800 species are found in the Nearctic fauna.

Caddisflies are of little economic importance; however, they must be regarded as beneficial since the larvae are important sources of food for fish. In river towns the adults are occasionally pestiferous since great numbers may be attracted to lights.

ORDER LEPIDOPTERA[2]
MOTHS, SKIPPERS, AND BUTTERFLIES

The Lepidoptera are one of the largest and most important orders of insects. They are exceeded in numbers of species only by the Coleoptera (Beetles). The number of species in the order is estimated to be almost 150,000, of which 10,000 species are thought to occur in North America.

The chief distinguishing characteristics of the Lepidoptera are summarized as:

1. Two pairs of membranous wings (rarely absent) covered with overlapping scales.
2. Mouthparts formed for sucking.

[2] *Lepis,* scale; *pteron,* wing.

3. Complete metamorphosis.
4. Larvae, known as caterpillars, with chewing mouthparts.

Members of the order are readily recognized by the scales on the wings and body. When a section of a wing is examined under magnification, the scales in the more specialized groups will be seen to be arranged like shingles on the roof of a house. The scales provide strength and rigidity for the wings and are also the source of color. The brilliant, striking colors of these insects are produced by pigmentation, and by diffraction of light by the striae on the scales or by the thin filmlike plates which make up their walls.

Insects of this order are commonly known as moths (Figure 176), butterflies, and skippers. Moths have stout bodies, and the wings when at rest are held in a rooflike horizontal position over the abdomen, or wrapped about the body. The antennae of moths are variable in form but are usually filamentous or featherlike in appearance. They fly chiefly at night. Bodies of butterflies are slender, the wings are held vertically when at rest, and the antennae are slender and clublike at the tips. They are day fliers. Skippers dart or skip through the air in flight during the day. Their bodies are intermediate in form between the moths and common butterflies, and their wings are held erect when at rest. The antennae of skippers are clublike at the tips, but usually a hooklike process is present on the end of the club or knob.

Wings of lepidopterous insects are usually broad and somewhat triangular in form, with the front pair larger. Venation in the more generalized forms closely resembles the hypothetical

Figure 176. A giant silkworm moth (*Hyalophora calleta*).

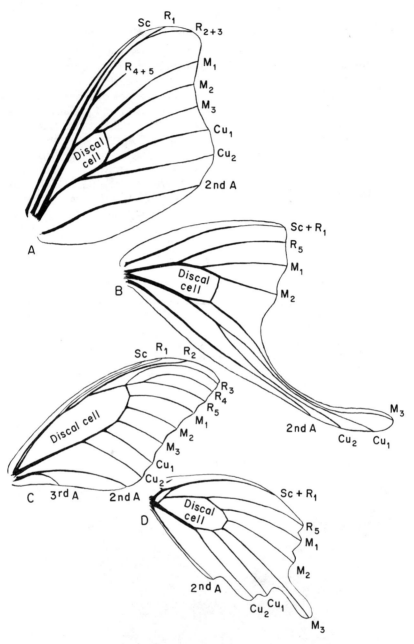

Figure 177. Wings of Lepidoptera showing venation. A and B. Wings of luna moth (*Actias luna*). C and D. Wings of the giant swallowtail butterfly (*Papilio cresphontes*).

type (Figure 177). In the more specialized groups there is a reduction of the wing veins, especially in the hind wings. Special structures are often present to synchronize the front and hind pairs of wings in flight. These may be (1) an enlargement of the humeral angle of the hind wing to extend well underneath the front wing; (2) a group of bristles (one stout bristle in the male), the frenulum, arising from the humeral angle of the hind wing, extending underneath the front wing, and fitting into a pocket or clasp; or (3) rarely, a fingerlike process (jugum) extending from the base of the front wing underneath the hind wing.

Mouthparts of most adults are specialized for sucking. In typical mouthparts the palpi and maxillae are well developed. When only one pair of palpi is present, it is the labial palpi. If the maxillary palpi are present, they may be recognized by the attachment to the maxillae. If mouthparts are not vestigial, a long, sucking tube (the proboscis) is found coiled underneath the head like a watch spring. This tube is formed by the elongate galeae of the maxillae fused together on the inner margins. Each of the galeae is grooved on the inner surface; when the two are brought together, a sucking tube is formed. The proboscis is adapted for feeding on nectar of flowers and plant juices. In some species spines are present on the tip of the proboscis. These enable the insect to lacerate the thin skin of some fruits and suck the juices. As an example, the cotton leafworm moth may damage figs and late peaches. However, this type of injury by moths is quite rare. In visiting flowers, moths and butterflies perform some service in the pollination of plants. Small moths are frequently pestiferous around lights during warm seasons.

Larvae are commonly known as caterpillars (Figure 178). They do not have the least resemblance to the adults into which they develop. Caterpillars are wormlike, usually cylindrical, and vary

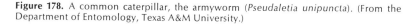

Figure 178. A common caterpillar, the armyworm (*Pseudaletia unipuncta*). (From the Department of Entomology, Texas A&M University.)

much in form and appearance. In addition to the three pairs of thoracic legs, there are two to five pairs of abdominal legs, termed prolegs, which are thick, fleshy, membranous, and not segmented. They are shed with the last larval molt. The pair of prolegs on the last (tenth) abdominal segment is termed the anal prolegs. When all pairs of prolegs are present, they are borne by the third, fourth, fifth, sixth, and tenth abdominal segments. The tip of a proleg is called the planta; upon it are borne hooks or claws known as crochets. The crochets are an aid in crawling and cling-ing to surfaces. The arrangement and form of the crochets are of much value in the identification of lepidopterous larvae.

Most caterpillars have relatively few inconspicuous setae or hairs on their bodies. However, some are woolly in appearance. All graduations in density of setal vesture occur. With the excep-tion of highly specialized forms, setae on the segments of the bodies of the larvae are quite definite in number and arrange-ment. The number and position of the setae differ, thus affording valuable characters for identifying caterpillars. The head is usu-ally well developed and bears short antennae, ommatidia (simple eyes), and chewing mouthparts. Caterpillars feed, with the excep-tion of the larvae of clothes moths and a few others, upon plants or their products. Almost every plant has some species of cater-pillar feeding upon some part of it or its products. Inasmuch as many of the most important insect pests are caterpillars, the order is of much economic importance.

When larvae are mature they usually spin silken cocoons in which they pupate. The silk is secreted by silk glands (modified salivary glands) and spun from a spinneret located on the tip of the labium. Hairs, leaves, or soil may be incorporated with the silk in the formation of the cocoon. Some cocoons are very elabo-rate, e.g., the cocoons of silkworms, while others may be quite simple. Larvae of butterflies form naked pupae, known as chrysa-lids, which have the tip of the abdomen secured to a branch, stem, or other object by a pad of silk—some are held in an upright posi-tion by a silken belt placed around the body.

Lepidopterous pupae are of the obtect type, having developing antennae, legs, wings, and mouthparts firmly cemented to the body. This characteristic, together with the long slender sclerites which form the maxillae, located along the midventral surface of the body, identifies most pupae of the order.

Heterocera (Moths)

Family Incurvariidae (Yucca Moths)

Of chief interest in this family of small moths are the yucca moths, *Tegeticula* (*Pronuba* spp.). A remarkable biological relationship exists between these moths and the yucca plant. The flowers are pollinated only by these insects (Figure 179) and the larvae feed exclusively on their seeds. Each is dependent upon the other for perpetuation of the species.

Figure 179. The female yucca moth (*Tegeticula yuccasella*) collecting pollen from the yucca flower. (After Folsom, *Entomology*, Blackiston, 1906; from C. L. Metcalf and W. P. Flint, *Fundamentals of Insect Life*. Copyright 1932 by McGraw-Hill Book Co. Used by permission of McGraw-Hill Book Co.)

The female of these small white moths has maxillae modified for the collection of pollen. Balls of pollen are collected and deposited on the stigmata of flowers, in the ovaries of which eggs have been laid. This ensures development of seed as food for the pinkish larvae that hatch from the eggs. Only enough larvae are provided to eat part of the seeds and thus permit some to mature so the plant species may be perpetuated. Most species of these insects are confined to the South, Southwest, and Mexico.

The bogus yucca moths of the genus *Prodoxus* are closely related to the yucca moths. The larvae develop in the flower stems, base of the seed capsules, and main stems of the yucca and century plants. The bogus yucca moth is dependent, at least in part, on the yucca moth for a source of food for its larvae, inasmuch as the seed capsules and flower stems of the yucca plant would not develop without fertilization of the yucca flowers.

Family Cossidae (Carpenterworm Moths)

This is a small family of moths; the larvae are wood borers and often do considerable injury to trees (Figure 180). The larvae are almost devoid of hairs; are grublike in appearance; but may be distinguished readily from beetle larvae by the presence of prolegs. Pupation occurs within the feeding tunnels of the larvae. The pupa works its way partly out of the tunnel before emerging

Figure 180. Carpenterworm (*Prionoxystus robiniae*). Stages of development and type of injury. (From Agricultural Research Service, USDA.)

as an adult. After the adult has emerged, the empty pupal case may be seen projecting partly out of the tunnel. These moths are stout bodied and large or medium in size. The shape of the body and wings in some species resembles the sphinx moths. Mouthparts are vestigial.

Several species are common. The best known of these is the carpenterworm or goat moth (*Prionoxystus robiniae*). This is a widely distributed insect in the United States and southern Canada. The larvae attack a large number of forest and shade trees, especially oaks. Eggs are laid in crevices of the bark. The size of the pinkish-white larvae varies, but they may attain a length of 2 inches or more. The larvae tunnel in the trunks and larger branches of trees. Some of the tunnels extend to the outside from which frass may be eliminated and sap exuded. Winter is passed in the larval stage, and the adults emerge during the summer months. The moths are large, with a wing expanse of as much as 3 inches in the female. The wings are gray with light and black markings, and the hind wings are slightly tinged with yellow. Probably 3 years are required for the development of the larvae. In valuable shade trees, the larvae may be killed by injecting small amounts of carbon disulfide in the tunnels and closing the hole with putty or mud.

The pecan carpenterworm (*Cossula magnifica*) is found only in the southern states. The larva attacks pecans, hickories, and oaks. Infested trees may be recognized by the presence of coarse sawdust at the base of the tree where it has dropped from the entrance of the larval burrows.

Fully grown larvae are more than 1 inch in length and are pinkish white. The moths, which appear in late spring or early summer, deposit eggs on small branches. The larvae tunnel in successively larger branches. Before cold weather, the partly grown larvae crawl down and tunnel into the trunks of the trees to pass the winter. There appears to be one generation annually. Control measures are the same as recommended for the carpenterworm.

Family Megalopygidae (Flannel Moths)

Wings of the Megalopygidae are clothed with loose scales mixed with long hairs which produce a flannellike appearance. Bodies of the larvae are heavily clothed with fine hairs or setae, with which are intermixed venomous setae.

The best known member of the group is the puss caterpillar (*Megalopyge opercularis*) (Figure 181A). This caterpillar is frequently abundant in the South and often becomes a pest in shade trees around homes, schools, and in parks. They are of little importance as enemies of shade trees, but they are capable of inflicting rather severe stings to man. When the body of a cater-

Figure 181. A. The puss caterpillar (*Megalopyge opercularis*). B. Cocoon showing trapdoor for the escape of the moth.

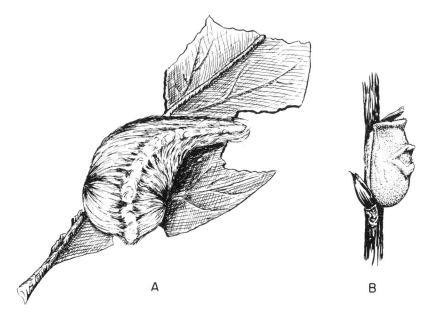

A   B

pillar is pressed against tender skin, it is pricked by the venomous setae which are hollow and supplied with a poison. Some of the setae are pulled out and others are broken off, resulting in severe dermatitis and other symptoms. The larvae are short, thickset, and woolly in appearance. Their color is variable, being yellow, gray, reddish brown, or a mixture of colors. The mature larva is about 1 inch in length and possesses 7 pairs of prolegs.

Winter is passed as a larva within a cocoon. Following pupation, the adults emerge, and several hundred eggs are laid by each female in late spring or early summer. The larvae feed on foliage of hackberry, elm, oak, and other trees. The mature larva constructs a rather unique cocoon on the trunk or branches of the host plant in which to pupate. At one end of the cocoon a trap door is provided for the escape of the adult as it emerges from the pupal case (Figure 181B). The dorsal surface of the cocoon is marked by a structure similar to a leaf scar. The color of the cocoon is about the same as that of the larva, because the larval hairs are incorporated in the silk. Adults are yellowish brown with wings clothed with long wavy hairs. Wing expanse of the moths ranges from 1 to 1½ inches. One or two generations of the puss caterpillar occur annually. Should the puss caterpillar appear in numbers large enough to be pestiferous, the insect may be controlled by spraying the trees with lead arsenate or toxaphene.

The crinkled flannel moth (*Megalopyge crispata*) is found in the North. The sting of this larva is not so severe as that of the puss caterpillar. The caterpillar feeds on foliage of elm, oak, apple, and many other trees. The larva is short, thickset, and densely clothed with long brown hairs. The adult is yellowish white with the front wings crossed by irregular lines formed by brown and black hairs. The species is somewhat larger than the puss caterpillar.

Family Tineidae (Clothes Moths)

The family Tineidae is composed of a large number of small moths; however, only a few species, the clothes moths, are of economic importance. The two most common species are the webbing clothes moth (*Tineola bisselliella*) and the casemaking clothes moth (*Tinea pellionella*), both of which are native to Europe. The moths do not feed on clothing since their mouthparts are imperfectly developed. Damage is caused by the larvae feeding upon wool, feathers, furs, hair, and products made from them. They will also feed upon beef meal, casein, skins, dead insects, and other animal matter. The larvae do not feed upon products of vegetable origin, such as cotton, linen, and rayon; silk is rarely attacked.

The webbing clothes moth is the more important species. The adult has a wing expanse of about ½ inch, and is uniformly pale yellow. The larvae are small white caterpillars about ½ inch in length. The webbing clothes moth takes its name from the habit of the larvae which spin transparent tubes as they feed, and produce a weblike mass of silken threads upon the food materials. When maturity is reached, the larvae spin silken cocoons in which are incorporated bits of excrement and food materials. Within the cocoon, the larvae transform into pupae from which the adults emerge later.

The adult of the casemaking clothes moth (Figure 182) is about the same size as the webbing clothes moth. The front wings are grayish yellow, marked by indistinct dark spots while the hind wings are lighter in color. The larvae spin small portable cases which they seldom leave. The biologies of the two species are quite similar.

The adult females each lay 100–150 small white eggs on the food materials of the larvae. The eggs hatch in 4–8 days during warm weather. In colder weather the egg stage may be prolonged as much as 3 weeks. The period of larval development is most variable, ranging from 6 weeks to 4 years. The pupal period is 1–4 weeks in duration, depending upon the temperature. A life cycle of clothes moths may be completed in 2 or 3 months or be prolonged over several years.

Frequently, small moths of various species are seen in the home and are mistaken for clothes moths. Many of these are attracted to lights from the outside, while others may be breeding in foodstuff. The Angoumois grain moth is most often mistaken for clothes moths. A characteristic which readily distinguishes this insect from clothes moths is the decidedly narrowed and pointed apex of the hind wing.

Figure 182. The casemaking clothes moth (*Tinea pellionella*) showing larval case, larva, and adult. (From USDA.)

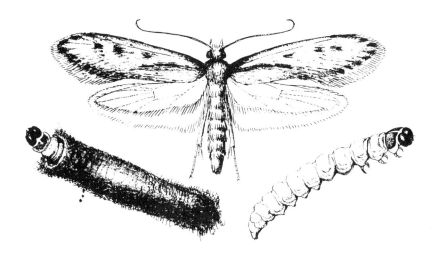

Control of clothes moths is similar to that of carpet beetles and begins with good housekeeping. It is advisable to dispose of all old woolen clothing and scraps, or place the materials in tight boxes or chests and spray with household spray, or sprinkle liberally with paradichlorobenzene or naphthalene crystals. Frequent vacuum cleaning of rugs, carpets, and floors will remove lint, hair, and bits of other materials upon which the larvae feed. Woolen clothing may also be sprayed. With precautions, rugs, carpets, and upholstered furniture may be sprayed also. Spraying with commercial products containing fluorine compounds is another means of protection against the insects. Brushing and sunning articles will remove the pests; dry cleaning destroys all stages. The latter two measures do not prevent reinfestation of the materials. Cedar chests, while new, afford some protection against damage.

Family Psychidae (Bagworm Moths)

Larvae of members of this family construct bags in which they live (Figure 183A). Adult females are wingless, while the males bear wings which are sparsely covered with scales. Members of the family are rather widely distributed over the world.

The most important species of this family in the United States is the common bagworm (*Thyridopteryx ephemeraeformis*) (Figure 183B). This insect is found from Massachusetts to Kansas and

---

Figure 183. The common bagworm (*Thyridopteryx ephemeraeformis*). A. Typical bag. (Prepared by the Clemson University Cooperative Extension Service's Entomology-Plant Pathology and Agricultural Communications Sections, Federal Extension Service Cooperating.) B. a, full-grown larva; b, larval head; c, male pupa; d, female pupa; e, adult female; f, male. (From USDA.)

A   B

south to Central Texas and Florida. The common bagworm attacks a long list of trees and shrubs, but its feeding is most destructive on arborvitae and cedars. Many beautiful ornamental plants around homes, public buildings, in parks and cemeteries are defoliated and killed each year by the feeding of these larvae.

Winter is passed as eggs in the female bags which remain suspended by silken strands on the host plants. The eggs hatch in the spring and the young larvae disperse in search of food, some of them being blown by the wind to other plants. The young larvae immediately construct small bags of silk in which are incorporated bits of leaves or twigs. As the larva grows, the size of the bag is increased correspondingly. In feeding, the larva protrudes the head and thorax and carries the bag with it as it crawls. Pupation occurs within the bag in the latter part of summer or September.

Prior to pupation the larva reverses its position in the bag and hangs with its head downward. Before emergence of the male moth, the pupa pushes its way partly out of the small opening at the lower end of the bag. The pupal case then splits and the male moth emerges. The moth is medium in size, dark colored, and the wings are almost devoid of scales. The female does not emerge completely from the pupal case, pushing only the head and part of the thorax out of a T-shaped slit. The mature female is grublike, devoid of wings, functional eyes, legs, and antennae. She remains concealed in the bag and hangs head downward.

Males are attracted to receptive females by odor. The end of the abdomen of the male is inserted in the lower opening of the bag in which the female is found until the entire abdomen of the male is hidden in the bag. Following fertilization, the abdomen of the male is slowly retracted from the bag. Soon after mating, the female begins egg deposition. Eggs are packed in the pupal case with down from the body. After the eggs are laid, the female moth forces her way out of the pupal case and bag, drops to the ground, and dies. There is one generation annually.

Bagworms are readily controlled by spraying with lead arsenate before the larvae are more than halfgrown. Carbaryl sprays are also recommended. When the infestation is localized on small shrubs, effective control may be obtained by picking and burning the bags containing the overwintering eggs during the winter months.

Family Gelechiidae (Gelechiids)

The family Gelechiidae is comprised of a large number of species of small moths. Many of the species may be recognized as members of this family by the pointed apex and the sinuate outer margin of the hind wing. Feeding habits of the larvae vary greatly. Some are miners; others feed in stems or rolled leaves; some produce galls; and the food of many is seed. Some of our most serious pests are found in this family.

THE PINK BOLLWORM (*Pectinophora gossypiella*). The pink bollworm (Figure 184) is the most destructive insect pest of cotton in many parts of the world. In Egypt, India, China, and Brazil it has been an important pest for many years. Indications are that southern Asia, probably India, is the native home of the insect. It has spread to distant parts of the world, such as Egypt, Brazil, and Mexico, through shipments of infested cottonseed. In 1917, the insect was first found in Texas. Eradication measures were successful in east Texas and Louisiana, but failed in the western districts along the Mexican border. Indications are that these districts were reinfested periodically by moths drifting in from infested areas in Mexico, for the moths are known to be carried long distances by winds. Extensive spread of the insect was prevented for many years by quarantine and control measures in the infested areas. In recent years, unfavorable weather conditions greatly hampered control measures in the infested areas, and the insect has spread rapidly, especially in Texas.

Primary damage of the pink bollworm is caused by feeding on the seeds of green bolls. Seeds from infested bolls are of low viability, light in weight, and their oil content is low and of inferior quality. As the bollworm makes pathways through the immature lint, it becomes cut and stained, and of inferior quality. Bolls may be completely or partially destroyed, and much of the lint produced is not worth picking. Squares and blooms are also attacked, but this damage is not significant.

In addition to feeding on cotton, the pink bollworm attacks okra, hollyhock, species of native *Hibiscus*, *Thurberia*, and other malvaceous plants. Infestations in okra and hollyhock depend chiefly on the proximity of fields of infested cotton.

The moths, or adults, are small, with a wing expanse of about ¾ inch, grayish brown, and resemble clothes moth or Angoumois grain moths in general appearance. They are nocturnal in habit and are not attracted to ordinary lights. Eggs may be laid

Figure 184. The pink bollworm (*Pectinophora gossypiella*). (From the Department of Entomology, Texas A&M University.)

on stems, squares, and buds; but when large green bolls are available, most of them are deposited in masses underneath the calyx at the base of the bolls. Eggs are white, oval, and about ⅕₀ inch in length with the surface finely reticulated by longitudinal and irregular cross veins. Each female lays 100–200 eggs.

The fully grown caterpillar is about ½ inch in length and is pinkish or light cream colored. Other larval characteristics are crochets of abdominal prolegs uniordinal and arranged in a penellipse (horseshoe shape) opening to the outside, four denticles present on each mandible, and three triangularly arranged setae located on the prespiracular shield of the prothorax. Several habits of the larvae are also helpful in recognizing the insect. Infested bolls are rarely filled with frass and excrement. The larvae make clean cut "shot holes" through the partitions and carpels in their feeding activities, and in making their exit from the bolls.

Another characteristic of the larvae is the frequent webbing together of seed late in the season prior to hibernation. The seed feeding and seed inhabitating characteristics of the larvae are also valuable in recognizing the insect.

Immediately following emergence from the eggs, the larvae begin searching for food. If suitable food is not found soon, they die. Larvae may feed slightly on foliage, but squares or bolls are essential for development. Cotton is attacked as soon as squares are found. Larvae feeding in squares may web the tips of the corolla together prior to blooming so that the petals will not unfold normally, and the blooms have a rosetted appearance. Larvae developing in squares may drop to the ground and pupate in trash or the soil.

When large bolls are attacked, the newly hatched larvae tunnel through the carpels to the inner membrane. When the membrane is reached, a small, brown, tortuous tunnel is made before the lint is entered in search of seed. The formation of this small tunnel or mine is a characteristic habit of this insect. Upon reaching maturity within green bolls, larvae may cut small holes through the carpels and drop to the ground to pupate—or pupation may occur within the bolls. Pupae are about ⅖ inch in length, brown, and covered with a fine pubescence. They are usually found in cocoons.

There may be 4–6 generations of the pink bollworm annually, a generation being completed in 25–30 days during warm weather. The egg stage averages about 5 days, while the feeding period of the larvae is 10–14 days. Pupae transform into moths in about 8 days. Three or 4 days following emergence, female moths begin oviposition. Larvae of the summer or warm season generations are known as short-cycle larvae, while the overwintering forms are termed long-cycle larvae.

The pink bollworm overwinters as larvae in cocoons. The overwintering or long-cycle larvae are found in old bolls, dropped squares, trash, and surface soil of the cotton field. Gin trash and seed in heavily infested areas contain many diapausing larvae. A larva may diapause in a single seed or in two seeds webbed together, forming what is known as "double seeds." Larvae pupate and moths emerge in the spring; however, emergence may be prolonged into the summer months.

Quarantine measures are maintained in infested districts, and movements of all products in those areas which may harbor the pest are regulated. In heavily infested districts, sterilization of the seed with heat is a part of the ginning process. Burning or mechanical treatment of the gin trash is also required. Fumigation with methyl bromide may be required before seed can be shipped to areas free of the pest.

Good cultural practices materially aid in control of the pink bollworm and other insects. The planting of early maturing varieties is advisable. In those areas where the crop is harvested before frost, the cotton stalks should be destroyed with a shredder and the residue later plowed under. Insecticidal control of the pink bollworm consists of the use of Guthion or Sevin applied at weekly intervals either as dusts or as sprays.

THE ANGOUMOIS GRAIN MOTH (*Sitotroga cerealella*). The Angoumois grain moth (Figure 185) is second in importance to the rice and granary weevils as a pest of stored grains. It was given this

Figure 185. Larva and adult of the Angoumois grain moth (*Sitotroga cerealella*). (From the University of California, Division of Agricultural Sciences.)

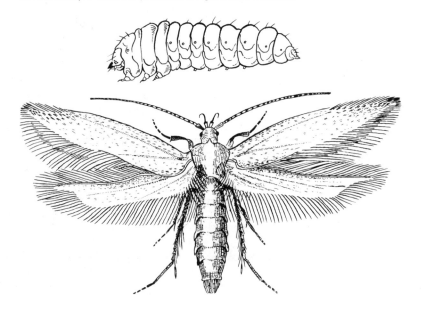

common name because its destructiveness as a grain pest was first reported from the old province of Angoumois, France. The insect has a wide distribution, but it is most destructive in warm climates. The larvae feed in and destroy seeds of corn, wheat, oats, sorghum, barley, and other crops.

Adults are small yellowish moths with a wingspread of about ⅗ inch. They may be seen flying in infested bins or crawling on the surface of the grain. Each female normally deposits about 40 small, white or reddish eggs on tips of ears of corn or heads of small grain or grain sorghums in the field, or on grain in storage. The newly hatched larvae bore into the kernels where they feed upon either the endosperm or the germ. Prior to pupation, each larva constructs a tunnel to the outside but keeps it closed with a thin layer of the seed coat. The larva then changes to a reddish brown pupa within a silken cocoon. The adult later emerges from the pupal case, pushes aside the thin layer of the seed coat, and escapes to the outside. A generation of the Angoumois grain moth may be completed in about 5 weeks. There may be as many as 6 generations in warm climates. If temperature conditions permit, breeding continues in stored grains throughout the winter months; otherwise, the insect overwinters in the larval stage.

Before storage of a new crop of grain, the bins should be thoroughly cleaned and the surfaces sprayed with either methoxychlor or malathion. Field infestations may be reduced to a minimum by harvesting as soon as the grain is sufficiently dry for storage. Malathion as a grain protectant may be applied as a spray or dust during the process of storage. Several fumigants are effective in control of the pest. Those most commonly employed are mixtures of carbon tetrachloride and ethylene dichloride or carbon disulfide. Methyl bromide is an effective fumigant, but its use requires a recirculation system built into the storage facilities. Drying systems often may be adapted for this type of fumigation.

THE PEACH TWIG BORER (*Anarsia lineatella*). The peach twig borer is an important pest of peaches in several sections of the country, particularly on the Pacific Coast. This is an old European insect which was first found in this country in 1860. Injury is caused by the feeding of the larvae in the fruit and tunneling in the twigs; damage to fruit is important. Peaches, almonds, apricots, cherries, and plums are attacked.

Winter is passed as immature larvae in hibernacula closely attached to the bark. The overwintered larvae emerge, tunnel out, and kill the young succulent shoots in the spring. Pupation occurs in cracks, pruning scars, and rough places of the bark. Small, gray moths with a wing expanse of ⅓ to ½ inch later emerge from the pupal cases and deposit eggs on the twigs. Larvae of the summer generations prefer fruit to the twigs. The majority of fruits are attacked at the stem end, where the fruits touch or where the leaves are in contact with the fruit. Most of the worms penetrate only a small distance; however, large larvae sometimes feed to the pit. The mature larvae are about ⅜ inch long and chocolate brown. The number of generations annually is one to four, with the larger number occurring in warm climates.

In the central states, delayed dormant sprays of lime-sulfur or oil emulsion are the most effective control measures. The spray kills the larvae in their hibernacula. These sprays, however, have not proved effective in all sections of the country. Sprays containing basic lead arsenate, applied in the spring, provide satisfactory control on the Pacific Coast. The use of azinphosmethyl sprays has shown promise. Dust mixtures of basic lead arsenate and sulfur are recommended for use on mature fruit to avoid poisonous residues.

THE TOMATO PINWORM (*Keiferia lycopersicella*). In warm climates this insect is a pest of importance in field grown tomatoes, and its injury may be particularly extensive when the crop is grown in greenhouses. Under greenhouse conditions its range is extended northward. In addition to tomatoes it may attack potatoes, eggplants, and certain other species of solanaceous plants. Dissemination is primarily through transplants. Shipments of infested fruit and packing crates are also means of dispersal, as well as railroad cars and trucks. The flight of the moths may account for much of the local infestation of the pest.

On young plants the most common injury is made as leaf miners. The young larva feeds as a leaf miner until it is half grown. It then leaves the mine and rolls together a small part of a leaf; it lives and feeds within this enclosure. Stems are attacked sometimes. All leaves may become heavily infested, and the plants may not set fruit. However, the most important damage is fruit injury. The insect most often enters the fruit under the calyx at the stem end. The side of the tomato may be entered where two fruits touch or at the point of contact of a leaf and a fruit. A tiny hole is made which may not be readily observed.

The adult is a small moth resembling the clothes moth in color and size. The general color of the small larva is light green, but it changes to a purplish black when fully grown. The mature larva is about ¼ inch in length. Pupation is within a cell in the topsoil. The female lays 100–150 eggs which are deposited in an erratic pattern, but usually on the lower surface of the leaves of the upper half of the plant. The life cycle is rather short with 7 or more generations under greenhouse conditions over a production period of 4–5 months.

Destruction of crop residues, plowing, and rotation of crops aid materially in control of the pest. However, supplemental chemical control may become quite necessary. Satisfactory insecticidal control is rather difficult to obtain. Carbaryl, toxaphene, and parathion are suggested.

Family Plutellidae

About 50 species of the Plutellidae are known to occur in North America. The diamondback moth (*Plutella xylostella*) (Figure 186A-C) is the best known member of the family. It is a pest of some economic importance on cruciferous plants and attacks certain ornamental and greenhouse plants such as stock, candytuft, and sweet alyssum. The larva feeds on the underside of the leaves, eating out small areas but leaving the thin epidermis intact. This produces a transparent spot on the leaf surface. Upon drying, the thin epidermis breaks, producing characteristic holes in the leaves (Figure 186D). Young plants may be rather severely injured. The full-grown larva is about ⅓ inch in length and pale green with small black setae on its body. When the larva is disturbed, it wriggles actively or drops from the plant on a silk thread. This habit aids in distinguishing this caterpillar from small cabbage worms. Prior to pupation, the larva spins a transparent gauzy cocoon which is attached to a leaf or some other part of the plant. Adults are small, grayish moths with a wing expanse of about ⅓ inch. The front wings of the male have an irregular yellow

Figure 186. Diamondback moth (*Plutella xylostella*). A. Adult. B. Larva. C. Pupa. D. Damaged leaf. (From USDA.)

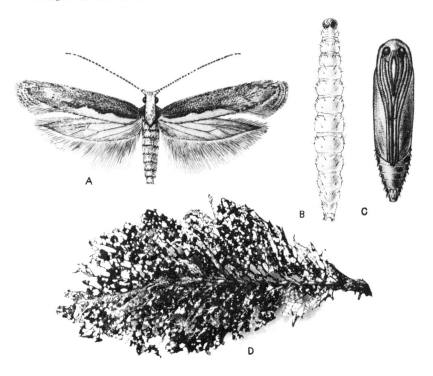

stripe along each inner margin. When the wings are folded, the two yellow stripes are brought together and form three diamond-shaped yellow spots which have suggested the common name. Females lay the small, yellowish white eggs on leaves of the host plants. The length of a generation is relatively short; there are probably two to six or more generations annually. Winter is usually spent as adults, hidden beneath cabbage leaves or other cover in the fields. However, all stages may be found during the winter in the insect's southern range. Dusts and sprays of malathion and methoxychlor are recommended. *Bacillus thurinigensis* is also being recommended for control of the pest.

Family Aegeriidae (Clear-Wing Moths)

The most striking characteristic of most members of the Aegeriidae is that one or both pairs of wings are relatively free of scales. Many of the adults are wasplike in general appearance. The moths are moderate in size, with the front wings exceptionally narrow. They are active during the day. The larvae are borers, infesting a number of plants. More than 100 species are known in this country. Several are important pests.

THE PEACH TREE BORER (*Sanninoidea exitiosa*). The peach tree borer ranks with the San Jose scale and plum curculio in importance as a pest of the peach. Many trees die each year as a direct or indirect result of the attacks of the larvae of this insect. Larvae tunnel and feed in the cambium or inner layer of the bark (Figure 187A), usually in the base and occasionally in the larger roots. Masses of gum mixed with frass, soil, and bits of bark are usually seen

Figure 187. The peach tree borer (*Sanninoidea exitiosa*). A. Larvae feeding in young peach tree. B. Adult male. (From USDA.)

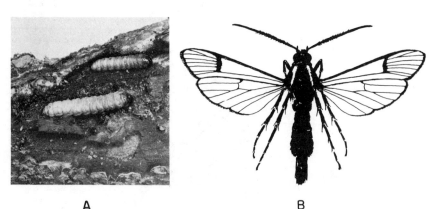

A   B

around the base of trees infested by the borers. The presence of gum does not always indicate the presence of borers, however, as injury, sun scald, and other agencies may cause the exudation of gum. Other hosts of the peach tree borer are plum, apricot, almond, nectarine, and related plants. The range of distribution of the insect is east of the Rocky Mountains from Canada to the Gulf Coast.

Winter is passed as larvae. All the larger larvae remain in their tunnels but some of the smaller forms overwinter in a protective covering on the bark of the tree. Feeding and growth is resumed when the weather becomes warm. Upon completion of larval development, brownish cocoons in which the larvae pupate are formed either in the soil near the tree trunk or at the exit of the tunnels. The fully grown larvae are about 1 inch long and yellowish white with brown heads.

The length of the pupal stage is 3 or 4 weeks. A few moths (Figure 187B) may emerge during May in the southernmost range of the insect; however, most moths emerge in July and August in the North, and June through September in the South. The female moth is blackish blue with clear hind wings and one or two orange bands around the abdomen. The male is lighter colored than the female with both pairs of wings clear and the abdomen ringed with several narrow yellow bands. The wing expanse of the adults is slightly more than an inch.

The females usually lay 500–600 eggs each, most of which are deposited on the tree trunks. In warm weather, eggs hatch in 9 or 10 days. The newly hatched larvae find their way to the base of the trees and enter near the ground level. They bore into the cambium and inner bark layers where they feed until cold weather. Normally only one generation is completed each year.

Several control measures may be employed in combating this pest. Azinphosmethyl and endosulfan may be sprayed on the lower parts of the large branches and trunks of the trees during the time the moths are emerging and ovipositing. Recommended strength of the sprays and time of application vary in different parts of the country. Paradichlorobenzene treatment has been successfully used for more than 50 years. Crystals of the compound are applied in a ring around the base of the tree. A gas is formed as the crystals vaporize, which penetrates the bark and tunnels, and kills the larvae. The paradichlorobenzene treatment should be made at the close of the oviposition period in the fall. Ethylene dichloride treatment is efficient and relatively safe for use on young trees when properly applied. Applications may be made with this insecticide in the fall or spring, or in periods of warm weather during the winter in the South. Most satisfactory results are probably obtained by fall treatments. Worming the trees is an old control measure. If the worming is carefully done, reasonable control will be obtained. The time of application of control measures and dosages vary so much in different sections of the country that the grower should consult the local state agricultural experiment station or extension service, or refer to available USDA publications for local recommendations and details of control.

THE LESSER PEACH TREE BORER (*Synanthedon pictipes*). This insect is quite similar to the peach tree borer in appearance. Its injury is confined chiefly to the trunks and limbs. The larvae work in crotches, under old bark, and in places injured by mechanical means (freezes, sun scald, or disease).

Overwintered larvae change to pupae in the spring. Shortly after emergence from the pupal cases, the female moths lay their eggs on trunks and limbs. One and a partial second generation occur annually in the South, but only one is completed in colder climates.

Proper care of orchards is important in preventing infestations of the lesser peach tree borer. Care should be taken to prevent mechanical injuries. Wounds and areas killed by sun scald and disease should be treated. The removal of dead and broken limbs is advisable. The sprays that are recommended for the peach tree borer are suggested for control of this pest.

THE SQUASH VINE BORER (*Melittia cucurbitae*). This insect is an important pest of squashes and pumpkins. Usually the first indication of the presence of the borer is the sudden wilting of leaves and masses of yellowish excrement pushed out of holes in the vines. Examination of an infested vine will show it to be tunneled out by white, brown headed larvae which may measure up to 1 inch in length. Heavily infested plants are killed. In addition to squashes and pumpkins, gourds, cucumbers, and melons are attacked. The insect is found from Canada to Brazil, westward to the Rocky Mountains.

Larvae mature in 4–6 weeks. They leave their tunnels in the plant, enter the ground, and spin silken cocoons which are covered with particles of soil. In the North, larvae remain in the cocoons until spring before transforming into pupae. In warmer climates, the larvae change to pupae from which moths soon emerge, and eggs are laid for a second generation.

The moths are medium in size. The fore wings are opaque and olive brown; the hind wings are transparent. The abdomen is ringed with red or orange, black, and bronze; and long hairs fringe the hind legs. Each female deposits singly 150–200 eggs chiefly on the stems, but also on other parts of the plant.

Vines should be raked and destroyed following harvest to destroy the larvae remaining in them. Fall, winter, or spring plowing will destroy many of the larvae and pupae in the cocoons. As the larvae are internal feeders, insecticidal control is difficult. Heavy dust applications of rotenone or carbaryl will destroy many of the young larvae before they enter the stems. The dusts should be applied at weekly intervals during the growing season.

Family Tortricidae (Tortricids)

The Tortricidae is a large family of rather small moths. There are probably more than 1000 North American species. The front wings are broad and truncate at the outer margins. The larvae feed on a wide variety of plants. Many species are leaf rollers; others feed in the fruits, buds, or stems. A number of important pests are found in this group. This family is considered a superfamily, *Tortricoidea*, and subdivided into several families by a number of authorities.

THE CODLING MOTH (*Laspeyresia pomonella*). The codling moth is the most serious insect pest of apples, causing most of the wormy fruit which is so familiar to everyone. The core of the fruit is eaten out by the pinkish-white caterpillars which have brown heads and are about ¾ inch long when fully grown. Apples, pears, English walnuts, and occasionally other fruits are attacked. This insect is found wherever apples are grown.

The winter is passed as mature larvae in tough silken cocoons underneath the bark of trees, in crotches, crevices, pruning scars, debris on the ground, and similar environments (Figure 188A). Many larvae overwinter in packing sheds or other places where

Figure 188. Codling moth (*Laspeyresia pomonella*). A. Larvae and pupae in cocoons underneath bark. B. Moth. (From USDA.)

apples have been stored. In the spring the larvae transform within the cocoons into brownish pupae. Three or 4 weeks following pupation, grayish moths with a wingspread of about ¾ inch emerge from the pupal cases (Figure 188B). Near the tip of each front wing is a copper brown spot which is bordered internally by a cross band of chocolate brown. The moths are active mainly at twilight in warm weather. They are not strong fliers.

Moths that develop in the spring from overwintered larvae emerge over a period of several weeks. Egg deposition is usually heaviest about 4 weeks after the petals of the apple blooms have fallen. Each female moth deposits 50–75 eggs on the leaves, twigs, and fruit. Eggs hatch in about a week. Many of the young larvae of this generation enter the fruit by way of the calyx cup or blossom end and eat their way to the core. Larvae of later generations enter the fruit at almost any point and commonly produce a type of injury known as codling moth stings. Larvae complete development in 3–5 weeks. Then they leave the fruit and seek suitable places for pupation, such as underneath bits of loose bark and other protected places on the tree, and in debris on the ground. Here cocoons are spun and pupation occurs. In the New England states a small number of the larvae of the first generation pupate before the next spring, so there is a partial second generation. Farther south the size of the second generation increases. Two full generations occur in the middle Atlantic states. In warmer climates there may be three or four generations annually.

Recommendations for the control of the codling moth vary somewhat in different sections of the country. This insect is difficult to control, and correct timing of the sprays, thorough applications, and the use of proper materials are essential. It is necessary for the grower to obtain detailed information on the most satisfactory spray program and materials for his section of the country from the local state experiment stations and extension service entomologists. A number of insecticides and combinations of these are employed to control this insect. Diazinon, Guthion, carbaryl, parathion, malathion, lead arsenate, and methoxychlor are commonly used. In most sections 3–4 sprays applied at 10–14-day intervals are recommended in control of the first brood larvae. Their application should begin 10–14 days after petal fall. For control of subsequent broods 1–3 applications of spray should be made at the same intervals.

In the Pacific Northwest the spray program usually begins 3 weeks after petal fall. Two to 4 applications of spray should be applied at 3-week intervals as needed. Lead arsenate is used only in control of light infestations or in those sections where it has proved satisfactory. Carbaryl and Guthion are recommended to control resistant strains, and carbaryl also, for use in late applications to prevent excessive residues of other insecticides. Guthion and parathion should not be used on small plantings around homes, and where used they should be applied only by trained applicators. Parathion should not be used on such varieties as the McIntosh.

Several minor practices help in the control of the codling moth. Cleaning up and removing trash and rubbish in the orchards, and scraping loose bark from all old trees aid in the elimination of places of pupation and hibernation. The removal of cull apples is advised. Packing sheds and their immediate surroundings should be cleaned up and the rubbish destroyed.

THE ORIENTAL FRUIT MOTH (*Grapholitha molesta*). The oriental fruit moth is believed to have been imported into the United States from the Orient prior to 1915. It is now found in most of the peach-producing sections of the country. The injury produced by the insect ranges from slight to heavy, varying with the locality and the season. The larvae feed on both twigs and fruit (Figure 189). Injury to the twigs is similar to that done by the peach twig borer. Damage to fruit is suggestive of the feeding of the plum curculio in peaches and the codling moth in apples. Peaches, plums, apples, and pears are the fruits chiefly attacked. The larvae

Figure 189. Larva of oriental fruit moth (*Grapholitha molesta*) feeding in twig of peach. (From USDA.)

are pinkish white, not chocolate or reddish brown as is the peach twig borer, and about ½ inch long. The last segment of the abdomen bears a plate with five teeth.

Winter is passed as larvae in cocoons which are found in such protected places as cracks in the bark of the tree, mummied fruit, or rubbish on the ground. In the spring the larvae transform to pupae, from which stage the moths emerge about the time peach trees are in bloom. The grayish adults have a wingspread of about ½ inch and resemble codling moths, except that they are smaller.

Eggs are usually laid on the underside of the leaves, but occasionally they may be deposited on the twigs. While the new growth is tender in spring and early summer, the larvae bore into the twigs and eat out the centers. This twig injury may seriously interfere with the growth of young trees. Fruit is attacked in the summer when the twigs become tough and fibrous. There are three to seven generations of the insect annually. In those sections where fruit is not available after midsummer, the insect is rarely an important pest. In the absence of fruit, the larvae must feed on hardened twigs which are not satisfactory food material.

Properly timed sprays containing dieldrin, azinphosmethyl, or parathion will control the oriental fruit moth. Sprays should not be applied later than 30 days prior to harvesting. A small wasp, *Macrocentrus ancylivorus*, is an important parasite and has provided effective control of the pest in some sections of the country.

Destruction of dropped and culled fruit will aid in reducing infestations. The paradichlorobenzene treatment for the control of the peach tree borer will destroy many overwintering larvae around the base of the trees. The application of fertilizers late in the season is not advised, because new twig growth may be promoted which could then provide food for the larvae at this season.

THE GRAPE BERRY MOTH (*Paralobesia viteana*). The grape berry moth (Figure 190) is distributed over most of the eastern part of the United States where it is frequently a pest of importance of both wild and cultivated varieties of grapes. In early season the larvae feed in the blooms or the young berries. The second and third generations attack the green or ripening fruit. They are greenish and ⅓ to ½ inch long when fully grown. Prior to pupation the larvae leave the berries and each cuts out a bit of leaf which is folded over, and a cocoon is spun within this shelter. The moth are grayish, with a wing expanse of about ½ inch. About 5 weeks are required for development from egg to adult. There are 2 or 3 generations of this insect annually. Diapause is in silken cocoons which are usually found in the loose bark or trash on the ground.

Cleaning up and burning fallen leaves and trash in the fall or winter will destroy many of the diapausing pupae. Carbaryl, methoxychlor, and parathion are among the insecticides recommended for the control of this pest.

Figure 190. Grape berry moths (*Paralobesia viteana*). (From USDA.)

Family Pyralidae (Pyralid Moths)

This is a very large family of moths; more than 1000 species occur in North America. The family is considered by many authors as a superfamily with four or more families which are divided further into a number of subfamilies. The members of the family are a diverse group with much variation in appearance and habits. Most of the moths are small or moderate in size with the labial palpi often projecting snoutlike. Larvae of the family may be recognized by the presence of two setae in the prespiracular group of the thorax, by setae IV and V of a proleg-bearing segment located close together below the spiracle, and by the arrangement of the crochets of the prolegs in a circle or a penellipse. A number of important pests are found in the family.

THE EUROPEAN CORN BORER (*Ostrinia nubilalis*). This serious pest of corn was probably brought into this country in shipments of broom corn from Europe about 1908 or 1909. Its presence here has been known since 1917. The insect is now found in most of the major corn-producing sections of the country. Its distribution extends from the Atlantic seaboard westward to North Dakota, South Dakota, and Nebraska, and southward to Kentucky and North Carolina. Some conception of the destructiveness of this insect may be obtained from the estimate that it caused a loss of 85,000,000 bushels of corn in 1948. Primary injury of the larvae is by tunneling through the stalks and ears (Figure 191). Injury is sometimes so severe that the plants break and fall in the fields.

Figure 191. European corn borer (*Ostrinia nubilalis*). A. Larva. (Prepared by the Clemson University Cooperative Extension Service's Entomology-Plant Pathology and Agricultural Communications Sections, Federal Extension Service Cooperating.) B. Hill of sweet corn destroyed by borers. (From USDA.)

There are two biological races of the European corn borer. A one-generation race is predominant in the North Central states. This race does not generally attack plants other than corn. In eastern and southern regions of the insect's range, a multiple-generation race predominates. The number of generations annually of this race may vary from one in colder climates to three in Virginia, and five in Guam. These larvae are more destructive because of the greater number of generations and the wider range of host plants. More than 200 different kinds of herbaceous plants are attacked.

The insects diapause as larvae in stems of the food plants. The larvae are brownish or pinkish with the body marked by small dark spots, and they attain a length of almost 1 inch when fully grown. When the weather becomes warm in the spring, the larvae construct flimsy cocoons for pupation within the tunnels in the host plants. The moths, which emerge from June until August, have a wingspread of about 1 inch. They are yellowish to pale brown with dark wavy lines extending across the wings. The male moths are darker than the females. They are rather strong fliers and are most active at night. Females lay an average of 500–600 eggs, which are usually deposited on the underside of the leaves of the food plants in groups of 5–50. The duration of the egg stage is about 1 week. On corn the young larvae feed in the whorls of developing leaves, between the leaf sheaths, or between the ears and the stalks. Tassels, which frequently break over, are heavily attacked until ears are formed. When the larvae are about half grown they become borers and tunnel into the stalk and ears. Here they feed until they complete their development. Dry weather destroys many larvae before they enter the stalks. Cold weather and heavy rainfall also are beneficial in checking the insect.

Since the insects diapause as larvae in the tunnels of the food plants, utilization or destruction of the plant residues before emergence of the adults will appreciably reduce the population for the next season. Plowing plant residues under deeply and completely is a very effective control measure. Residues that cannot be plowed under should be raked together and burned. The planting of resistant varieties of corn is advisable. If corn is utilized for silage or fodder, the plants should be cut as close to the ground as possible; no stubble should be left more than 2 inches high. Correctly timed applications of insecticidal dusts and sprays will greatly reduce corn borer injury. DDT was the first insecticide generally used. Ryania as a dust has been recommended. Recently, carbaryl, EPN, and toxaphene appear to be the chief insecticides used.

THE SOUTHERN CORNSTALK BORER (*Diatraea crambidoides*). This is often a corn pest of importance in the South, but because of the nature of its attacks, the full extent of its damage is not generally realized. Injury is caused by the yellowish-white larvae which are about 1 inch in length and marked with brown spots when fully grown (Figure 192). The insect overwinters as mature larvae which are generally found in the taproots of the cornstalks. In the spring the larvae change to pupae from which the moths emerge 10 or

Figure 192. The southern cornstalk borer (*Diatraea crambidoides*). (Prepared by the Clemson University Cooperative Extension Service's Entomology-Plant Pathology and Agricultural Communications Sections, Federal Extension Service Cooperating.)

more days later. The moths are light yellow with a wing expanse of barely more than 1 inch. Each female usually lays 300–400 eggs on the undersurface of the leaves. Eggs hatch in 7–10 days. The young larvae feed first on the surface of the leaves but later tunnel into the stalks and feed as borers until their development is completed. They may leave and reenter a stalk several times or change to other plants in the course of their development. The length of the larval stage in the summer is 20–30 days. There may be as many as three generations annually. Although corn is the principal host, sorghums and Johnson grass are attacked also.

Cultural practices are the most effective control measures in combating this insect. Cleaning up and destroying cornstalks and stubble following harvest are the most satisfactory measures. Fall and winter plowing will destroy many of the diapausing larvae. Crop rotation is also of value in decreasing the injury caused by the pest.

THE SOUTHWESTERN CORN BORER (*Diatraea grandiosella*). Larvae of the southwestern corn borer are not readily distinguished from those of the southern cornstalk borer. The two species also have similar life histories and habits. Their habits differ in that the southwestern corn borer may girdle the stalk internally prior to diapause in the taproots (Figure 193). This injury results in lodging as the stalks are readily blown over. The southwestern corn

Figure 193. The southwestern corn borer (*Diatraea grandiosella*) in base of a cornstalk. (From Texas Agricultural Experiment Station.)

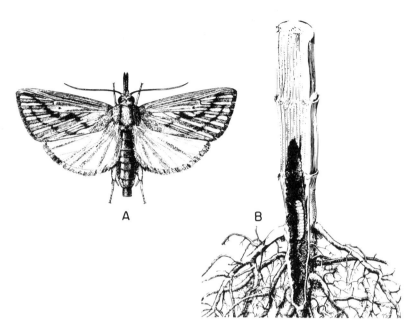

Figure 194. Sugar cane borer (*Diatraea saccharalis*). A. Adult. B. Larva in stalk. (From USDA.)

borer is a native of Mexico. It spread into Arizona, New Mexico, and Texas prior to 1913. In addition to those states, the insect is now found in Oklahoma, Colorado, Kansas, and Nebraska.

Corn is the primary host of this insect. As sorghums are not heavily attacked, it is advisable to substitute planting of these crops for corn, at least in those areas where borer damage is the heaviest.

In those regions where extremely cold winter weather normally prevails, plowing out the corn stubble is recommended. This practice exposes the larvae to low temperatures and most of them will be killed. Other practices, such as those recommended for the southern cornstalk borer, are suggested for the control of this insect.

THE SUGARCANE BORER (*Diatraea saccharalis*). The sugarcane borer is the most important insect pest of sugarcane in Louisiana (Figure 194). Annual loss due to this insect amounts to several million dollars. It is also a serious pest of rice. In addition to sugarcane and rice, the larvae attack corn, sorghums, sudan grass, and native grasses. Biology, habits, and general description of the insect are quite similar to those of the southern cornstalk borer. The life cycle of the insect is somewhat shorter and four to five generations may be completed annually. The insect, which is of tropical or subtropical origin, was introduced into Louisiana about 100 years ago and is now found in Texas, Louisiana, Mississippi, and Florida.

Since the larvae overwinter in crop residues, it is important that this material be destroyed. Cane tops, pieces of stalks, leaves, and other trash should be thoroughly burned or plowed under (wrapped) between the rows. Infested rice fields should be burned, grazed, or flooded following harvest. The destruction of stalks and stubble of infested cornfields during the winter months will reduce the number of diapausing larvae. The growing of resistant varieties of sugarcane is recommended. Insecticides recommended for control of this pest are carbaryl, diazinon, methyl parathion, and parathion.

THE LESSER CORNSTALK BORER (*Elasmopalpus lignosellus*). This insect is often a troublesome pest of corn, peanuts, cowpeas, beans, sorghum, and several other crops in the South. Injury is caused by the larvae tunneling into the stalks or stems of the plants. The lower portions of the stalks or stems are attacked. Injury is most severe where the plants are grown in sandy soils. The larvae are bluish green with darker markings, rather slender, and about ¾ inch long.

Winter is passed in the larval, pupal, or adult stages, but most commonly as larvae in its southern range. Moths emerge in the spring, and eggs are deposited on the foliage and stems of the food plants. The moths are brownish gray with a wingspread of less than 1 inch. Larvae hatching from the eggs feed first on the leaves and roots and later tunnel into the stems of the plants. Larval development is completed in 2 or 3 weeks. The larvae pupate in silken cocoons which are found under trash on the surface of the ground. There may be as many as four generations annually in the South with a lesser number occurring in cooler climates. The most effective control measures are cleanup schedules after harvest and crop rotation. Fall and winter plowing is also helpful in reducing the numbers of the insect.

THE GARDEN WEBWORM (*Loxostege rantalis*). The foliage of cotton, alfalfa, clover, cowpeas, beans, and other plants (including a number of weeds) are fed upon by the larvae of this insect. Because the most common native host is the careless weed (*Amaranthus* spp.), the larvae are often referred to as "careless weed worms." Frequently infestations on cultivated crops are caused by migrations from weeds which have become overpopulated or destroyed. The larvae usually spin webs over the leaves upon which they are feeding.

The insect overwinters as larvae or pupae in the soil where the host plants grow. Adults emerge in the spring and lay their eggs on foliage of the host plants of the larvae. The moths are small and yellowish or grayish brown with irregular shading on the wings. They are nocturnal in habit and often collect around lights in numbers. The fully grown larvae are about 1 inch in length, greenish yellow with 3 conspicuous black spots arranged in a triangle on the side of each abdominal segment. Larvae complete development in 3–5 weeks, and then enter the soil to transform into the pupal stage. The insect may complete as many as 5 generations in the South, with probably 2 or 3 occurring in its northern range.

The garden webworm may be controlled with a number of insecticides. Both dusts and sprays are effective. Carbaryl and trichlorfon are most commonly employed in controlling the pest. Arsenicals and cryolite are also used. Rotenone may be dusted on vegetable crops. The alfalfa webworm (*Loxostege commixtalis*) and the beet webworm (*Loxostege sticticalis*) (Figure 195) are two related insects with similar biologies, and the same insecticides may be used in their control.

THE GREATER WAX MOTH (*Galleria mellonella*). This widely distributed insect is most destructive to colonies of bees in warm climates. The larvae burrow through honeycombs and construct silken tunnels as they feed on wax, pollen, cocoons, and impurities in the combs (Figure 196). Old, dark combs are preferred to those that are new and light colored. The combs in a heavily infested colony of bees may be reduced to a mass of webs, fragments, and excrement. Damage and destruction of combs occur in weak colonies when the bees are unable to adequately police the hives and keep out the intruders, and when combs are stored. The fully grown larvae are rather plump, dirty gray, and about 1½ inches in length. Pupation occurs in a tough silken cocoon within the hive or in other protected places. The adults have a wing expanse of about 1¼ inches and are grayish brown. There are two or three generations of the insect annually. Winter is passed either in the larval or the pupal stage, although moths may emerge in the winter months in the South during periods of warm weather.

Control of the wax moth consists essentially of good beekeeping. With adequate care of the colonies, broken combs and cappings, and stored combs, wax moth injury may be kept to a

Figure 195. The beet webworm (*Loxostege sticticalis*). (From USDA.)

Figure 196. Damage to comb of the honeybee by larvae of the greater wax moth (*Galleria mellonella*). (From R. Grout, *The Hive and the Honey Bee.* Copyright 1949. Used by permission of Dadant & Sons, Publishers of American Bee Journal, Hamilton, Ill.)

minimum. Stored combs should be fumigated with hydrogen cyanide, methyl bromide, or paradichlorobenzene.

THE MEDITERRANEAN FLOUR MOTH (*Anagasta kuhniella*). This insect is very troublesome in flour mills. As the larvae feed, they spin silken threads which result in masses of flour being webbed together. This matted material clogs the flour machinery and impedes operations. Flour is the principal food material, but the larvae may be found also feeding on corn, wheat, wheat bran, buckwheat flour, cornmeal, cottonseed meal, cereals, and other grain products. The fully grown larvae are whitish or pinkish and about ⅝ inch long. Pupation occurs in silken cocoons which are found in flour, meal, and mill machinery. The moths have a wingspread of less than 1 inch and are blackish gray with wavy black lines crossing the wings near the tips. Eggs are laid in the food materials, on containers, carton walls, floors, or in milling machinery. A generation may be completed in 9 or 10 weeks. When temperature conditions are favorable, breeding is continuous throughout the year.

Elimination of accumulations of flour, meal, and grain in flour mills, bins, loading docks, and other places will aid in minimizing infestations. General fumigation with methyl bromide or hydrogen cyanide is a highly effective treatment. Sprays of methoxychlor or malathion applied as a residual treatment to woodwork of flour mills, warehouses, and storage bins aid in controlling the pest.

THE RICE MOTH (*Corcyra cephalonica*). This moth is similar in appearance to the Mediterranean flour moth. It commonly attacks rice in the South and is found occasionally in other farinaceous products. It is not usually found in flour mills. The pest may be controlled by the recommendations given above.

THE INDIAN-MEAL MOTH (*Plodia interpunctella*). The larvae (Figure 197A) feed on a wide variety of materials such as grains, grain products, dried fruits, nuts, roots, herbs, and powdered milk, but the insect is seldom a pest in flour mills. Infested materials become

Figure 197. The Indian-meal moth (*Plodia interpunctella*). A. Larva. B. Adult. (From Agricultural Research Service, USDA.)

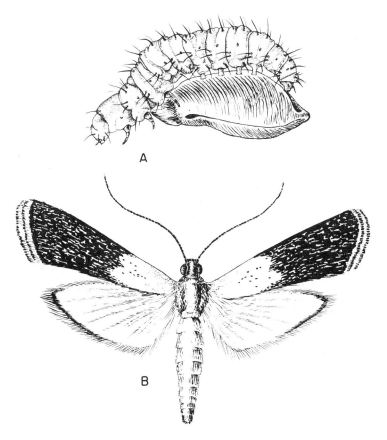

fouled with cast skins, excrement, webbing, and cocoons. The larvae are dirty white, and are frequently marked with pinkish or greenish hues. The mature larvae are about ½ inch in length. The cocoons in which the larvae pupate are found on the surface of the food materials or in cracks and crevices. The moths (Figure 197B) are readily recognized by the markings of the front wings, the bases of which are grayish white and the apical two-thirds reddish brown. The wing expanse is almost ¾ inch. The Indian-meal moth may pass through its developmental stages in 6–8 weeks. Breeding is continuous throughout the year under favorable conditions. As many as 5 generations may develop annually. The insect may be controlled by the same measures recommended for the Mediterranean flour moth.

THE PECAN NUT CASEBEARER (*Acrobasis caryae*). This is the most important insect pest of the pecan, which is its only known host. Injury is caused by the larvae which bore into and destroy the nuts (Figure 198). Larvae of the first generation are the most destructive. They are active in May and early June when the nuts are small, and one larva may destroy several nuts in a cluster. Second generation larvae also tunnel into the nuts, but the nuts are larger at this time and fewer are destroyed. Later generations usually feed in the shucks of the nuts, buds, or axils of the leaf stems. The larvae are olive green and are about ½ inch long when fully grown.

Figure 198. A. Pecan nuts destroyed by the pecan nut casebearer (*Acrobosis caryae*). B. Adult resting on a nut. (From Texas Agricultural Experiment Station.)

The insects diapause as partly grown larvae in small silken cases, or hibernacula, attached to buds of the trees. In the spring, the overwintered larvae feed first on the buds to which the hibernacula are attached, and later tunnel into the young growing shoots. Development is completed in the shoots, and the larvae transform into the pupal stage within their tunnels.

The moths that have developed from the overwintered larvae emerge in largest numbers when the nuts are setting. These moths are small, with a wing expanse of about ⅗ inch. They are gray, with a ridge of dark scales extending across the front wings, one-third the distance from the base. Pupation of the first and second generations is within the nuts. Larvae of the third and fourth generations usually pupate within the shucks of the nuts. There are two to four generations of the pecan nut casebearer annually.

The most effective control of the nut casebearer is obtained by spraying soon after the nuts have set in the spring when eggs and young larvae are found. Parathion, malathion, toxaphene and carbaryl are recommended for control of the insect.

THE PICKLEWORM (*Diaphania nitidalis*). The larvae of this insect bore into the underside of the fruit of cantaloupes, squashes, and cucumbers. Before fruit is formed the larvae feed in blooms, buds, leaf stalks, and stems. This widely distributed insect is particularly destructive in the South. The young larvae are whitish or greenish with small black spots on the body. When fully grown the larvae are coppery or greenish and about ¾ inch in length.

Winter is passed as pupae in silken cocoons which are usually found in the leaves of the host plants. Adults emerge in late spring or early summer. The moths have a brown body with a brush of black hairs on the end of the abdomen and a wing expanse of about 1 inch. The wings are brownish with yellow areas in the middle of the front wings and basal half of the hind wings. Each female moth deposits 300 or more eggs upon those parts of the plants which are used as food by the larvae. The size of the first generation of larvae is small but the numbers increase rapidly as the season advances. A generation may be completed in 4 weeks during the summer. There may be as many as 4 or 5 generations during the year.

Cultural control measures are valuable in reducing infestations for the next season. Following harvest, crop residues should be collected and burned to destroy larvae feeding in them. In the fall the land should be plowed to eliminate the pupae on the ground. Trap crops of squash are often recommended as preventive measures since the insect prefers this plant as food. When these plants become infested, the blossoms and fruit may be picked and destroyed or the entire plant removed and burned. Insecticides most commonly used in control of the pest are malathion (for home garden use), lindane, and carbaryl.

THE MELONWORM (*Diaphania hyalinata*). This insect is similar to the pickleworm in its biology, habits, and hosts. Since the larvae feed on foliage, at least in part, the insect can be controlled by using methoxychlor or lindane should control measures be justified.

Family Sphingidae (Sphinx Moths)
The moths of this family are recognized by the spindle-shaped bodies, narrow wings, and the long sucking tube coiled like a watch spring underneath the head. They usually fly at dusk and are often seen poised in the air over flowers, like hummingbirds, feeding on the nectar. Their feeding habits have suggested the name of hummingbird moths. The caterpillars feed on the foliage of plants. They are large, cylindrical, naked, and usually bear a horn on the eighth abdominal segment. The horn is not provided with a sting and serves no purpose, unless it terrifies enemies. Some of the larger and more conspicuous moths and caterpillars are found in this family.

THE TOBACCO HORNWORM (*Manduca sexta*) and the TOMATO HORN-
WORM (*Manduca quinquemaculata*). These two closely related insects are the most common tomato pests. The caterpillars feed voraciously on the foliage; green tomatoes are also attacked. They are also pests of importance on tobacco, eggplant, potato, and other solanaceous plants. The two species are distributed over most of the United States, and larvae of both may be found feeding on the same plant. However, the tobacco hornworm (Figure 199) is more common in the South, and the tomato hornworm occurs more frequently in the North. The larvae are large, green (some-times brownish black) worms about 3 or 4 inches long with white stripes on the side of the body and a horn on the end of the abdomen. The larger larvae of the two species may be readily

Figure 199. The tobacco horn-worm (*Manduca sexta*). (Pre-pared by the Clemson University Cooperative Extension Service's Entomology-Plant Pathology and Agricultural Communications Sections, Federal Extension Service Cooperating.)

distinguished. The tobacco hornworm is green with 7 white stripes extending obliquely along each side; the horn on the end of the abdomen is red and curved. The tomato hornworm is green or brownish black with 8 white V- or L-shaped markings along each side; the horn on the end of the abdomen is black and usually almost straight.

The pupae, which are about 2 inches long, dark brown, and spindle shaped, diapause in the soil. The case within which the proboscis develops arches from the head and is bent downward like a pitcher handle. The moths emerge in the spring. They are large and gray, with a wing expanse of about 4 inches. Moths of the tobacco hornworm are dark gray, with the front wings marked by a group of white dots at the base, and the hind wings blackish and crossed by more or less broken diagonal white bands. The abdomen is marked with 6 pairs of more or less rounded orange yellow spots. The tomato hornworm adult is light gray; the front wings bear no white dots at the base; and the hind wings are ash gray crossed by black and whitish diagonal bands. The abdomen bears 5 pairs of quadrangular orange yellow spots.

The greenish yellow eggs, which are deposited on the underside of the leaves, hatch in a week. The larvae reach maturity after 5 molts in 3 or 4 weeks. The fully grown larvae enter the soil to a depth of 3 or 4 inches, form cells, and pupate. The number of generations varies from 1 in the North to possibly 3 in the Gulf states.

Small larvae may be readily poisoned with carbaryl, endosulfan, or methoxychlor. The large caterpillars are more difficult to kill. Hand picking is often resorted to as a control measure. The insect has a number of natural enemies such as insect parasites, birds, and diseases.

THE WHITE-LINED SPHINX (*Hyles lineata*). This is one of the most common sphinx moths. The body and front wings are brown with six light lines on the thorax and a yellowish-white stripe extending from the inner margin of the base to the apex of each front wing (Figure 200A). The hind wings are black with a broad rosaceous band across the middle of each. Wing expanse of the moths varies from 2½ to 3 inches. The larvae are nearly 3 inches in length, with the characteristic horn on the end of the abdomen (Figure 200B). Markings and coloration of the larvae are extremely variable, the most common color being greenish yellow with black markings. Some larvae are almost black and marked with yellow lines.

This insect has a biology similar to the tomato and tobacco hornworms. There are two and possibly three generations annually. Larvae feed on the foliage of a wide range of plants such as purslane, chickweed, cotton, vegetable crops, roses, apple trees, watermelons, and buckwheat. On rare occasions the larvae become so abundant that they swarm over the plants like armyworms.

Figure 200. The white-lined sphinx (*Hyles lineata*). A. Adult. B. Caterpillars. (From Department of Entomology, Texas A&M University.)

When control measures are needed, the larvae may be killed by the insecticides recommended for the control of the tomato and tobacco hornworms.

THE PANDORUS SPHINX (*Pholus pandorus*). This is a large and beautiful moth with a wing expanse of about 4 inches. The color of the wings consists of shades of olive and gray with inner margins marked with yellow and rose. The larvae feed on Virginia creeper. *Pholus labruscue* is a related species but more tropical in its habitat.

One group of sphinx moths has the central portion of the wings transparent. The hummingbird clear-wing (*Hemaris thysbe*) and the snowberry clear-wing (*Hemaris diffinis*) are examples of this group. Larvae of the former feed on the virburnums; those of the latter are found on bush honeysuckle and snowberry.

Family Geometridae (Geometrid Moths or Measuring Worms)
Moths of this large family are rather delicate and are usually medium in size. They are weak fliers and are ordinarily found around woods. The larvae are known as measuring worms or loopers because they crawl by means of looping movements. They do not have the full complement of prolegs; the first three pairs are usually absent. The larvae feed primarily on the foliage of trees.

Pupae are found in flimsy cocoons or cells in the ground. More than 1000 species of this family are found in North America.

CANKERWORMS. The spring and the fall cankerworms are the best known of the geometrids. The caterpillars of these two species defoliate many fruit and forest trees such as elm, apple, oak, hickory, and maple. Maximum injury occurs in the spring as the new foliage is completing its growth.

The moths of spring cankerworms (*Paleacrita vernata*) emerge and lay eggs in the spring. The fully grown caterpillars are dark greenish or blackish measuring worms with only two pairs of prolegs and are about 1 inch in length. They feed for 3–5 weeks and then enter the soil where they transform into pupae in earthen cells. Here they remain until the next spring when the adults emerge. The female moths are wingless with a gray, spider-like body. The male moths have functional wings and are gray in color. Only one generation occurs annually.

Infestations may be prevented by banding the trunks of trees with sticky materials, such as tanglefoot, to prevent the wingless females from ascending to lay eggs. This must be done early, for the moths emerge in February or March. The caterpillars are easily killed by applications of lead arsenate or carbaryl.

The fall cankerworm (*Alsophila pometaria*) has a biology similar to the spring cankerworm. It differs from the latter in that the moths emerge and the females lay eggs in the fall instead of the spring. Winter is passed in the egg stage. The larvae are similar in appearance to the spring cankerworm, but they have three pairs of prolegs instead of two pairs (Figure 201). This insect can be controlled by following the recommendations given for the spring cankerworm, except that trees need to be banded in the fall instead of the spring if this control measure is employed.

Family Notodontidae (Notodontid Moths)

Moths of the Notodontidae are of moderate size, with a wing expanse of usually less than 2 inches. They are stout in form, and the body is densely clothed with hairs. Many resemble the owlet moths. Some species have a posteriorly projecting lobe or prominence on the inner margin of the front wings, and this character has suggested the common name "prominents" for the group. Larvae feed on the foliage of trees and shrubs. Pupation is in flimsy cocoons or in the soil.

THE HANDMAID MOTHS (*Datana* spp.). Members of this genus are the most common insects of the family. The moths are brown with the front wings marked by transverse stripes of a different color (Figure 202). Most species have a dot on the discal cell.

The larvae are gregarious in habit and feed on the leaves of a number of forest and fruit trees, such as apple, oak, pecan, and hickory. They are black or reddish with longitudinal stripes of white or yellow. Winter is passed as pupae in the ground.

Figure 201. The fall cankerworm (*Alsophila pometaria*). (From Agricultural Research Service, USDA.)

Figure 202. Datana moths and egg cluster. (From Texas Agricultural Experiment Station.)

The yellow-necked caterpillar (*Datana ministra*) is generally distributed over the United States and Canada. The mature larvae are about 2 inches long with a black head, immediately behind which is a yellow band. The body is black with yellow stripes and is sparsely clothed with hairs. Eggs are laid in clusters on the leaves. Only one generation occurs annually in the cooler climates. A related species (*Datana robusta*) is double-brooded in its southern range. Colonies of the walnut caterpillar (*Datana integerrima*) often defoliate small walnut and pecan trees. The species has two broods in the South. Tachinid parasites are important natural enemies (Figure 203). Datana caterpillars are rather easily controlled by the use of azinphosmethyl and carbaryl.

THE RED-HUMPED CATERPILLAR (*Schizura concinna*). The caterpillars of this widely distributed insect feed on the leaves of elm, apple, cherry, rose, and other plants. When fully grown the larvae are about 1 inch in length. The head is red; the body is marked by black and yellowish lines with a prominent red hump on the dorsal surface of the first abdominal segment (Figure 204); the adults are dark brown. The insect diapauses as larvae in cocoons found in debris or in the topsoil. There are one or two generations annually, depending on the climate. Control measures are the same as for the Datana caterpillars.

THE SADDLED PROMINENT (*Heterocampa guttivitta*). The larvae of this insect feed on the foliage of beech, apple, and sugar maple.

Figure 203. Datana caterpillars showing tachinid parasite eggs deposited on their bodies. (From Texas Agricultural Experiment Station.)

Figure 204. The red-humped caterpillar (*Schizura concinna*). (Prepared by the Clemson University Cooperative Extension Service's Entomology-Plant Pathology and Agricultural Communications Sections, Federal Extension Service Cooperating.)

Mature larvae are about 1½ inches long, and are usually yellowish green or light green (Figure 205). The body is quite devoid of hairs and a brownish or purplish saddle-shaped patch is usually present on the back. The moths are grayish, with a wingspread of 1½–2 inches. Only one generation occurs annually in the northern states. *Heterocampa manteo* and *H. umbrata* are related species.

Family Lymantriidae (Tussock Moths)
The common name of this family refers to the characteristic tufts of brightly colored hairs with which the larvae are clothed. The larvae feed on the foliage of deciduous trees and may do serious damage. The female moths of many species are practically wingless.

THE GYPSY MOTH (*Porthetria dispar*). This is the best known insect in the family. The insect was brought from Europe to Medford, Massachusetts, about 1869 by a naturalist who was investigating the possibility of silk production of this and other caterpillars. Some of the experimental insects escaped and became established in adjacent woodlands. The caterpillars feed on the foliage of both deciduous and evergreen trees (Figure 206). The insect is known to attack more than 500 species of plants. The larvae are hairy, dark colored, and attain a length of 2 or more inches. On the dorsal surface of the body is a double row of 5 pairs of blue spots followed by 6 pairs of red spots. The insect is found in the northeastern part of the United States and Canada. In 1954 an infesta-

Figure 205. *Heterocampa* sp. Larva feeding on oak. (Prepared by the Clemson University Cooperative Extension Service's Entomology-Plant Pathology and Agricultural Communications Sections, Federal Extension Service Cooperating.)

Figure 206. Larvae of the gypsy moth (*Porthetria dispar*). (From Connecticut Agricultural Experiment Station, New Haven.)

tion was discovered in Michigan where eradication measures were undertaken.

Diapause is in the egg stage. Eggs are laid in masses of 400–500 and are covered with hairs from the body of the female moth. The eggs hatch in the spring as the young leaves are expanding. Most of the larvae reach maturity by midsummer and spin flimsy cocoons within which they change to dark brown pupae. Duration of the pupal stage is 10–14 days. The male moths are brownish and have a wing expanse of about 1½ inches. The females are somewhat larger, almost white, and have dark irregular markings across the wings. Fortunately the females are unable to fly. Soon after mating the females lay their clusters of eggs on trunks of trees, stones, buildings, and other objects. Only one generation occurs annually. The insect is spread chiefly in the larval stage. Egg masses may also be transported on lumber, boxes, nursery stock, and other materials.

Several control measures are used against this pest. Its spread has been restricted by strict quarantine measures. Egg masses may be destroyed by brushing them with coal-tar creosote. Spraying with carbaryl is currently recommended.

THE BROWN-TAIL MOTH (*Nygmia phaeorrhoea*). The larvae of the brown-tail moth are important pests of fruit trees, such as apple and pear, and deciduous shade trees; evergreens are not attacked. The insect is found in New England, New Brunswick, and Nova Scotia. The fully grown caterpillars are about 1½ inches in length, dark brown, hairy, and have a row of white tufts along each side of the body (Figure 207A). The body bears barbed nettling hairs which produce a dermatitis on contact with the skin, not unlike that caused by poison ivy. The larvae pupate the latter part of June in flimsy cocoons which are found in sheltered places. Two or 3 weeks following pupation the moths emerge. The moths, which have a wing expanse of slightly more than 1½ inches, are white with a tuft a golden brown bristles on the end of the abdomen, which has suggested the common name (Figure 207B). The females lay 200–400 eggs each on leaves in an elongate mass. The eggs hatch in about 3 weeks, and the young larvae feed gregariously on terminal leaves which they soon web together to form hibernation shelters. Only one generation occurs annually. Destruction of the overwintering webs or tents and spraying with carbaryl is suggested as control measures.

THE WHITE-MARKED TUSSOCK MOTH (*Hemerocampa leucostigma*). The caterpillars of this moth are frequently a pest of deciduous shade and fruit trees, particularly in the eastern United States. The mature larvae are yellowish black, hairy, and about 1¼ inches long (Figure 208). They are recognized by a red head, by tufts of long black hairs on either side of the head with a third tuft on the

Figure 207. The brown-tail moth (*Nygmia phaeorrhoea*). A. Larvae. B. Adults. (From USDA.)

Figure 208. Larva of the white-marked tussock moth (*Hemerocampa leucostigma*). (From Illinois Natural History Survey.)

eighth abdominal segment, and by two reddish spots near the end of the abdomen.

Family Phalaenidae or Noctuidae (Noctuids or Owlet Moths)

The owlet moths form the largest family of the Lepidoptera in North America. More than 2500 species are known in America north of Mexico. From an economic viewpoint this is also the most important family of the order in this country, as many agricultural pests are found here.

A majority of moths seen around lights are members of this family. Most of the adults are inconspicuously colored and of average size. Typically, the body is large in relation to the size of the wings. The front wings are rather narrow and somewhat elongate. A triangular body outline is formed when the wings of the moths are folded upon the abdomen. The caterpillars are ordinarily dull in color, naked, and usually provided with the full complement of prolegs. They generally feed on foliage of plants, but some are borers in stems and fruits. The larvae may be identified by the presence of two setae in the prespiracular group of the prothorax; by the proleg-bearing segments of the abdomen with setae III above, IV behind, and V below the spiracle; and by the arrangement of the crochets of the prolegs in a longitudinal mesoseries.

THE COTTON LEAFWORM (*Alabama argillacea*). The cotton leafworm is one of the oldest and best known of the cotton insects. The caterpillars feed on the leaves of the plant, and vast areas of cotton may be defoliated late in the growing season. The fully grown larvae are about 1½ inches long and rather slender in form (Figure 209A). The anal prolegs stand out quite prominently, and

Figure 209. A. The cotton leafworm and B, moth (*Alabama argillacea*). (From Department of Entomology, Texas A&M University.)

in crawling the larvae move in a semilooping manner. The cater-pillars of the first generations are lighter colored than those found at the end of the season. The lighter forms are yellowish green with three narrow white stripes down the back and a white line along each side. There are four equally spaced black spots on the dorsum of each abdominal segment. Each spot bears a black seta and is surrounded by a light ring. With the exception of the first instar, there are 30 black dots on the head. There is an increase of pigmentation between the white stripes in the dark specimens. In extreme cases the caterpillars are almost black. Length of the larval period varies from 1 to 3 weeks.

The mature larvae pupate in slight cocoons protected by a folded corner of a leaf. Pupae range in color from chestnut brown to almost black. When conditions are favorable the adults may emerge in a week (Figure 209B). They are light brown, tinged with olive green and wine. The wing expanse varies from 1⅛ to 1¼ inches. The adult females deposit singly 400–600 bluish-green eggs on the underside of the leaves during a period of 7–10 days. The eggs hatch in 2 or 3 days in warm weather. A life cycle may be completed in 3 or 4 weeks and there may be 3–7 genera-tions annually. Wet weather favors outbreaks of the insects.

Here is an exceptional case of a moth capable of causing injury. The tip of the proboscis is armed with many sharp, stout spines by means of which skins of fruit may be lacerated. Con-siderable damage may be done to figs and ripening peaches.

The cotton leafworm is a tropical insect; it does not overwinter in the United States. With the advent of cold weather in the fall, all stages of the insect die. In the spring moths drift into the Cotton Belt from the tropics. The first leafworms are generally reported from southwest Texas near the coast. The moths are strong fliers and may be found as far north as Canada by the end of the season.

The production of earlier crops of cotton and the widespread use of insecticides for the control of the boll weevil and other insects have eliminated most of the injury caused by this pest. The caterpillars may be controlled by several poisons, such as carbaryl, methyl parathion, and Guthion.

CORN EARWORM (*Heliothis zea*). This species is widely distributed in both North America and South America, and also occurs in Hawaii where it was probably introduced from this country. The insect is listed as a pest of importance throughout its range of dis-tribution, but it is most destructive in the southern United States. Other common names of the insect are cotton bollworm, tomato fruitworm, vetch worm, and false tobacco budworm. The corn earworm is a general feeder, attacking many plants, particularly corn, cotton, tomato, tobacco, vetch, and cowpea.

The corn earworm is most destructive in feeding in the fruits of plants, such as ears of corn (Figure 210A), flower buds

Figure 210. The bollworm or corn earworm and B, the moth (*Heliothis* zea). (From Department of Entomology, Texas A&M University.)

(squares) and bolls of cotton, and fruit of the tomato. However, foliage and tender stems may be attacked. Early in the season the larvae feed in the whorl of terminal leaves of young corn plants, damaging leaves and developing tassels. When silks develop, numbers of eggs are laid on them. The larvae which hatch from these eggs tunnel into the ears and feed on the kernels. On cotton, newly hatched larvae feed on the squares. Older larvae tunnel out large green bolls. Leaves and succulent stems of the cotton plant are sometimes attacked. On the tomato plant, the larvae feed first on the foliage and later tunnel into the fruit. Both foliage and seed pods of alfalfa and vetch are attacked. Often foliage of the peanut is severely riddled by the feeding of the larvae in the Southwest.

Eggs of the corn earworm are waxy white and about $\frac{1}{50}$ inch in diameter. They have a flat base, are dome shaped and ribbed. The mature larvae are about $1\frac{1}{2}$ inches in length. Their color is quite variable, ranging from very dark to light green or pink. Their bodies are marked by alternating longitudinal dark and light stripes, but these markings are not dependable. The most distinctive characteristics are the presence of short, sharp microspines with which the skin is covered, except on the dorsal abdominal tubercles, and the feeding habits. The brown pupae, which are quite similar to those of cutworms, are found in the soil. Color and markings of the moths are variable (Figure 210B). One of the most common forms is tan or buff. In another form, the front wings are grayish brown marked with dark gray irregular lines and darker spots.

Moths feed on nectar of flowers and other sweet liquids. They are strong fliers and are active at dusk. Eggs are deposited singly on host plants of the larvae. A moth may deposit a maximum of 3000 eggs, with an average number of eggs probably in excess of 1000.

The length of the life cycle depends upon weather conditions. Eggs may hatch in 2 or 3 days during the summer. The length of the egg stage is increased in cooler weather in the spring and fall. The length of the larval stage varies from 2 weeks in the summer to a month or longer during spring and fall. When larval maturity is reached, the insect leaves the plant and enters the ground for pupation. The depth to which the soil is entered varies from 1 to 7 inches, depending upon the type of soil and moisture. The pupal stage ranges in length from less than 2 weeks in warm weather to more than 6 months in the period of diapause. A generation may be completed in 1 month under warm conditions, while in cool weather it may extend over a period of 2 months. There are 4–7 generations annually in the southern states with only 1 or 2 occurring in the insect's northern range.

The corn earworm has many natural enemies. One of the most important natural checks is cannibalism of the larvae. Cannibalism is more marked in corn than in other crops because of the proximity of the larvae in feeding in the ears. Birds, toads, spiders, the insidious flower bug, larvae of lacewing flies, lady beetles, wasps, and other insects prey upon the pest. *Trichogramma evanescens* is an important egg parasite.

Control measures depend upon the crops attacked. Strains of corn are being developed which show a measure of resistance to corn earworm attacks. Carbaryl is recommended for use as a spray on both field and sweet corn. Young plants should have the spray directed into their whorls. When corn is in the silk stage, the silks should be soaked with frequent applications of the spray. Associated with the insect on cotton is a closely related species, the tobacco budworm (*Heliothis virescens*). Both have developed resistance of varying degrees to insecticides. This is true particularly of the tobacco budworm which in some sections is not being controlled with any pesticide or their combinations. Azodrin, carbaryl, methyl parathion, toxaphene or their combinations afford a measure of control if resistance is not too much of a factor. Carbaryl is recommended for use on tomatoes.

THE ARMYWORM (*Pseudaletia unipuncta*). Somewhere in the United States east of the Rocky Mountains outbreaks of this insect occur almost every year. The hordes of the greenish-brown caterpillars feed on leaves and stems of grains and grasses and other plants. The larvae are about 1½ inches long when fully grown. On each side of the body are three stripes of approximately equal width. The upper stripe is pale orange; the middle one, dark brown; and the bottom stripe, pale yellow. The skin is smooth, the spiracles are black, and the mandibles are devoid of denticles.

The larvae feed at night and hide underneath clods of soil or other protection during the day. When the host plants have been destroyed, the caterpillars crawl in great numbers to adjacent fields in search of more food. This habit of travel has suggested the name "armyworm." The length of the larval stage is 3–4 weeks in the northern states. The caterpillars enter the ground to transform into pupae. About 2 weeks later the moths emerge from the pupal cases. The moths, which have a wingspread of about 1½ inches, are brownish gray with a white spot near the middle of each front wing. Each female lays 500 or more eggs in rows of 10–50 on the lower leaves of the host plants. There are usually 2 or 3 generations each year; however, it is possible for more generations to occur in the South. Diapause is chiefly as immature larvae, but indications are that adults or pupae also may survive the winters in southern regions. Applications of toxaphene, carbaryl, or methyl parathion will effectively control the armyworm.

THE FALL ARMYWORM (*Spodoptera frugiperda*). Feeding habits of the fall armyworm are similar to those of the armyworm. Grain and grass crops are most generally attacked, but the range of host plants is greater than for the latter species. Peanuts, alfalfa, potato, tomato, cotton, cowpeas, and a number of other plants may also serve as hosts. The larvae may feed in the buds and ears of corn like the earworm. In parts of the West Indies the insect is commonly known as the corn earworm. The caterpillars are greenish or brownish and are about 1⅓ inches in length when fully grown (Figure 211). They have three yellowish-white, hairlike stripes down the back, a conspicuous inverted Y on the head, and prominent black tubercles on the body from which the body hairs grow.

Figure 211. The fall armyworm (*Spodoptera frugiperda*). (From Department of Entomology, Texas A&M University.)

When serious outbreaks of the insect occur, the larvae exhaust the food supply and begin crawling, literally by the thousands, seeking more plants to devour. The first generations are well defined and do not overlap as the later broods. The larvae mature and suddenly disappear, having gone into the ground for pupation. The length of the larval period is dependent upon climatic conditions and may vary from 12 days to more than a month. In warm weather the pupal stage may not be more than 8–10 days in duration.

The moths resemble the adults of cutworms. The wing expanse is about 1½ inches. The hind wings are grayish with the front pair dark gray, mottled with light and dark areas, and with a light spot near the tips. The life span of the moths is 10–14 days, but in this brief period they may fly hundreds of miles and the females lay an average of 1000 eggs. The eggs are laid in clusters on or near the food plants. In hot weather the egg stage may be as short as 2 days. The length of a generation may vary from less than a month to 2 months, depending upon climatic conditions.

The biology of the insect is similar to that of the cotton leafworm in many respects. The insect is of tropical origin and, through flight of moths, tends to spread over the United States east of the Rocky Mountains each season. But, unlike the cotton leafworm, it is able to overwinter in the United States along the Gulf Coast. All stages may be found there during the winter months. As with the cotton leafworm, wet seasons are favorable for outbreaks of the insect. The number of generations completed annually depends upon the section of the country in which the insect is found. Only one generation may occur in the North; there may be as many as 9–11 completed in the southernmost range of the insect. A small hymenopterous parasite, *Chelonus texanus*, is a common natural enemy of the larvae (Figure 212). Control measures are the same as for the armyworm.

THE YELLOW-STRIPED ARMYWORM (*Spodoptera ornithogalli*). This caterpillar feeds on the leaves of a wide range of plants, such as corn, wheat, cabbage, turnip, potato, tomato, and cotton. Also, it may tunnel into cotton bolls in much the same manner as the bollworm. The mature larvae are 1½ to 1¾ inches in length (Figure 213). The head is quite small in relation to the size of the body, and the color is quite variable, some specimens being much darker than others. Typical specimens are readily recognized by the presence of three light lines down the back with a double row of triangular dark spots lying between the outer lines. The front wings of the moths are dark velvety brown marked with black and light yellow with the hind wings lighter colored. The wingspread is about 1½ inches.

The life history of this insect is not very well known. Diapause is usually in the pupal stage, but some moths may overwinter also. Two generations may be produced annually in the North with the possibility of four completed in the southernmost states. Should infestations become large enough to warrant control measures, applications of carbaryl or related compounds are recommended.

CUTWORMS. Cutworms are inconspicuously marked, dull colored caterpillars. The color and markings of the body harmonize quite well with the soil, with which they are usually associated. They range in length from 1½ to 2 inches when fully grown. This is a rather large group of noctuid larvae with diverse feeding habits. The most commonly observed injury is the severance of the stems of young plants at the ground level. Based on feeding habits, cutworms may be classified into (1) surface feeders, (2) tunnel makers, (3) climbers, and (4) subterranean feeders. Most species of cutworms attack a wide range of plants, including all common farm and garden crops. Feeding usually at night, the larvae hide in the soil, under clods, trash, or in other protected places during the day. Transformation is within pupal cells in the soil. Cutworms have 1–5 generations annually; depending upon the species and climatic conditions. They overwinter as larvae, pupae, and in some cases as adults. The moths are dark, and the front wings are usually rather inconspicuously marked with darker or lighter narrow bands and spots. The hind wings are lighter than

Figure 212. *Chelonus texanus*, a parasite of the fall armyworm (*Spodoptera frugiperda*). (From USDA.)

Figure 213. The yellow-striped armyworm (*Spodoptera ornithogalli*). (From Department of Entomology, Texas A&M University.)

the front wings. The armyworm, fall armyworm, yellow-striped armyworm, cabbage looper, and the corn earworm are cutworms also, but because of their importance they are discussed separately. Only a few of the more common species can be mentioned here.

SURFACE-FEEDING CUTWORMS. The granulate cutworm (*Feltia subterranea*) is a widely distributed form and is an important pest in the South. Three types of feeding by this cutworm have been reported; namely, cutting off small plants near the surface of the soil, feeding on the foliage, and tunneling into the fruits of tomatoes and eggplants. The caterpillars are dark gray with many small dark granules over the surface of the body. This species may produce five complete generations annually in the South. A related species, the dingy cutworm (*Feltia subgothica*), produces only one generation annually. This species has a wide distribution and is a common pest. The larvae are dull brown with a yellowish-gray dorsal stripe.

The army cutworm (*Euxoa auxiliaris*) is found in the Great Plains region. Winter wheat and alfalfa are chiefly attacked. The larvae may assume the habit of armyworms and migrate to adjacent fields when they become extremely abundant and exhaust the food supply.

TUNNEL-MAKING CUTWORMS. The black cutworm (*Agrotis ipsilon*) is a widely distributed and well known species. It is most destructive east of the Mississippi River. The larvae make burrows in the soil into which the food is dragged. They are very destructive as they cut off many more plants than they consume. The caterpillars are greasy gray or brown with indistinct stripes. Four generations of this insect may be completed annually. The pale-sided cutworm (*Agrotis malefida*) also lives in a tunnel into which food is pulled. This is also a multiple-generation species. It is found most generally in the southern United States, Mexico, and Cuba.

CLIMBING CUTWORMS. The variegated cutworm (*Peridroma saucia*) (Figure 214) is probably the most widely distributed and most important cutworm. This species is not only found through North America and South America, but it occurs in Europe and Asia Minor also. The caterpillars are feeders on most kinds of plants, but they show some preference for vegetable and forage crops. Feeding activity is chiefly during the night, but the larvae may be active on cloudy days.

The mature larvae are pale yellow or brown and about 2 inches long. They are differentiated from other noctuid larvae by the presence of a row of dull yellow spots down the middorsal line and a more or less distinct black or brownish W on the eighth abdominal segment. Larvae, pupae, and adults may be found throughout the winter in the South. In the North the insect hibernates in the pupal stage. As many as four generations may be completed annually in southern climates.

The spotted cutworm (*Amathes c-nigrum*) is one of the most important species in the northern United States. The caterpillars are general feeders but prefer garden plants. These insects overwinter as immature larvae and complete two generations a season. The caterpillars are brownish or grayish with a row of triangular spots along each side of the dorsal surface of the body.

SUBTERRANEAN CUTWORMS. The pale western cutworm (*Agrotis orthogonia*) is the most important of the subterranean forms. It

Figure 214. The variegated cutworm (*Peridroma saucia*). (From Department of Entomology, Texas A&M University.)

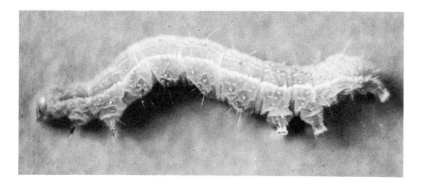

Figure 215. The cabbage looper (*Trichoplusia ni*). (From Department of Entomology, Texas A&M University.)

feeds almost entirely under the surface of the ground and cuts off the plants slightly above the crowns. Wheat and barley are the most important food plants. The caterpillars are grayish without spots or other markings. The insect overwinters as larvae within the eggs. There is only one generation annually. This insect is confined to the arid and semiarid sections of the United States and Canada.

CONTROL OF CUTWORMS. Dusting or spraying plants and the ground around them with trichlorfon, toxaphene, or chlordane will control most species of cutworms. Rotation of crops in such a manner that corn does not follow sod land is advised, unless the land is plowed the previous summer or fall. Cultural control is usually employed in combating the subterranean cutworm, but recent investigations have shown that applications of dieldrin to the soil will control the insect.

THE CABBAGE LOOPER (*Trichoplusia ni*). This caterpillar is the common green looping worm found feeding on the leaves of cabbage, turnip, lettuce, pea, cotton, and a number of other plants. It is frequently mistaken for a measuring worm. In some sections the insect is a more destructive pest of cruciferous plants than the imported cabbageworm. The caterpillar attains a length of more than 1 inch, is naked, and green in color (Figure 215). There is a noticeable narrow white line along each side of the body. Other less distinct lines appear on the back. The larvae have only 3 pairs of prolegs, in contrast with the imported cabbageworm and most other caterpillars which have 5 pairs. The larvae feed for a period of 2–4 weeks and then spin a flimsy cocoon, usually on the underside of the leaf of the host plant, in which transformation to the pupal stage occurs. During the summer months the adults emerge 10–14 days following pupation. The moths have a wingspread of about 1¼ inches, and are grayish brown with the front wings marked near the center by a silvery spot which is shaped somewhat like the figure 8. Eggs are laid singly on the upper surface of the leaves of the host plants. Diapause is in the pupal stage. The number of generations varies from 2 in the northern range of the insect to 4 or more in the South. Quite a few insecticides have been recommended for control of this pest on various crops. Those compounds quite commonly used are toxaphene, Azodrin, malathion, and *Bacillus thurinigensis*. Precautions must be taken to avoid harmful residues on vegetable crops.

THE STALK BORER (*Papaipema nebris*). The common stalk borer is widely distributed east of the Rocky Mountains. The caterpillars bore or tunnel in the stems of giant ragweed, corn, cotton, and numerous other plants. Cultivated plants are usually injured around the weedy margins of fields. The brownish larvae are found within the stalks or stems and reach a length of about 1½ inches when fully grown. There are five white lines on the back and sides. The two lines on either side fade out between the first and fourth abdominal segments and produce an injured appearance. The body lines disappear completely prior to the pupation of the caterpillars. The adults are grayish brown in general color, with considerable variation in markings. The wingspread of the moths is more than 1 inch.

The insect passes the winter as eggs attached to the stems of the wild hosts. Eggs hatch in the spring, and the larvae mature the latter part of the summer. Pupation is within the larval burrows. There is only one generation each year. Cutting and burning of wild host plants, and cleaning up the margins of fields and gardens by early spring are the most effective control measures in combating this insect pest.

THE GREEN CLOVERWORM (*Plathypena scabra*). The green cloverworm frequently infests alfalfa, clover, cowpeas, and the related crops. The caterpillar may be readily differentiated from the alfalfa caterpillar by the presence of four pairs of prolegs, whereas the latter possesses the full complement of five pairs. The larvae are green with two white lines along each side of the body and are about 1¼ inches long (Figure 216). The adults are dark brown, and the front wings have a mottled appearance. The larvae pupate in light cocoons under litter or slightly underneath the surface of the soil. Three or four generations develop annually in southern climates. There are probably two generations in the North. The insect hibernates as pupae or adults. Cutting the alfalfa or clover of infested fields is usually the only control measure needed. This eliminates the food supply and exposes the larvae to bright sun-

Figure 216. The green cloverworm (*Plathypena scabra*). (Prepared by the Clemson University Cooperative Extension Service's Entomology-Plant Pathology and Agricultural Communications Sections, Federal Extension Service Cooperating.)

light and natural enemies. Insecticides suggested for control are carbaryl, methoxychlor, and phosdrin. Phosdrin should be applied only by a trained operator.

THE UNDERWINGS OR CATOCALAS (*Catocala* spp.). The underwings or catocalas are an attractive group of moths, specimens of which are prized by all amateur collectors. Some of the moths are quite large, with a wing expanse of as much as 3 inches. The front wings are generally gray or brown and marked with wavy lines (Figure 217A). The hind wings are often bordered by yellow, red, or white. The conspicuously marked hind wings have suggested the common name of underwings. The larvae feed on the foliage of forest trees such as oak, hickory, and pecan (Figure 217B). They are rarely numerous enough to cause much injury to the foliage.

THE BLACK WITCH (*Erebus odora*). This species is the largest of the noctuids; some specimens have a wingspread of as much as 6 inches. The moths are dark brown. The front wings have an eyespot near the middle and the hind wings are marked by double eyespots near the anal angles. This insect is a native of the West Indies, but there are reports that it may breed in the extreme southernmost part of the United States. Certain leguminous trees serve as hosts of the larvae. These moths are strong fliers and are sometimes found as far north as Canada in the late summer or fall.

Figure 217. An underwing (*Catocala*). A. Larva. (From Florida Agricultural Experiment Station.) B. Adult.

Family Arctiidae (Tiger Moths or Arctiids)

The common name of tiger moths has been suggested by the prominently striped or spotted wings of a majority of the adults of this family. The larvae are generally densely clothed with hairs. Most of the common woolly caterpillars are the larvae of tiger moths.

THE SALTMARSH CATERPILLAR (*Estigmene acrea*). The common name of this insect (Figure 218) is misleading, for it is widely distributed throughout the country and is not confined to coastal regions as the name implies. The larvae feed on the foliage of most garden and field crop plants in addition to numerous weeds, grasses, and other uncultivated hosts. The caterpillars are about 2 inches long when fully grown and are clothed in long black, brownish or yellowish hairs. The moths have a wingspread of about 2 inches. They are predominantly white with a number of black spots on both the upper and lower surfaces of the wings. In the female the wings are white on both surfaces, and the abdomen is brownish yellow with the exception of the first and last segments, which are white. The males are brownish yellow on the underside of the front wings, on both surfaces of the hind wings, and on the abdomen excepting the tip, which is white. The thin brownish cocoons which the larvae spin have incorporated in them many body hairs. These are found under trash and in loose soil. Eggs are laid in clusters, usually on the underside of the leaves of the host plants. Winter is passed either as larvae or pupae. In the insect's northern range there is only one generation annually, while there may be as many as four in the South.

Control should begin with the destruction of weeds and trash where the insect overwinters. This insect is rather difficult to control with insecticides, especially when the caterpillars are almost grown. Applications of toxaphene at the rate of 3 pounds of the technical product per acre, however, have proved to be fairly satisfactory in its control.

THE FALL WEBWORM (*Hyphantria cunea*). The unsightly webs of the fall webworm are most commonly observed in late summer and fall. The webs enclose the leaves of the twigs and smaller branches; occasionally small trees are almost completely enveloped by them. The larvae are gregarious and feed upon the upper and lower surfaces of the leaves within the webs (Figure 219). As the food requirements increase, the webs are enlarged to enclose more foliage. Hickory, persimmon, pecan, elm, and numerous other forest, shade, and fruit trees serve as hosts of the caterpillars. Evergreens are not attacked. Winter is passed as pupae in cocoons secreted underneath scales of bark, debris on the ground, or in loose soil. The moths emerge in the spring. They are pure white,

Figure 218. The salt-marsh caterpillar (*Estigmene acrea*). Larvae, pupa (removed from cocoon), and adult. (From Department of Entomology, Texas A&M University.)

Figure 219. Fall webworm (*Hyphantria cunea*) on tent. (From Agricultural Research Service, USDA.)

except that in some specimens the front wings are marked with black or brown dots. The eggs are greenish white and are laid in clusters on the leaves of the host plants.

The fully grown larvae are slightly more than 1 inch in length and are clothed with long black and white hairs. In its northernmost range of distribution the insect has only one generation annually, while in the South there are two generations. When infestations are light it is practical to remove the webs by pruning and burning them. Sprays of toxaphene, azinphosmethyl, or parathion will control the pest.

THE YELLOW WOOLLYBEAR (*Diacrisia virginica*). These caterpillars are about 2 inches long and are clothed with long yellowish hairs. They are seen most commonly in the fall crawling across highways and pathways in search of suitable hibernation quarters. Hibernation is in the pupal stage enclosed in silken cocoons. The moths are white except for a few small black spots on the wings.

THE BANDED WOOLLYBEAR (*Isia isabella*). These caterpillars are clothed with hairs of even length, which are black on the ends of the body and brown in the middle. The adults are grayish yellow with a few small black spots on the wings. The insects diapause as larvae in protected places.

Family Nolidae
This is a small family of moths which is frequently classified as a subfamily of the Arctiidae. Less than two dozen species are known to occur in the United States.

THE SORGHUM WEBWORM (*Celama sorghiella*). This is the best known and most important insect of the family. It is an important pest of grain sorghums. The larvae feed in the heads on the developing seeds (Figure 220). Late-planted and late-maturing crops tend to suffer the heaviest losses. In the United States the insect occurs in the Gulf and South Atlantic states, and the Great Plains region as far north as Nebraska. The mature larvae are sluggish caterpillars about ½ inch long, clothed with bristly spines of varying lengths. The basic color of the body is green with four red to blackish dorsally located stripes. The adults are whitish and have a wing expanse of about ½ inch. The insect passes the winter as larvae in crop residues. There may be six complete generations annually in its southern range. Control consists chiefly in destruction of crop residues, growing early crops, and the use of carbaryl, parathion, or toxaphene sprays as soon as the infestation is found.

Family Citheroniidae (Royal Moths)

This family contains a limited number of species of medium to large moths. Their bodies are stout and hairy, and they are provided with strong wings. The basal half or two-thirds of the antennae of the males are strongly pectinate, and the head is sunken into the prothorax. The larvae bear long, curved horns or spines on the second thoracic segment and sometimes on the third also. The larvae pupate within earthen cells in the ground.

Figure 220. Sorghum webworm (*Celama sorghiella*) on head of grain sorghum. (From Texas Agricultural Experiment Station.)

THE REGAL MOTH (*Citherona regalis*). This moth has a wing spread of 4½–6 inches. The front wings are olive gray with reddish veins and yellow spots. The hind wings are orange red with yellow markings. The larvae, which are known as hickory horned devils or persimmon-bulls, attain a length of 4–5 inches. Their bodies are greenish, bluish, or reddish brown. They are recognized by the long horns on the body, particularly those on the mesothorax and metathorax which are much longer than the others. Food plants consist of hickory, persimmon, cotton, black walnut, and deciduous plants of other species. Hibernation occurs as pupae in the ground. The moths emerge by early summer. Larvae may be found in the late summer and early fall.

THE IMPERIAL MOTH (*Eacles imperialis*). The wing expanse of this moth is 4–6 inches. It is yellow with markings of purplish yellow (Figure 221). The larvae, which attain a length of 4 inches, are usually green but may have a red or brown cast. The body is lightly covered with long whitish hairs. The second and third thoracic segments bear noticeable spiny horns. The larvae feed on the foliage of a large number of shade and forest trees. The insect overwinters in the pupal stage in the soil. There is only one generation annually.

ANISOTA SPP. There are several species of common moths in this genus. The moths are brownish or dark yellow with the front wings marked by a white discal spot. The larvae are cylindrical in form and bear two conspicuous, slender, recurved horns on the

Figure 221. The imperial moth (*Eacles imperialis*).

mesothorax; the other dorsal and lateral spines are small. Their bodies are conspicuously striped and are 1½–2 inches in length. They feed chiefly on the foliage of various species of oak.

Family Saturniidae (Giant Silkworm Moths)
These large moths and their silken cocoons are known to almost all naturalists. The moths are stout and hairy, with broad wings; the heads are more or less sunken into the prothorax. Members of the family may be distinguished from regal moths by the antennae of the males, which are pectinate to the tips. The caterpillars commonly feed on the foliage of shade and forest trees; however, some species feed on grass. They are large and are more or less armed with tubercles and spines. Most larvae pupate in dense, silken cocoons which are frequently found attached to trees or enveloped within a leaf.

THE POLYPHEMUS MOTH (*Antheraea polyphemus*). This is one of the more common moths of the family. The adults are brownish or yellowish with a transparent windowlike spot on each wing (Figure 222A). A grayish border is present on the costal margin of the front wings, and there is a dark band near the outer margin of both pairs of wings. The wingspread may be between 5 and 6 inches. Larvae are about 3 inches long, light green, and marked by silvery white lines on each side of the abdomen. They feed on the leaves of hickory, oak, maple, birch, and a number of other trees. The cocoons are dense and usually wrapped in a leaf. Diapause is in the pupal stage (Figure 222B). Two generations of the insect develop in the South and one in the North each season.

THE CECROPIA MOTH (*Platysamia cecropia*). The cecropia moth is the largest member of the family; the wingspread of large specimens slightly exceeds 6 inches. The wings are dusky brown, margined with gray, and marked beyond the middle by a white band which is bordered on the outer edge by red (Figure 223). Near the center of each wing is a crescent-shaped light spot. Fully grown larvae are 3–4 inches in length and are bluish green. Their bodies are armed with tubercles. Those located on the dorsal surface of the second and third thoracic segments are larger than the others and are coral red. The remaining dorsal tubercles are yellow except those on the first thoracic segment, the last abdominal segment, and those on the sides of the body, which are blue. The tubercles are armed with black spines. The larvae feed on the leaves of a number of trees and shrubs, among them, members of the *Rosaceae*, willow, and maple. The cocoons are quite large and are fastened lengthwise to branches or other objects. Winter is passed in the pupal stage.

THE LUNA MOTH (*Actias luna*). The wings of the luna moth are light green with the costal margins of the front wings marked by a purplish brown band. Each wing has a transparent spot, and the anal angle of the hind wings is extended into a taillike prolongation. Larvae attain a length of 3 inches. Their color is bluish green with a pale yellowish stripe along each side and yellowish marks between the abdominal segments. The larvae feed on hickory, pecan, sweet gum, and other forest trees. The cocoons are somewhat similar to those of the polyphemus moth, but are considerably thinner in texture. The insect overwinters in the pupal stage.

Figure 222. A. The polyphemus moth (*Antheraea polyphemus*). B. Cocoon.

A

B

Figure 223. The cecropia moth (*Platysamia cecropia*).

A   B

Figure 224. A. The io moth (*Automeris io*). B. The Nevada buck moth (*Hemileuca nevadensis*).

THE IO MOTH (*Automeris io*). Adults of this species have a wing expanse of 3–4 inches. The color of the sexes differs; the color of the male is a deeper yellow, and the front wings of the female are purplish red. Near the center of each hind wing of both sexes is a large, circular, dark spot (Figure 224A). Larvae are about 2 inches in length when fully grown. They are green and have a reddish stripe bordered below with white along each side of the body. The body is clothed with venomous spines which produce nettling of tender skin on contact. The larvae feed on many shade and forest trees and are also known to feed on cotton. Cocoons are found among leaves on the ground during the winter.

THE PROMETHEA MOTH (*Callosamia promethea*). This species is probably the most common of the giant silkworm moths. The moths have a wingspread of about 4 inches. The sexes differ so much in their coloration and markings that the males and females may be mistaken for different species. The male moths are dark brown or black except for the outer margin of the wings, which is grayish. The female moths are brown and each front wing is marked with a white triangular discal spot. The outer margin of the front wings is clay colored. The larvae attain a length of about 2 inches and are bluish green. The body is armed with longitudinal rows of shining tubercles which are black, except the four on the second and third thoracic segments which are larger and coral red, and a yellow one located near the end of the abdomen. The larvae feed on the foliage of many forest and fruit trees but appear to prefer cherry, ash, and sassafras. The elongate cocoons are partially enveloped in a leaf of the host plant. Winter is passed as pupae within the cocoons.

THE RANGE CATERPILLAR (*Hemileuca oliviae*). The range caterpillar is one of a number of species of the genus *Hemileuca* found in the United States. Other common species are the buck moth (*H. maia*) and the Nevada buck moth (*H. nevadensis*) (Figure 224B). The range caterpillar feeds on grasses and is a serious pest of the range in parts of the West. The larvae are black, gray, or yellow and are densely clothed with venomous spines. Hibernation is as minute larvae within the eggs, which are attached in masses to the stems of plants. The adults have a wingspread of 2–2½ inches. The body is black, brown, or reddish, and the wings are buff with the front wings crossed by two lighter colored bands.

Family Bombycidae (Silkworm Moths)

This family is quite small in number of species, and none are native to North America. The silkworm (*Bombyx mori*) is the only member of this group represented in this country. It was introduced many years ago in an attempt to establish a silk culture industry here, which never proved economically feasible. The silk of commerce is obtained from the cocoons of this insect. Although synthetic fibers are replacing the use of silk, and the industry is not so important as it was previously, it still provides an important source of income in Japan, China, and other parts of the world.

Silkworms are carefully raised on mulberry leaves. Three or 4 weeks after hatching, the creamy white larvae are full grown and are about 3 inches in length. Soon after the formation of the cocoons the insects are killed; the cocoons are then soaked in water, and the silk is unwound by skillful operators.

The moths are cream colored with two or three ill-defined brownish lines across the front wings. Several generations are produced each season.

Family Lasiocampidae (Tent Caterpillars)

Adults of this family are stout bodied, hairy, and of average size. The larvae, which are covered with hairs, feed on the foliage of a number of deciduous trees, including fruit trees. Periodical outbreaks of the caterpillars occur, and serious damage may result if these insects are not controlled.

THE EASTERN TENT CATERPILLAR (*Malacosoma americanum*). This insect makes its tents in the crotches of haw, wild cherry, plum, apple, peach, and other trees and shrubs in early spring. Within the tents are found many brown, hairy caterpillars. When fully grown the caterpillars are about 2 inches in length. They are marked by a white stripe down the back, which is bordered by reddish brown (Figure 225A). On either side of the body are blue and white spots.

This insect is found throughout the United States and Canada east of the Rocky Mountains. Closely related species are found on the Pacific Coast. Winter is passed as small larvae within the eggs. Eggs are laid in brown masses which form varnishlike rings around small limbs of the host plants. The larvae emerge from the eggs as the leaves begin to unfold in the spring, and crawl to a convenient crotch where the tent is made. They travel back and forth from the tent to the feeding areas.

Length of the larval stage is 4–6 weeks, at the end of which time the caterpillars disperse and seek protected places to spin cocoons in which they pupate. The cocoons are white and tough, and have a yellowish powder intermingled with the silk. Two or 3 weeks following pupation the moths emerge. They are brown, and each front wing is marked by 2 oblique lines. Shortly after eggs are deposited, the larvae develop but do not emerge from the eggs until the next spring. The life cycle may be completed and eggs deposited by late spring in the South, and during the summer in colder climates. There is only one generation each season. These caterpillars are readily controlled with applications of malathion or methoxychlor sprays.

THE FOREST TENT CATERPILLAR (*Malacosoma disstria*). This species is closely related to the eastern tent caterpillar, has a similar biology, but does not make a tent. The larvae feed on the foliage of oak, maple, gum, ash, birch, and other trees. The larvae are somewhat larger than the eastern tent caterpillars, the body is generally a pale bluish color, and there is a row of diamond or keyhole shaped light spots down the back (Figure 225B). These insects may be controlled by the same measures suggested for the eastern tent caterpillar.

Figure 225. A. The eastern tent caterpillar (*Malacasoma americanum*). (Prepared by the Clemson University Cooperative Extension Service's Entomology-Plant Pathology and Agricultural Communications Sections, Federal Extension Service Cooperating. B. The forest tent caterpillar (*M. disstria*). (From Department of Entomology, Texas A&M University.)

Rhopalocera (Skippers and Butterflies)

Family Hesperiidae (Skippers)

Skippers are stout bodied and moderate in size. The name has been given this group of butterflies because of the erratic and fast mode of flight. They may be separated from other butterflies by the tips of the antennae which in most cases are recurved and form a hook, and by their stout bodies which resemble the moths more than the butterflies. The larvae are characterized by their large heads and strongly constricted necks. They are usually naked and are found concealed by the leaves of the host plants (Figure 226). The pupae are rounded and resemble those of moths more than the chrysalids of butterflies. This stage of development is passed in slight silken cocoons protected by leaves fastened together with silken strands.

THE BEAN LEAF ROLLER (*Urbanus proteus*). The wings of this skipper are chocolate brown with the front pair marked by silvery white spots. The hind wings have taillike prolongations like those of the swallowtail butterflies. The wing expanse is about 1¾ inches. In the southern states the larvae are sometimes pests of beans, turnips, and other plants. They cut and roll the leaves around themselves and feed within the rolls that are formed.

THE LARGER CANNA LEAF ROLLER (*Calpodes ethlius*). This insect is also known as the Brazilian skipper. The larvae live in folds of leaves of the canna. The body is greenish and semitransparent and has a characteristic large head and constricted neck. The fully grown larvae are about 1¾ inches in length. The adults have a wing expanse of more than 1 inch, are dark brown, and both front and hind wings are marked by several small, white spots near the middle. Cannas may be severely injured by the feeding of the larvae if control measures are not taken. Hand picking of the larvae and the application of carbaryl, either in the form of dusts or sprays, are suggested for control.

Family Papilionidae (Swallowtails)
Most members of the Papilionidae are large. They are usually identified by the taillike prolongations of the hind wings. The wings are basically black and are usually marked with yellow, and frequently with green and blue. Species of this group may be found in almost every section of the country, but they are seldom of any economic importance, as the larvae do not feed on a wide range of economic plants and are rarely abundant. The larvae are naked or very sparsely clothed with fine hairs. All of the caterpillars of this unusual family are provided with an organ known as an osmeterium. This is an orange-colored, forked, and eversible tubular process which is projected through a slit on the dorsal surface of the prothorax when the caterpillar is disturbed. An unpleasant odor is diffused which is thought to be repellent to its enemies. The chrysalids are suspended on convenient objects by an

Figure 226. Larva of the silver-spotted skipper (*Epargyreus clarus*). (Prepared by the Clemson University Cooperative Extension Service's Entomology-Plant Pathology and Agricultural Communications Sections, Federal Extension Service Cooperating.)

attachment of silk on the end of the abdomen and a silken belt around the middle of the body. They are angular in outline and bear two conspicuous projections on the sides.

The giant swallowtail butterfly or orange dog (*Papilio cresphontes*) (Figure 227A) is the largest of this group of butterflies, with a wingspread of 4–5½ inches. The wings are mostly yellow underneath and black above. The dorsal surface of the front wings is crossed by a broken band composed of yellow spots. The costal area of the hind wings is yellow and there is a broken yellow band near the outer margins. The larvae attain a length of 2½ inches and are grayish brown with lighter colored patches (Figure 227B). Larvae feed on the leaves of prickly ash, citrus, poplar, and other plants. They are a minor pest of citrus trees in the Gulf coastal regions where they are known as orange dogs.

The black swallowtail butterfly (*Papilio polyxenes asterius*) (Figure 230A) has two rows of yellow spots crossing its black wings. The larvae of this species feed on celery, dill, parsnip, caraway, and other umbelliferous plants. They are green, ringed with black, and marked with yellow. There are two or three generations each season. If control measures become necessary, the use of rotenone is suggested.

The tiger swallowtail butterfly (*Papilio glaucus*), appears in two color phases. The *turnus* phase has yellow wings with a broad black margin in which a row of yellow spots (Figure 228A).

Figure 227. A. The giant swallowtail butterfly (*Papilio cresphontes*). B. Larva.

Figure 228. A. The tiger swallowtail butterfly (*Papilio glaucus*). B. Larva.

The front wings are marked with four black bars. Both sexes are represented in this form. In the *glaucus* phase the wings are entirely black with a marginal row of yellow spots. Only the female is found in this phase. The larvae of the tiger swallowtail are quite striking. They are dark green and bear on either side of the thorax an eyespot which is greenish yellow margined with black (Figure 228B). Larvae feed on the leaves of birch, poplar, ash, wild cherry, and other trees.

The bodies of the larvae of the pipevine swallowtail (*Battus philenor*) are dark brown with coral red dots and bear fleshy filaments. The larvae feed on Dutchman's pipe, Virginia snakeroot, and related plants. The wings of the adults are black with a greenish cast. The hind wings are somewhat lighter than the front wings and bear a row of whitish spots along the outer margins.

Family Pieridae (Whites and Sulphur Butterflies)
These are our most abundant butterflies, and are seen commonly in fields and along roadsides. They are ordinarily medium in size; however, some are quite small. Their wing colors are almost always yellow, orange, or white, usually marked with black. The larvae are green and clothed with fine, short hairs. Some species are pests of cultivated plants.

THE IMPORTED CABBAGEWORM (*Pieris rapae*). This is the best known member of the family. The larvae are the velvety green caterpillars that feed on the leaves of cabbage, mustard, turnips, and related plants (Figure 229). The adults are the common white but-

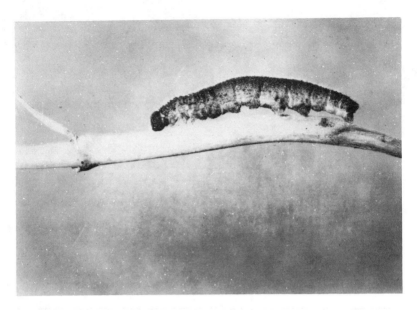

Figure 229. The imported cabbageworm (*Pieris rapae*) on stem of a plant. (From USDA.)

terflies with the black tipped front wings seen flying around gardens and truck farms. The female butterfly has two black spots on the front wings and one on the hind wings, while the male has one spot on both the front and hind wings. The yellowish, ribbed, and bullet shaped eggs, which are laid on the underside of leaves, hatch into small green caterpillars which are voracious feeders. They attain a length of about 1¼ inches in about 2 weeks and pupate.

Three to six generations may be completed in one season. Diapause is as a pupa. Malathion, parathion, rotenone, and other toxicants are used in control.

THE ALFALFA CATERPILLAR (*Colias eurytheme*). This is another common insect. It is a pest of alfalfa, particularly in the Southwest. In addition to alfalfa, the caterpillars feed on the foliage of other legumes. They attain a length of about 1½ inches when fully grown and are green with a white stripe along the side of the body through which passes a fine red line. The butterflies are yellow with a wingspread of about 2 inches. The wings are solid yellow on the underside; the dorsal surface is trimmed in black. This insect may complete 2–7 generations annually. Winter is passed in the pupal stage throughout most of its range of distribution. Cutting alfalfa closely and removing the hay is an effective control measure as this eliminates the food supply of the caterpillars and exposes them to natural enemies and the effects of the sun. Sprays of methoxychlor, carbaryl, and trichlorfon are recommended in control of the larvae.

The roadside butterfly (*Eurymus philodice*) is quite common. This yellow butterfly is often seen around damp places. The larvae feed on clover and related plants. The orange sulphur (*Eurymus eurytheme*) and the dog's head (*Zerene caesonia*) are other common yellow butterflies.

Family Nymphalidae (Brush-Footed Butterflies)

A majority of the species of butterflies are found in the Nymphalidae. The members of the family are differentiated from all others in that the first pair of legs is greatly reduced in size. The most commonly known groups are the fritillaries, the angle wings, the emperors, and milkweed butterflies.

The fritillaries are butterflies of medium size. The wings are tawny or dull yellow, checkered and bordered with black. Their underside is often marked with rows of silvery spots. The larvae are cylindrical, their bodies are more or less clothed with hairs, and they are sometimes armed with branching spines.

In the angle wing butterflies the outer margins of the front wings are ragged in appearance as if parts were missing. The red admiral (*Vanessa atalanta*) is a common representative of this group. The wings are dark with a bright orange band crossing the front pair from the middle of the costa to near the inner angle. Lying between this band and the apex are several white spots. The larvae feed on elm, nettle, and other plants.

The painted beauty (*Vanessa virginiensis*) is widely distributed, occurring throughout the United States, and in Canada and South America. The wings are marked with brownish black and golden orange. The apical portions of the front wings are marked with several white spots. The painted lady (*Vanessa cardui*), (Figure 230B) is related to the painted beauty in appearance; however, it is not so brightly colored.

The mourning cloak (*Nymphalis antiopa*) (Figure 230C) is one of the better known butterflies. The purplish-brown wings are bordered by a yellow band on the outer margins. The larvae, which are gregarious in habit, feed on the foliage of willow, hackberry, elm, and poplar.

Butterflies of the genus *Polygonia* are marked by a metallic spot on the underside of each hind wing. Some of the more common species are the hop merchant (*Polygonia comma*) and the questionsign (*Polygonia interrogationis*).

The viceroy (*Limenitis archippus*) is of much interest because of its close resemblance to the monarch butterfly (Figure 231). The mimicry is thought to be for protection, as the bodies of milkweed butterflies contain acrid substances which are distasteful to insectivorous animals. This is a brownish butterfly and may be readily differentiated from the monarch by its smaller size and by the presence of a black transverse band on the hind wings. The larvae feed on the foliage of willow, cottonwood, aspen, and other trees.

The best known representatives of the hackberry butterflies are the gray emperor (*Asterocampa celtis*) and the tawny emperor (*Asterocampa clyton*). These are brown butterflies marked with both darker and lighter spots. The larvae feed on the leaves of hackberry.

The monarch (*Danaus plexippus*) and the queen (*Danaus berenice*) (Figure 230D) are interesting representatives of the milkweed butterflies. The wings of the monarch are light brown with black veins and borders, and with white spots on the costal and outer borders. The wings of the queen are light chocolate brown with the front wings spotted white, and the costal and outer margins bordered with black. The outer margins of the hind wings are also black bordered. Milkweed butterflies are provided with acrid secretions which are distasteful to birds and other insectivorous animals. Larvae of both species feed only on milkweeds (*Asclepias*).

The monarch butterfly has migratory habits. There is a migration of the adults southward in the fall and again northward in

Figure 230. Some common butterflies. A. The black swallowtail (*Papilio polyxenes*). B. The painted lady (*Vanessa cardui*). C. The mourning cloak butterfly (*Nymphalis antiopa*). D. The queen (*Danaus berenice*).

A   **B**

Figure 231. Protective mimicry. A. The monarch butterfly (*Danaus plexippus*) which is distasteful to insectivorous animals. B. The viceroy (*Limenitis archippus*), an edible butterfly which mimics the monarch so closely that animals are thought to avoid it.

the spring. It is thought all stages of the insect die in the northern part of the United States each winter. There are several life cycles each season.

Family Lycaenidae (Blues, Coppers, and Hairstreaks)
The butterflies of the Lycaenidae are small and quite delicate. Their larvae are rather sluglike in form with short broad bodies. Some species have osmeteria which are protruded between the seventh and eighth abdominal segments. These osmeteria excrete honeydew, which is fed upon by ants.

Probably the best known group of this family is the hairstreaks. They are so named because of their delicate striped markings. The cotton square borer (*Strymon melinus*) is the only member of the family that is economically injurious. The velvety, green, sluglike caterpillars eat holes in pods of lima beans and cowpeas, and in cotton squares. The fully grown larvae attain a length of slightly more than ½ inch. The posterior margin of each hind wing of the adults bears a taillike prolongation which is marked with an orange-red spot near the base. There are three generations of this insect annually in the South, and two are produced in the North. Winter is normally passed in the pupal stage.

CHAPTER 15
ORDER DIPTERA[1]

FLIES

All types of small insects with membranous wings are called flies, and the term fly has been used to form compound names for insects of other orders, such as butterfly, dragonfly, and mayfly. However, from an entomological viewpoint, a fly is a two-winged insect belonging to the order Diptera.

The general characteristics of the order are:

1. Winged members with only 1 pair of wings borne on the meso-thorax; the second pair of wings represented by a pair of threadlike, knobbed structures, known as halteres.
2. Mouthparts adapted for piercing and sucking, or for lapping or sponging.
3. Complete metamorphosis.
4. Larvae of the more common forms known as maggots.

The Diptera (Figure 232) are one of the largest orders of insects, consisting of more than 80,000 species of worldwide distribution. In many respects, this is the most important group of insects with which man has to contend. Many species, such as mosquitoes, gnats, and flies, suck the blood of man and other animals. These insects are also vectors of a number of important diseases such as malaria, yellow fever, filariasis, and encephalitis. Houseflies and other flies associated with filth are distributors of such diseases as typhoid fever and dysentery. Larvae of screw-worm flies, botflies, and other forms attack animals. Some, e.g., the hessian fly, fruit flies, and cabbage maggot, are crop pests.

However, all flies are not harmful. Larvae of some species aid in the decomposition of organic matter. Many are parasitic on other insects, e.g., the *Tachinidae* and a number of the *Sarcophagidae*. Some are predators on insects, such as the robber flies (*Asilidae*) and the larvae of a number of *Syrphidae*. Also, other dipterous insects are beneficial as pollinators of useful plants.

[1] *Dis*, two; *pteron*, wing.

Figure 232. A crane fly (*Pedicia albidivittata*). (Courtesy of C. O. Mohr.)

A majority of the members of the order are rather small, soft bodied insects. Most of them are readily distinguished from other insects by the possession of only one pair of wings, the front pair, and a pair of small, knobbed structures, the halteres, which function as balancing organs and represent the reduced hind wings. The wings of flies are relatively small, transparent, and have rather simple venation (Figure 233). Some Diptera are wingless but the halteres are usually present.

The head is large, attached to the thorax by a slender neck, and is quite mobile. The compound eyes are usually large and often occupy much of the surface of the head. Usually, three ocelli are present. Antennae of the more generalized families consist of many segments, but in the specialized groups there is a reduction in number of segments. Mouthparts of the adults are formed for piercing and sucking, sponging or lapping. There are several subtypes of the former. They are usually quite complicated. Most adult Diptera feed upon nectar, sap, honeydew, and liquid materials from decaying organic matter. However, a number feed on the blood of man and other animals. Some Diptera partake of no food in the adult stage and their mouthparts are nonfunctional.

Metamorphosis of Diptera is complete. The larvae are more highly specialized than this stage of other orders. They are distinctly separated from the adults in both habit and morphology.

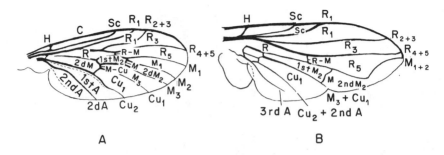

Figure 233. Wings of Diptera. A. Wing of *Anisopus*. (Based on J. H. Comstock, *An Introduction to Entomology*. Copyright 1940. Redrawn with permission of Comstock Publishing Associates.) B. Wing of housefly (*Musca domestica*).

Seldom are larvae and adults found in the same environment partaking of the same food, as so often is the case in the Coleoptera (beetles). All larvae are legless, and most of them have no distinct head. In those generalized families with a distinct head, the mouthparts are of the chewing type. In the other forms, the bodies taper from the rear forward and terminate in a small conical segment which can be retracted. This segment bears no true mouthparts but is provided with a pair of mouth hooks which move vertically, tearing the food or tunneling into tissues. These larvae are known as maggots.

Pupae of Diptera are usually either naked or encompassed by the last larval skin; only rarely are cocoons spun. When the larval skin serves as a covering for the pupa it is called a *puparium*. It often has the appearance of a large seed and is a watertight case.

The order is divided into two suborders, the *Orthorrhapha* and the *Cyclorrhapha*. Adults of the *Orthorrhapha* have antennae which are usually longer than the head and consist of six or more segments. If the antennae are not distinctly six-segmented, the last segment is annulate. Larvae often have a distinct head. When the head is not well developed, it is retractile. The pupae are not enclosed in a puparium. Pupae escape from the larval skin through a T-shaped or straight slit down the dorsal surface, or a transverse slit between the seventh and eighth segments of the abdomen. The adult *Cyclorrhapha* have three or fewer segments in the antennae. The third segment bears a dorsal or terminal arista. The larvae have no distinct head. Pupation is within a puparium from which the adults emerge by pushing off the anterior end.

Suborder Orthorrhapha (Straight-Seamed Flies)

More than 30 of the families of Diptera are included in the *Orthorrhapha*. Only the more common families can be mentioned here.

Family Tipulidae (Crane Flies)

Most of the common species of crane flies resemble overgrown mosquitoes with slender bodies and long legs (Figure 232). They are sometimes referred to as the daddy-longlegs of the air. Some species attain a length of more than an inch while others are quite small in size. The most distinctive characteristic of these insects is the V-shaped transverse suture on the dorsal surface of the thorax (Figure 234).

Crane flies are found chiefly in damp environments, especially where a heavy growth of vegetation occurs. However, they are sometimes seen in numbers in pastures and fields. Most species are sluggish in flight, although the power of flight seems to be quite well developed in certain of the smaller species. These often collect in swarms and dance up and down in the air as do some of the midges.

Habits of the larvae of crane flies vary, both as to food and the environment in which they are found. Some are aquatic, a number of species are found in the moist soil of marshes, along margins of bodies of water, or in woods; while others live in the soil of grasslands. Most larvae feed on decaying vegetable matter, but some attack tissues of living plants, and others are carnivorous in habit. A few species occasionally are destructive to grain, grasses, and alfalfa in the West. The best known of these species is the range crane fly (*Tipula simplex*). These larvae and related forms are frequently called "leatherjackets." Some crane flies complete one generation annually while others have two life cycles.

Family Culicidae (Mosquitoes)

Mosquitoes are familiar to everyone. They are small insects and are readily identified by the presence of scales on the body, and along the fringes and veins of the wings. They possess long antennae, most joints of which bear whorls of hairs. In the males the whorls of hairs are so dense that they produce a bushy appearance. Females of most species feed upon blood. Mouthparts of the males are not developed for piercing and they do not suck blood. Their food consists of plant juices, nectar, and other liquids. The larvae and pupae of all species are found in water. More than 100 species are native to North America.

The biology of mosquitoes varies considerably. Many species overwinter in the egg stage, some as adults, and others as larvae in the water. Eggs are laid in water, or in those places where water will collect later. The larvae are commonly known as "wrigglers." They have large heads and chewing mouthparts and feed on microscopic plant and animal material in the water. The thorax is large but does not bear legs. The abdomen is slender, and on the eighth, or next-to-the-last abdominal segment, is located a respiratory tube which is known as a siphon. The larvae thrust this tube above the water at intervals to breathe. Oxygen is also supplied in part by four tracheal gills located on the last segment of the abdomen.

LATERAL VIEW

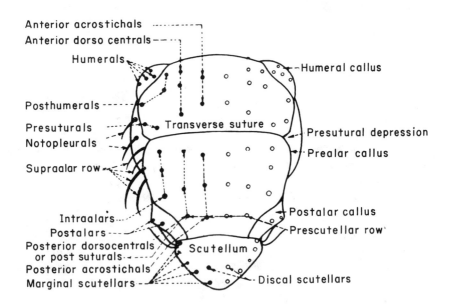

DORSAL VIEW

Figure 234. Bristles and regions of the thorax of a blowfly (*Calliphora viridescens*). (After W. R. Walton, from *Entomological News*, 1909, Vol. 20, p. 314, xiv, 1909.)

The larvae pass through four instars or growing stages. Then, they change into pupae which are commonly known as "tumblers," and unlike most insect pupae, are quite active. Respiration in the pupal stage is through two trumpetlike tubes located on the thorax. Following a pupal period of short duration, usually 2 or 3 days, the insect's skin splits down the back, the adult emerges and after a few moments flies away. The length of the life cycle of mosquitoes from egg to adult varies from 10 days to several weeks. Most mosquitoes have a number of generations each year. The females live from one to several months, but the length of life of male mosquitoes is usually much shorter.

ANOPHELES. Members of this genus are known as malaria mosquitoes. *Anopheles* mosquitoes are recognized by their spotted wings, maxillary palpi as long as the proboscis, cresent-shaped scutellum, and characteristic resting position (Figure 235). They rest with the proboscis, head, and abdomen in nearly a straight line, with the body lifted at an angle from the surface. Other species rest with the body almost parallel to the surface.

Eggs of anophelines are laid singly upon the surface of the water. The *Anopheles* larvae are readily recognized by their resting position, which is parallel to the surface. Larvae of other species rest with the head downward and the body at an angle of 45° with the surface. The adults of the most common species are weak fliers. The length of a life cycle is dependent on temperature, and may vary from 18 days to several weeks. Usually only adult females overwinter. Several generations are produced during the year.

Anopheles quadrimaculatus (Figure 236A) is the most common vector of malaria in the United States, but *Anopheles freeborni* is more important in the western part of the country.

CULEX. *Culex* mosquitoes develop in standing water, such as polluted ponds, marshes, tanks, street gutters, and water barrels. Eggs are laid in rafts; these masses may contain 100 or more eggs each. Breeding may continue through the winter months in the warmer parts of the Gulf Coast region. In colder climates, the adult females hibernate in hollow trees, buildings, or other protected places. The males die with the arrival of cold weather.

The southern house mosquito, *Culex pipiens quinquefasciatus* (*fatigans*) (Figure 236B), is probably the most abundant house mosquito in towns and cities of the South. *Culex pipiens pipiens*, a closely related species, is the common house mosquito in the North. The life cycles of the two species are similar. In warm weather, the life cycle from egg to adult may be completed in 10–14 days, but it is prolonged by cool weather. There are several generations each year. *Culex tarsalis*, a common species west of the Mississippi River, breeds in a variety of places and large populations often build up.

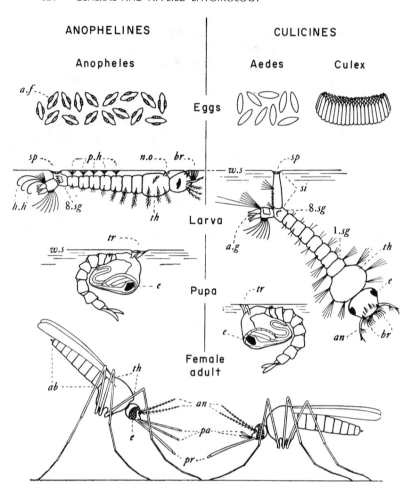

Figure 235. Distinguishing characteristics of anopheline and culicine mosquitoes. *a.f,* air floats; *a.g,* anal gills; *ab,* abdomen; *an,* antenna; *br,* mouth brush; *e,* eye; *h.h,* hooked hairs; *n.o,* notched organ; *pa,* maxillary palpus; *p.h,* palmate (or float hairs); *pr,* proboscis; *1 sg,* first abdominal segment; *8 sg,* eighth abdominal segment; *si,* siphon; *sp,* spiracle; *th,* thorax; *tr,* respiratory trumpets; *w.s,* water surface. (From J. Smart, *Insects of Medical Importance,* after J. F. Marshall. Copyright 1943. Used by permission of British Museum of Natural History, London.)

Culiseta inornata is related to the *Culex* mosquitoes and is found throughout the United States and southern Canada. It breeds throughout the winter where weather permits, and is usually present only during the winter months in southern climates.

AEDES. With the exception of the yellow fever mosquito (*Aedes aegypti*) and a few other species, *Aedes* mosquitoes usually breed in flood waters, rain pools, and salt marshes. Eggs are deposited singly, usually in depressions and on edges of pools, where they may survive long periods of desiccation. When these places are filled with water and the weather is favorable, some of the eggs hatch, while others do not hatch until subsequent flooding. Although some species may lay eggs on the surface of the water, most of them will not hatch until the water is evaporated and the pool refilled. Some species are single brooded; others produce a generation following each wet season.

The yellow fever mosquito (*Aedes aegypti*) is the most important transmitter of this dreaded disease. Adults are characterized by the presence of white rings on the tarsi and white spots on the abdomen and thorax. There is also a lyre-shaped figure on the mesonotum. This mosquito is domestic in its habits and is found breeding almost entirely in the vicinity of dwellings, sometimes even breeding within homes. Eggs are deposited on the surface of the water or slightly above the water line on the sides of various receptacles where it is possible for them to survive desiccation for several months. Clean water is preferred for egg deposition to water polluted with sewage. Breeding may occur in vases, tin cans, old automobile tires, flower pots, and almost any other type of container. The females bite chiefly during the day and are trouble-

Figure 236. Two common mosquitoes. A. *Anopheles quadrimaculatus.* B. *Culex pipiens quinquefasciatus.* (From S. J. Carpenter and W. J. La Casse, *Mosquitoes of North America.* Copyright 1955 by University of California Press. Used by permission of the publisher.)

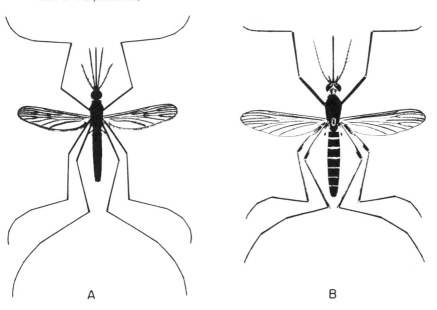

A   B

some during the summer months throughout the South. Although adults may live for several months, they are quite susceptible to cold and succumb to temperatures below 40° F. The species probably does not survive the winter in the United States except in the extreme southern portion of the country. The length of a life cycle may be as short as 10 days under optimum conditions. If the temperature and food supply are not favorable, a much longer period of time is required for its completion.

Aedes sollicitans, Aedes taeniorhynchus, and Aedes dorsalis are the most important salt-marsh mosquitoes. Aedes sollicitans is commonly known as the salt-marsh mosquito or the New Jersey mosquito. It is found breeding along the Atlantic and Gulf coasts. Aedes taeniorhynchus may be found breeding along the Atlantic, Gulf, and Pacific coasts. Aedes dorsalis is a common salt-marsh mosquito on the Pacific Coast. All are strong fliers and may migrate many miles from their breeding places. They are prolific and may increase to huge numbers, at which times they make life miserable for both man and beast (Figure 237).

Figure 237. Aedes mosquitoes. A. The yellow fever mosquito (Aedes aegypti). B. The salt-marsh mosquito (Aedes sollicitans). (From S. J. Carpenter and W. J. La Casse, Mosquitoes of North America. Copyright 1955 by University of California Press. Used by permission of the publisher.)

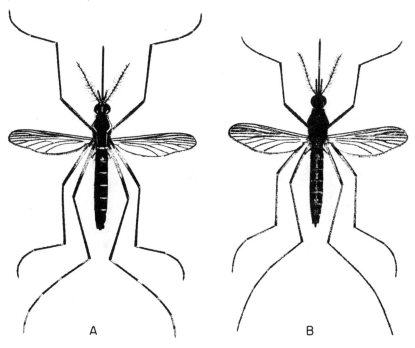

A   B

Mosquito control generally should be conducted on a large area basis. As larvae must develop in water, elimination of breeding places by drainage, filling, and other means is of primary importance. Domestic species, such as the yellow fever mosquito, may be largely controlled by eliminating receptacles that hold water such as tin cans, buckets, barrels, cisterns, and old automobile tires. Water should also be prevented from standing in gutters, drains, and depressions. Keeping the surface of water in lakes, reservoirs, and streams free of vegetation and floating materials aids materially in preventing larval development. This practice eliminates part of the source of food and places of protection, and provides the top-feeding minnows better opportunities to search out and feed upon the larvae and pupae. Adjusting the water level of lakes and reservoirs to prevent water from standing in marginal vegetation serves the same purpose. Fish, such as the top-feeding minnow (*Gambusia affinis*), are frequently used to prevent mosquitoes from breeding in small ponds and pools. However, they usually cannot be relied upon for complete control.

Elimination of breeding places, the proper care of lakes and other bodies of water, and the use of natural agencies, although important, usually are not sufficient for satisfactory mosquito control. Other measures such as insecticides, screens, and repellents must be employed. Oil (usually No. 2 fuel oil) applied to the surfaces of pools, ponds, streams, and other breeding places is most frequently used. Emulsifiable concentrates properly diluted or oil solutions of those insecticides which are approved for this purpose are quite effective.

Adult mosquitoes are most effectively combated in dwellings. Sixteen-mesh screen will prevent the entrance of all but possibly a few of the smallest individuals. The use of sprays that are recommended for household purposes are quite satisfactory. When persons are exposed to mosquito bites, protection from their attacks may be obtained for a few hours by the use of repellents such as dimethylphthalate and diethyltoluamide.

Family Chironomidae (Midges)

Members of this large family of insects are small, delicate, and mosquitolike in appearance. They may be distinguished from mosquitoes by the absence of scales on the body and wings. Antennae of the males are very plumose. The adults frequently collect in huge swarms in the late afternoon or evening near streams, ponds, and lakes. They produce a weak, rather high-pitched humming sound entirely unlike that of mosquitoes.

Midges breed chiefly in water, but some develop in decaying vegetable matter, manure, or under bark of trees (Figure 238). Because the larvae occur in huge numbers in water, they are an important source of food for many species of fish. Many of the larvae are known as bloodworms because of their red color. Com-

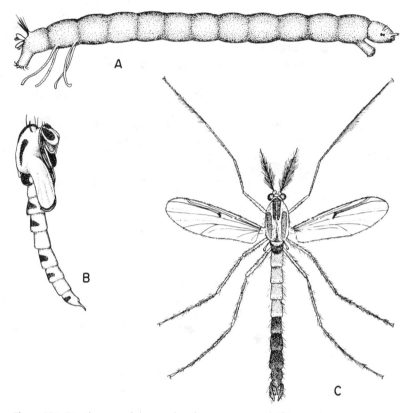

Figure 238. Developmental stages of midges. A. Larvae of *Chironomus tetans*. B. Pupa of *Cricotopus trifasciatus*. C. Adult of *Chironomus ferrugineovittatus*. (From Illinois Natural History Survey.)

mon species of midges have a rather short life cycle, producing a number of generations annually.

Most midges do not bite; however there are some, chiefly in the genus *Culicoides*, that are blood suckers. They are commonly known as "punkies," or "no-see-ums," because they are very small and are somewhat difficult to see. Because of their blood-sucking habits, they may become serious pests along seashores, and near rivers and lakes. The larvae are aquatic or semiaquatic and are probably scavengers. Satisfactory control has been obtained by treating breeding places with oil-emulsifiable concentrates as recommended for mosquitoes. An application of chlordane in kerosene to doors and window screens usually prevents adults from entering dwellings for several weeks. When persons are exposed to attacks of these insects, applications of approved repellents afford fair protection against their bites.

Family Cecidomyiidae (Gall Midges or Gall Gnats)
This is a family of very small midgelike flies. The insects are delicate, with long legs and antennae, and reduced wing venation.
The larvae are small maggots that feed only on liquid foods;
many of them are brightly colored. The mode of pupation differs;
some species form a puparium while others spin cocoons or provide no protection at all for the naked pupae.

Food habits of the larvae are quite varied. Most species feed
on plants where galls, which are typical of the species of midge,
are frequently formed. Some forms feed on fungi or excrement,
and others are parasitic or predaceous on such insects as aphids.
Winter is usually passed in the larval stage. The number of
generations produced annually varies from one to several.

An unusual type of reproduction has been observed in *Miastor
americana*, the larval stage of which is found in decaying bark.
Paedogenesis, that is, reproduction in the larval stage, occurs in
this species. The daughter larvae feed within the mother larva,
which is eventually consumed, after which they escape and may
reproduce likewise for several generations before pupation occurs.

THE HESSIAN FLY (*Mayetiola destructor*). The hessian fly is an
important pest of wheat; barley and rye are also common hosts.
A few specimens have been taken on wild grasses. The insect was
probably brought to this country during the Revolutionary War
in the straw bedding of Hessian soldiers. It has spread to all of the
wheat growing areas of the country with the exception of some
of the arid and semiarid sections of the West and Southwest
where climatic conditions are unfavorable for its development.

The small sooty black flies (Figure 239A) normally emerge
from their puparia in late summer or early fall and lay their
minute reddish eggs on the upper surface of the leaves of volunteer or early-sown wheat. In a few days they hatch into small
reddish maggots that soon turn white. The young larvae work
their way behind the leaf sheaths where they rasp the stems and
suck the sap. Infested wheat in the fall is stunted, and the leaves
are dark bluish green. The central shoot is frequently absent.
Severely injured plants usually die during the winter. When the
heads fill the next June, the infested straws often break over.
Heavily infested wheat may have a large percentage of fallen
straws, which considerably reduces yields.

The hessian fly usually overwinters as a mature larva within a
brown puparium called the "flaxseed." Partly grown larvae occasionally are able to survive the winter. The overwintering forms
are found between the leaf sheaths and the stems above the surface of the ground. In the spring the larvae pupate, and the adults
appear a week or two later. They are not strong fliers and are
never found far from their food plants. The adults are not known
to feed, and they usually die in 3 days or less after emergence.
During this time each female lays 250–300 eggs.

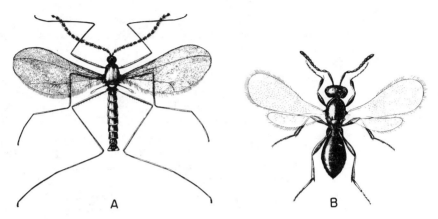

Figure 239. A. The hessian fly (*Mayetiola destructor*). B. A parasite (*Platygaster hiemalis*). (From USDA.)

Usually there is only one spring generation. The flaxseed stage is reached before the heads of grain are formed. This stage remains in the stubble during the summer. Pupation occurs and adults emerge in late summer or fall following rains and after the appearance of volunteer wheat. Generally, there are two complete generations each year, but when weather conditions are exceptionally favorable there may be a maximum of five.

No insecticidal control has been developed; only cultural practices are employed in combating this pest. The most valuable preventive measure is planting the wheat sufficiently late in the fall so that the plants will not be up and growing until after the emergence, egg deposition, and death of the adults. Satisfactory planting dates have been determined by research workers in the principal wheat production areas where the hessian fly is found. Naturally the time of emergence of the adults varies from year to year. However, the planting dates are sufficiently reliable to usually prevent all but light infestations, and still provide time for the plants to grow large enough to withstand winter weather. The destruction of volunteer wheat which may become infested in the fall helps prevent heavy infestations in the spring. Wheat stubble should be plowed under soon after harvest when practicable, since the adult flies are not able to emerge through the soil. However, the practice of planting grasses and clovers in the wheat fields prior to harvest frequently prevents the use of this effective control measure. Crop rotation and the maintenance of high soil fertility are of considerable value, inasmuch as lightly infested plants in fertile soil will overcome the injury and still produce fair yields. Varieties of wheat have been developed which are resistant to the hessian fly, and are in commercial use.

THE SORGHUM MIDGE (*Contarinia sorghicola*). This is an important pest of sorghums in the South. Most injury is produced in the more humid areas of the Gulf states, where almost entire crops of grain may be lost when conditions are most favorable for the insect. Losses of 20 percent of the crop occur frequently.

Injury is produced by the small larvae or maggots rasping the developing seed and feeding on the exuding sap. The seed fail to develop and the heads of grain appear blasted or blighted and produce practically no grain. It is said that one larva may destroy all the grain in a spikelet. The insect attacks all varieties of sorghums, Sudan grass, and Johnson grass.

The sorghum midge is a small, orange-colored, gnatlike fly (Figure 240). Each female in her short life span lays 30–100 small, white eggs in the spikelets or seed husks. The maggots or larvae are orange colored. Under average summer conditions a complete life cycle may be completed in only 14–16 days. The life cycle is somewhat longer in cooler parts of the season. As many as 13 overlapping generations have been observed. The insects overwinter as larvae within cocoons in the heads of the host plants, and transform to pupae the next spring, from which adults soon emerge. However, some do not transform or complete their development until the second or even the third spring.

Several practices may be employed which will reduce losses from the sorghum midge. Plowing under crop residues, and burning fields early in the spring to destroy hibernating larvae are recommended. Johnson grass near fields of sorghum should be cut to prevent the formation of heads before the plants bloom. It is advisable to plant uniformly blooming varieties of sorghum. Heads blooming prior to the main crop should be cut. With the recommended restrictions, carbaryl, diazinon, disulfoton, and other insecticides may be used against the pest.

Figure 240. The sorghum midge (*Contarinia sorghicola*). (From USDA.)

THE CLOVER SEED MIDGE (*Dasineura leguminicola*). The clover seed midge is an important pest in the production of red clover seed. Other clovers are attacked but the insect is of little importance on these plants. The seeds are destroyed by the maggots or larvae feeding on the ovules. Winter is passed as larvae within flimsy silken cocoons which are found on or slightly below the surface of the soil. The larvae pupate, and the tiny mosquitolike adults emerge in the spring and deposit eggs in the young clover heads. The young larvae find their way inside the flowers and attack the ovules. About a month later the mature larvae drop to the ground in which they pupate within cocoons. There are usually two generations each season, but in the southern part of the country there may be three.

When this insect occurs in damaging numbers it is advisable to cut the clover and remove the hay just before the uninjured heads are in full bloom. This is an effective control measure, as it eliminates all young midge larvae within the heads. Also, a measure of control may be obtained by clipping the clover about 2 weeks prior to blooming and again a month later. This practice brings the clover into bloom before the second generation of midges has emerged. This preventive measure does not always result in the greatest production of seed, however, when other clover insects are involved.

As the name gall midge suggests, a large number of species cause the formation of galls on a variety of plants such as willow, oak, hickory, and chrysanthemum. Each causes the formation of a gall which is characteristic for the species, and common species may be readily identified by the type of gall formed.

Family Simuliidae (Blackflies and Buffalo Gnats)

Adults of the Simuliidae are small, short, stout, and appear to be humpbacked. The antennae are slightly longer than the head and consist of 11 joints. The mouthparts are for piercing and sucking and are similar to those of the horsefly. Only females bite and many species are fierce bloodsuckers, and are important pests of man and animals. They are strong fliers; with the aid of favorable winds, they may drift considerable distances from their breeding places.

With rare exceptions the insects develop in running water. Rapidly flowing streams are preferred breeding places. The masses of eggs are laid on rocks, logs, and other objects at or slightly below the surface of the water. The larvae have a disclike sucker provided with hooks on the end of the abdomen with which they cling to submerged objects. The head is provided with two fanlike organs which are used to collect algae, protozoa, and diatoms for food. Respiration is by blood gills which are located on the dorsal surface of the last abdominal segment. Mature larvae pupate in cocoons which are attached to rocks or other objects where the larvae live. When the adults emerge, they escape from the pupal cases, float to the surface, and fly away immediately, before they are swept away by the current. Soon after emergence the females lay their eggs. Most species pass the winter as larvae. Some produce several generations each season, while others have one sudden emergence of adults early in the spring with only stragglers appearing later.

COMMON SPECIES. The southern buffalo gnat (*Cnephia pecuarum*) (Figure 241) is frequently a serious pest in the southern states, particularly along the lower Mississippi River and its watershed. The adults appear in early spring; and, when outbreaks occur, they make life miserable for livestock. In fact, there are many records of horses and mules having been killed by their vicious attacks. Indications are that, in addition to the bites and exsanguination, the animals are sometimes smothered by huge numbers of the gnats packing in the nostrils and blocking the air passages.

The turkey gnat (*Simulium meridionale*) is often a pest of poultry as well as other animals in the South. This species appears later in the spring than the southern buffalo gnat. It attacks the combs and wattles of the birds.

Simulium pictipes is a common blackfly in the East. This species does not attack man and is rarely found on animals. Its feeding habits are not known. The Adirondack blackfly (*Simulium hirtipes*) is a widely distributed form but is best known in the northeastern states. It is a vicious biting species and is feared by fishermen and hunters.

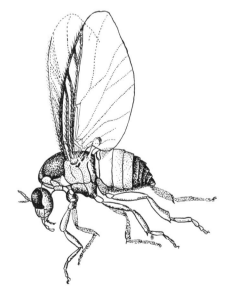

Figure 241. The southern buffalo gnat (*Cnephia pecuarum*). (From W. B. Herms, *Medical Entomology*, 4th ed. Copyright 1950 by the Macmillan Company. Used by permission of the publisher.)

Prevention and control of blackflies and buffalo gnats is a difficult problem. The removal of logs, roots, dipping branches, and other debris from streams will aid in preventing breeding, but this is often not practicable. Smudges are commonly used for the protection of livestock. Protective smears of oil and grease of various concoctions are employed by most farmers to protect their animals. One of the most commonly used is crankcase oil mixed with a small amount of pine tar. Approved aerosols have been found effective in control of the adults when applied over large areas.

When man is exposed to attacks of the insects, protective clothing and even head veils may be worn. Repellents, such as dimethylphthalate, will protect against attacks for several hours.

Family Tabanidae (Horseflies and Deerflies)

The Tabanidae is a large family containing more than 2500 species, of which nearly 300 are found in North America. They are medium to large, stout-bodied insects with large heads. Their size ranges from that of a housefly to a bumblebee. The adults are most common in the warmer months of the year and are encountered in greatest numbers along marshes and streams, and in wooded areas. The females of practically all species suck the blood of both wild and domestic animals such as horses, cattle, hogs, dogs, and deer. Man is also attacked. When animal hosts are not available, the females will feed on plant juices. The males do not suck blood but subsist on nectar, honeydew, and plant sap. Horseflies are strong fliers and are said to outstrip the fastest horse. They transmit various diseases such as anthrax, tularaemia, and trypanosomiasis of animals. However, most injury is caused by their bites and the blood that they take from the animals. It has been estimated that when horseflies are abundant, an animal may lose more than 3 ounces of blood daily. Wounds caused in feeding may also be predisposing causes of screwworm infestations.

Eggs of horseflies are deposited in masses on grasses, foliage of other plants, and rocks at the water's edge or in swampy places. The larvae drop to the surface of the water, mud, or damp earth and quickly go to the bottom of the water or burrow into the wet soil. Here they feed on small animal life, including each other. When the larvae complete their development they move into drier earth for pupation.

Most common species belong to the genera *Tabanus* and *Chrysops*. The species of *Tabanus* are the larger and the more common forms (Figure 242). Members of the genus *Chrysops* are called deerflies. They may be recognized by their smaller size, black or brown color, and dark markings on the wings. These forms are particularly troublesome around swamps in woodlands.

The striped horsefly or green head (*Tabanus lineola*) is one of the most common species. This insect has at least two generations annually in the south central states. The black horsefly (*Tabanus*

Figure 242. A horsefly (*Tabanus sublongus*). (From USDA.)

atratus) is a vicious biter. It measures about 1 inch in length and is black. This species generally has one generation each year.

No very satisfactory control measures for horseflies have been developed. The drainage of breeding places is of value, but this practice is usually considered impracticable in most instances. The oiling of stagnant pools has been found to be of value in some cases. Covering horses with fly nets or blankets and stabling during the day help protect the animals. Sprays are generally unsuccessful. A spray containing pyrethrins and piperonyl butoxide has been found to be fairly satisfactory.

Family Stratiomyidae (Soldier Flies)
Most soldier flies are of medium size, brightly colored, and wasp-like in appearance (Figure 243A). The abdomen is generally broad and flat. They are usually sluggish and are found around flowers. The larvae are flattened, elliptical or spindle shaped, and appear somewhat leatherylike. Some are found in privies, manure, and other decaying organic matter. Others are aquatic, or are found under loosened bark of trees, or in the nests of rodents and Hymenoptera. Several hundred species have been recorded from North America.

Family Bombyliidae (Bee Flies)
Bee flies are usually short, broad, and densely clothed with fine hairs (Figure 243B). Their most common colors are black, brown, or yellow with somewhat clouded wings. This is a large family; about 500 species are known in North America. The adults are most frequently observed hovering over flowers or resting in the sun on flowers, sticks, stones, or the bare earth. Food consists of nectar and pollen.

The larvae are parasitic or predaceous. The predators are the more common forms. Some species feed on pods of grasshopper eggs. Perhaps the best known of these species is *Aphoebantus mus*, the adults of which are often observed hovering over the oviposition grounds of grasshoppers. It is believed that the eggs are laid in crevices in the ground near egg pods of grasshoppers, upon which the larvae feed. There is one generation annually; the winter is passed in the larval stage.

The parasitic species infest larvae and pupae of a wide variety of insects. Perhaps the most important forms are found in the genus *Anthrax*. Several species of this genus are known to parasitize cutworms. Another species, *Anthrax anale*, is a parasite of tiger beetle larvae.

Family Asilidae (Robber Flies)

More than 500 species of this large family are found in North America. The adults are usually large with an elongate body and tapering abdomen (Figure 244). However, some are quite stout and resemble bumblebees, not only in form, but also in the dense clothing of black and yellow hairs.

The adults are predaceous on other insects. They are frequently observed during the summer months in flight over pastures, along roadsides, in open woodlands, or perched on limbs, dead weed stems, fence posts, or other places of vantage. The various species prey upon a wide variety of insects which they capture, pierce with the mouthparts and suck the body juices. Certain species of *Erax* and *Proctacanthus* appear to prey chiefly on grasshoppers. Others, such as *Sparopogon dispar*, collect in numbers around apiaries where they prey upon honeybees. They may cause considerable loss in young queen bees which are captured on their mating flights.

The larvae are reported as living in the ground or in decaying wood where they prey on larvae of beetles, pods of grasshopper

---

Figure 243. A. A soldier fly (*Hoplitimyia constans*). B. A bee fly (*Villa lucifer*).

A   B

Figure 244. Some common robber flies. (From Texas Agricultural Experiment Station.)

eggs, and possibly other insects; although some are thought to feed on the roots of plants.

Suborder Cyclorrhapha (Circular-seamed Flies)
The Cyclorrhapha is the larger of the two suborders of Diptera. Here are found more than 40 families, some of which are quite large. The suborder is so called because the pupa is always found in a puparium from which the adult escapes through a circular opening made by pushing off the anterior end of this pupal case. The adults are rather stout and short. The antennae are usually composed of three segments, the third bearing a style or arista.

Family Syrphidae (Syrphid Flies or Flower Flies)
The adults are also known as hover flies and sweat flies. The family is large and has more than 2500 species. Its members may be recognized by the presence of a longitudinal spurious or false vein in the wings between the radius and the media. Many are brightly colored and a number of them mimic bees, bumblebees, wasps, and other hymenopterous insects (Figure 245). They feed upon nectar and pollen of flowers and are of value as pollinators of many plants. Many hover motionless in the air except for the beating of the wings; others fly with a buzzing sound like that produced by bees.

The larvae vary much in appearance and habits. Several are predaceous on small insects, many feed upon decaying organic matter, a few attack living plants, and some have taken up their abode in the nests of wasps, bumblebees, and ants. *Syrphus americanus* and *Allographa obliqua* (Figure 246) are common examples of those species that prey upon aphids. They are valuable as natural enemies of these insects.

Figure 245. A syrphid fly (*Spilomyia fusca*), mimic of the ball-faced hornet (*Vespula maculata*). (Courtesy of C. O. Mohr.)

Figure 246. A syrphid fly (*Allographa obliqua*). (From USDA.)

The adult of *Eristalis tenax* so closely resembles the drone of the honeybee that it is known as the drone fly. The larvae of this species and others of the genus live in highly polluted water. They are known as "rat-tailed" maggots because of the presence of a long anal appendage. This is a breathing tube which can be lengthened or shortened at will and permits respiration even when the insect is submerged as much as several inches in the water.

Family Tephritidae (Trypetidae) (Fruit Flies)

The fruit flies constitute a large family of small to medium-sized flies. The wings are usually banded or spotted, and the bodies of many species are brightly colored. Adults of this family are identified by the apical part of the subcosta which abruptly bends forward and then becomes weak. The flies are frequently found on flowers and fruit. Many of them have the peculiar habit of raising and lowering the wings when at rest. Most larvae feed on living plants. Some are leaf miners, others tunnel in stems or form galls, but the most important injury is produced by those species that infest fruit.

THE MEDITERRANEAN FRUIT FLY (*Ceratitis capitata*). This insect is the most important of the fruit flies. It is widely distributed in the tropical and subtropical regions of the world where it attacks a wide variety of fruits. The peach is probably the favorite host. All citrus fruits are attacked, with the exception of lemons and sour limes. The larvae feed and develop in the pulp of the fruit.

The adults, which are slightly smaller than the housefly, are rather strikingly colored with black, brown, yellow, and white (Figure 247). Females may oviposit as many as 500 eggs each within the rind of the fruit. Under favorable conditions a generation may be completed in less than 3 weeks; however, the average period is considerably longer. The number of generations produced annually varies in different parts of the world under various weather conditions from 1 to probably as many as 16.

Infestations of the Mediterranean fruit fly have been discovered in Florida on three separate occasions. The basic procedure in the 1929–30 eradication program was the destruction of host fruits and the use of sugar bait sprays. The 1956–1957 infestation was

Figure 247. The Mediterranean fruit fly (*Ceratitis capitata*). (From USDA.)

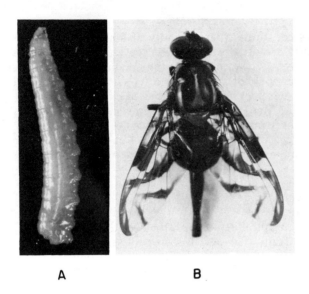

A   B

Figure 248. The Mexican fruit fly (*Anastrepha ludens*). A. Larva. B. Adult. (From Texas Agricultural Experiment Station.)

eliminated chiefly through the use of protein hydrolysate bait sprays and use of insecticides in soil-surface treatments under the infested hosts. The flies have sponging mouthparts and feed on liquid foods. Bait sprays are attractive to them and are effective in their control. The protein hydrolysate bait spray contains malathion as the effective killing agent. This spray is also effective against the Mexican fruit fly. In soil-surface treatment to destroy larvae entering the ground for pupation, dieldrin in granular form is very satisfactory. Strict quarantine measures are enforced in an effort to prevent reentry of the pest. Larvae in infested fruit may be destroyed by means of heat or cold treatment, or by fumigation with methyl bromide or ethylene dibromide.

THE MEXICAN FRUIT FLY (*Anastrepha ludens*). This is the principal fruit fly found in Mexico (Figure 248). During the fall and winter, numbers of these flies may drift across the Mexican border into the Lower Rio Grande Valley of Texas and infest citrus groves there. Infestations disappear the next spring and summer following the harvesting of the fruit. Habits and hosts of this pest are similar to those of the Mediterranean fruit fly. However, it has a longer life cycle and the females do not deposit as many eggs; consequently its capacity for injury is not so great. The adults are larger than houseflies and are of a yellowish-brown color. The females have a very long ovipositor sheath which is nearly as long as the combined length of the thorax and abdomen.

Quarantine measures are enforced to prevent the spread of the insect. Fumigation with ethylene dichloride or sterilization by means of either heat or cold treatment may be required before regulated citrus fruit may be shipped to nonregulated areas.

The oriental fruit fly (*Dacus dorsalis*) had been known as a pest in the Pacific islands for a long time. It was introduced into Hawaii during World War II. This is a serious pest of many tropical and subtropical fruits and it is considered by some to be more injurious than the Mediterranean fruit fly because it has a wider range of host plants.

THE APPLE MAGGOT (*Rhagoletis pomonella*). The apple maggot or railroad worm (Figure 249) is a pest of apples chiefly in the colder

Figure 249. Life cycle of the apple maggot (*Rhagoletis pomonella*). A. Adult. B. Eggs. C. Egg punctures. D. Egg below skin. E. Larva. F. Pupae. (From USDA.)

sections of the United States. In addition to apples, haws, wild crabapples, plums, blueberries, and other fruits are attacked. Injury is caused by the larvae burrowing through the pulp of the fruit. The medium-sized adults are black, yellow, and white with banded wings.

Diapause is in the pupa stage enclosed in brown puparia within the soil. Eggs are deposited singly in the skin of the fruit. Infested fruits usually drop. When growth is completed the larvae enter the ground and the puparia are formed. One generation develops annually except in the southern range where there may be a partial second brood. Some individuals have a prolonged life cycle and remain in the puparia for an additional year before the adults emerge.

Sprays applied to the trees when the adults are active are effective in the control of the pest. As the flies feed on moisture, they will be killed by the poisoned spray. Gathering and disposing of the fruit drops will prevent many larvae from completing their development and entering the ground.

The fruits of the cherry are infested by two related species (*Rhagoletis cingulata* and *Rhagoletis fausta*). Their biologies are similar to that of the apple maggot. They also may be controlled by poisoned sprays.

The larvae of *Eurosta solidaginis* produce the round goldenrod gall (Figure 250). This insect overwinters as larvae. Pupation occurs in the spring and the adults emerge to lay eggs in the apical portions of the young plants. Only one generation develops each season.

Figure 250. The goldenrod stem-gall fly (*Eurosta solidaginis*). A. gall. (From Chicago Museum of Natural History.) B. Adult (From Illinois Natural History Survey. Courtesy of C. O. Mohr.)

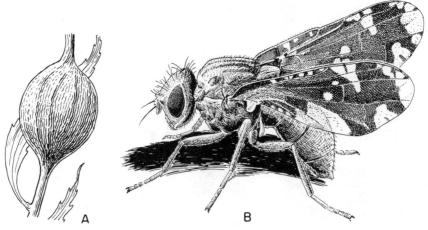

A   B

Family Drosophilidae (Vinegar Flies)

The adults are small yellowish flies, usually not more than 3 or 4 mm in length. They are most common around decaying or fermenting fruit. The small white larvae of the common members of the family burrow in the decaying fruit and feed on yeasts growing there.

Drosophila melanogaster has been employed extensively in the study of animal genetics. This insect has a short life cycle, is easily reared, and produces a number of mutant forms, so it has proved to be an ideal insect for the study of heredity. More is known about the heredity of this small fly than that of any other animal.

Family Agromyzidae (Leaf Miner Flies)

Members of the Agromyzidae are small flies and are usually colored yellowish or blackish. Most of the larvae are leaf miners and feed between the upper and lower epidermis of leaves; nearly all plants are attacked. The larvae of one genus (*Cryptochaetum*) are parasites of scale insects.

It is said of the leaf-mining forms that most species may be more readily recognized by the type of mines produced than by an examination of the insects themselves. Most larvae make narrow tortuous mines which become larger as the insect grows (Figure 251). The serpentine leaf miner (*Liriomyza brassicae*), together with several related species, attacks a number of field and vegetable crops. Their serpentine mines are often quite noticeable in leaves of cotton; however, actual damage to this crop is probably of little economic importance, but serious injury may be produced on peppers and tomatoes. Leafy vegetables, following attacks of this pest, are rendered less attractive to buyers. Biology of these insects is imperfectly known, but they are known to have a rather short life cycle, and a number of generations may be completed in a season. They are frequently highly parasitized. The corn leaf blotch miner is a common species and feeds on corn and various grasses. Control of leaf miners is difficult. Most insecticides are usually ineffective in combating these insects. Applications of parathion and dimethoate have provided the most satisfactory control measures.

Cryptochaetum iceryae is an important parasite of the cottony-cushion scale. It was introduced from Australia to aid in the control of this pest. It is now thought that much of the credit given *Rodolia cardinalis* in the control of the cottony-cushion scale is due this tiny parasite.

Family Gasterophilidae (Horse Bots)

The horse botflies have a superficial resemblance to honeybees. They are commonly seen buzzing around horses and mules, which greatly fear them. They do not bite or sting and their only purpose is to glue their eggs (usually known as nits) to the hairs of the animals.

Figure 251. Injury to foliage by a leaf miner (*Liriomyza*).

Three species of bots commonly occur in the United States. They are the common horse bot or nit fly (*Gasterophilus intestinalis*) (Figure 252) the throat bot or chin fly (*G. nasalis*), and the nose bot or nose fly (*G. haemorrhoidalis*). The larvae of all three species develop in the digestive tract where they attach themselves to its walls and remain for 8–11 months (Figure 253). The fully grown larvae or maggots are robust and tough skinned. Each body segment is provided with a circle of spines. The fully grown bots are pinkish or dirty white and about ¾ inch long. When development is completed the larvae release their hold and pass out with the excrement. Pupation takes place in the soil. Winter is passed as larvae within the digestive tract of the animal. There is one generation annually. The adults are usually most abundant during the summer months.

The common botfly lays eggs on the legs, shoulders, belly, and mane, but chiefly on the front legs. The eggs are incubated in about 7 days, but the larvae do not emerge until the animal licks or bites itself where the eggs are located. When this stimulus of moisture and friction is provided, the larvae emerge and attach themselves to the animal's tongue and lips. The larvae may remain alive in the eggs for as long as 3 months waiting for this stimulus. The larvae enter the mucous membrane of the lips and tongue where they burrow for about a month before they pass to the stomach and attach to its walls.

Eggs of the throat botfly are laid on the hairs beneath the

Figure 252. The common horse botfly (*Gasterophilus intestinalis*). (From A. Castellani and A. J. Chalmers, *Manual of Tropical Medicine.* Copyright 1919 by Bailliere, Tindall & Cox. Used by permission of the publishers.)

Figure 253. Section of a stomach of a horse showing lesions and attached bots (*Gasterophilus* sp.). (From USDA.)

jaws. Upon hatching, the larvae crawl into the animal's mouth. It is said they attach themselves between the molar teeth where they remain during the first larval instar. Then they pass to the stomach and small intestine where they are found in the pyloric end of the stomach and the duodenum.

Eggs of the nose botfly are attached to the hairs of the lips. Upon hatching, the young larvae enter the mucous lining where they burrow for more than a month before they pass to the stomach for attachment.

On rare occasions a young horse bot is found in the skin of humans. The behavior of the bots in this accidental and unfavorable host is quite unlike that in horses; they have never been known to grow to any size or to reach the digestive tract. They rapidly burrow in the skin where they cause severe itching and irritation.

The use of repellents and nets is of some value in protecting animals. Annoyance by the nose botfly and the throat botfly and their infestations may be partly prevented by covering those areas where the eggs are deposited. It is difficult, however, to provide such protection for animals in pastures. A high percentage of the young larvae of the common horse bot may be destroyed by applying warm water to the areas of the body where the eggs are deposited and rubbing vigorously with a sponge or swab. This stimulus causes the eggs to hatch and the larvae perish. The carbon disulfide treatment given by veterinarians is a satisfactory remedy for removal of bots. This treatment should not be administered until about a month after the first killing frost. At this time all the eggs for that season will have been laid and most larvae will have reached the digestive tract. Trichlorfon given in food or capsule is proving satisfactory for control of the parasites.

Family Oestridae (Botflies)

These are large, robust flies somewhat similar to bees in appearance. The larvae are parasites of various animals. The best known species is the sheep bot or nose fly (*Oestrus ovis*) (Figure 254). The adults are hairy, brownish or yellowish flies and are as large as the common horseflies. They deposit living young, not eggs, around the nostrils of sheep. The small larvae crawl into the nasal passages. Here they remain for a varying period of time before migrating to the frontal sinuses where they complete their larval development. The mature larvae find their way to the ground into which they burrow and pupate. The life history of the insect varies considerably since individuals may complete a life cycle in 3–5½ months, and others may not complete their development until the next season. In the Southwest, adults may be found throughout the year. A number of remedies for the prevention or treatment of sheep bots have been suggested, but most of them are of little or no value. In recent research Ruelene has been found to be effective and is being recommended for control.

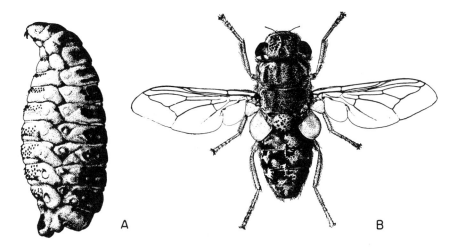

Figure 254. The sheep botfly (*Oestrus ovis*). A. Larva. B. Adult. (From A. Castellani and A. J. Chalmers, *Manual of Tropical Medicine.* Copyright 1919 by Bailliere, Tindall & Cox. Used by permission of the publishers.)

Larvae of the botflies of the genus *Cephenomyia* infest the sinuses of deer. The adults are large, grayish-brown flies which are reported to fly more rapidly than any other insect. They deposit living young in the nostrils of the hosts. The young larvae migrate to the sinuses where they develop.

Family Hypodermatidae (Warble Flies)

Warble flies are similar in appearance to the botflies and many authorities consider them in the family. The most important species of this family are the ox warbles (*Hypoderma lineatum* and *H. bovis*). The former is known as the cattle grub or heel fly and the latter is the northern cattle grub or bomb fly (Figure 255). The bomb fly is not found in the southern states but is the more prevalent species in the Northeast. Although cattle are the principal hosts of the warble flies, buffaloes and rarely, horses, goats, and man are attacked.

Heavy annual losses are attributed to cattle grubs. In the latter stages of development the larvae migrate to the backs of the animals and encyst underneath the skin in which holes are made. Occasionally as many as 100 grub holes may be found in a hide. Hides with a number of grub holes are worthless for making leather. There are also losses in meat and milk. Activities of the flies cause apprehension and fear among the cattle. Stampedes may occur. Cattle frequently seek protection in water to escape them. Feeding of the animals may be curtailed at this time, resulting in failure to gain weight and reduction in milk production.

A   B

Figure 255. A. The cattle grub (*Hypoderma lineatum*). (From Agricultural Research Service, USDA.) B. The bomb fly (*Hypoderma bovis*). (From A. Castellani and A. J. Chalmers, *Manual of Tropical Medicine*. Copyright 1919 by Bailliere, Tindall & Cox. Used by permission of the publishers.)

Heel flies first appear in late winter or early spring in the South. The period of their activity is about 6 weeks. The females glue the eggs to hairs usually just about the hoof. Eggs may be deposited also on hair of the belly, udder, or escutcheon when the animals are lying down. The northern heel flies appear later in the season and are active for a longer period of time. Their grubs also remain in the backs of cattle for a longer period.

The female warble fly rarely lays more than 800 eggs. The eggs hatch in 3–7 days, the larvae tunnel in the skin, and then bore into deeper tissues. Although they migrate slowly through the connective tissues of the body of the host animals, they are forever on the move, which prevents attack by the white corpuscles. About 9 months after entering the skin, they appear in the backs of the animals. The routes followed by the two species differ somewhat. The larvae of the heel fly are usually first discovered after tunneling into the skin in the walls of the gullet and esophagus in late spring or summer. The larvae then travel up the diaphragm, along the ribs, and through connective tissues to the back. Some may enter the neural canal in their passage to the back. When the skin is reached, holes are cut to obtain air. Around the grubs cysts or warbles are produced. In the South the grubs begin to appear in the backs of the animals in the middle of the fall. The northern cattle grubs appear to take a more direct route to the back of the animal. They are rarely found in the walls of the gullet and are more frequently observed in the neural canal.

Growth of the grubs is more rapid after the backs of the animals are reached. Development is completed here in 5 weeks to almost 3 months. The mature larvae work their way out of the cysts, drop to the ground, and pupate under trash or within the soil. The adult flies usually emerge from the puparia about 6 weeks later. Only one generation is produced annually.

Cattle grubs in beef animals are most effectively controlled by certain organic phosphorus compounds acting as systemic insecticides. Those which have been approved for use are coumaphos, trolene, and Ruelene. Coumaphos is applied as a spray. Sick animals and calves less than 3 months of age should not be treated, and animals 3–6 months old should be sprayed only lightly. Trolene, a drug grade of ronnel, may be administered in a bolus or by mixing it in the feed of the animal. Sick animals should not be fed the compound. Ruelene may be applied either by spraying or by pouring on the animals' backs. The above materials are recommended for use at the end of the heel fly season. In grub control on dairy cattle rotenone is the only insecticide permitted. It is applied as a wash, dust, or spray after the grubs appear in the backs of the animals during fall and winter.

A warble fly (*Oedemagena tarandi*) is a pest of reindeer in northern Europe and Alaska. Holes in the hides result in a large loss in leather. There is also a loss in meat and its quality.

Family Cuterebridae (Rodent Bots)

The adults are large, stout, hairy flies resembling bumblebees. Most of the larvae of this family are parasites of rodents such as rabbits, mice, and squirrels. *Cuterebra cuniculi* is a common species infesting rabbits. *Cuterebra emasculator* is said to attack the scrotum of squirrels, which may result in their emasculation.

The human botfly (*Dermatobia hominis*) is the most interesting member of this family. This insect is found in South America, Central America, and parts of Mexico. It is a pest of importance to man, cattle, and other animals. The female flies do not lay the eggs on the larval hosts, but deposit them on flies, mosquitoes, and ticks. When these parasites feed, the larvae hatch and bore into the skin of the animal, where they encyst. Infestations on cattle can be reduced by systematic use of a livestock spray such as toxaphene and lindane. Systemic insecticides are also effective.

Family Tachinidae (Tachina Flies)

The Tachinidae is the most beneficial family of Diptera. The group is very large and all its members are parasites of other insects. The flies have the general appearance of flesh flies and houseflies. Many are rather large, bristly, and somewhat resemble bees or wasps. Members of the family have bristles on both the hypopleura and pteropleura; the postscutellum is prominent, and the ventral abdominal sclerites are overlapped by the dorsal sclerites. See Figure 234.

Tachina flies parasitize a wide variety of insects. Most of them attack the larvae of Lepidoptera, larvae of sawflies, and adult Coleoptera; some parasitize Orthoptera, Hemiptera, and insects of other orders. Their life histories and host relationships are often quite intriguing.

Reproductive habits are diverse. Eggs are usually deposited directly on the hosts. Eggs glued to the body of a caterpillar are commonly observed. Some lay their eggs on the food and hatch after they are ingested by the feeding caterpillars. The maggots then attack the internal organs of the host. Others produce living larvae which are deposited upon the host or inserted into the body by means of the ovipositor. Other types of reproductive habits are known.

Winthemia quadripustulata is one of the most important native parasites (Figure 256). It is widely distributed, multiplies quite rapidly, and attacks a large number of caterpillars. Most of the eggs are placed on the thorax where the caterpillars cannot reach them with their mandibles. Upon hatching, the larvae bore into the host and feed upon the tissues. Pupation occurs in the soil. A generation may be completed in less than 3 weeks in warm weather. See Figure 203.

Compsilura concinnata was imported from Europe. It is an important parasite of larvae of the gypsy moth and brown-tail moth, and it also attacks a number of other caterpillars. The female inserts living larvae within the body of the host by means of its ovipositor. Three or four generations are produced annually. Overwintering is as small larvae within the body of the host.

Adult females of *Sturmia scutellata* deposit their eggs on the foliage to be ingested by the feeding caterpillars. This introduced

Figure 256. An important tachina parasite (*Winthemia quadripustulata*). (From Agricultural Research Service, USDA.)

European parasite is an important natural enemy of the larvae of the gypsy moth, its only host. Only one generation is produced annually by this parasite. Overwintering is within a puparium in the soil.

Archytas analis, which is a native parasite, preys upon the variegated cutworm (*Peridroma saucia*) and other caterpillars. The females deposit small larvae on the foliage of plants to which they are attached by means of minute membranous cups. The larvae patiently await the passing of a host. When the leaf is disturbed, a larva rears upward like a snake, and swings the head in a wide circle. If a host comes near enough it quickly attaches itself. Development is completed within the pupa of the host, where it also pupates. Several generations are produced each season.

Family Calliphoridae (Blowflies)

Many blowflies are brightly colored. Here are found the green-bottle flies and the bluebottle flies that are so familiar to almost everyone. These flies have the arista of the antennae plumose to the tip; the postscutellum is absent; both hypopleura and pteropleura bear bristles, and two notopleural bristles are present (Figure 234). Most blowfly larvae are scavengers, developing in decaying matter. Some are parasites of vertebrates, and others feed on invertebrates.

THE SCREWWORM (*Cochliomyia hominivorax*). This insect (Figure 257) is a parasite of livestock, various wild animals, and man. It is found in both North America and South America, but overwinters only in the southernmost parts of the United States and southward to Argentina. It spreads northward each season in infested livestock and through flight of the adults.

The screwworm is a livestock pest of considerable importance, especially in the Southwest. It does not breed in carcasses, but infests wounds of living animals. In fact, larvae have been known to enter the unbroken skin of experimental animals. Eggs are occasionally deposited in the nostrils of man.

The females deposit 250–300 eggs each in shinglelike masses on dry tissues near the wound. These hatch in 11–21 hours. The larvae tunnel into the live tissues with the head downward. After feeding for 4–8 days, the larvae drop from the wound to the ground in which they pupate in brown puparia. The fully grown larvae are about ⅔ inch long, of the typical muscoid type, and with elevated, spinelike circlets around each body segment which produce a screwlike appearance. The pupal period varies in length from 7 to 54 days. During warm summer weather in the Southwest the average length of a life cycle is about 24 days. The adults are larger than houseflies, blue-green with three dark stripes on the thorax and a reddish-orange to brown head. It is possible for this insect to produce a number of generations in a season.

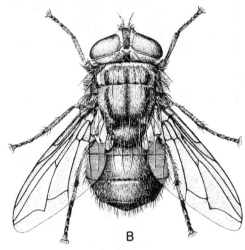

Figure 257. The screwworm (*Cochliomyia hominivorax*). A. Larva. B. Adult. (From USDA.)

Preventive measures are important in combating the screw-worm. Castration, dehorning, docking, and branding should be done, if possible, during the cold months when the flies are not present, or at least not abundant. Cuts while shearing sheep and goats should be treated until they are healed. It is desirable for animals to be born in late winter or early spring in most areas when there is least likelihood of infestations. Care should be taken to prevent unnecessary injury to livestock. In preventing or elimi-nating infestations in both dairy and beef animals, wounds may be treated with either Smear 62 which contains diphenylamine, or E.Q. 335 with lindane as the active ingredient. For beef cattle only, coumaphos, and ronnel are recommended. The spectacular use of male-sterile flies has practically eliminated this pest in the United States.

THE SECONDARY SCREWWORM (*Cochliomyia macellaria*). It closely resembles the primary screwworm. It is primarily a scavenger and breeds abundantly in dead animals. The larvae are found also in old infected wounds of living animals where they feed on dead tissues, and in urine-soaked wool; live tissues are not attacked.

THE BLACK BLOWFLY (*Phormia regina*). It is a common insect which usually breeds in animal wastes and carcasses. The larvae may infest sores, old wounds, and urine-soaked wool of sheep. It is the most prevalent of the wool maggots. Wool maggots may be controlled by use of several insecticides. A locally applied lindane or coumaphos spray; dips, sprays or smears of ronnel are used. Sick animals should not be treated.

THE BLUEBOTTLE FLIES (*Calliphora erythrocephala, C. vicina, C. vomitoria,* and others). The bluebottle flies are readily recognized by their large size and buzzing noise. They breed in carcasses, excrement, and wastes. Sometimes they enter houses in search of breeding places.

The greenbottle flies (*Lucilia sericata, L. illustris, L. sylvarium,* and related species) (Figure 258) breed in wastes of many types, as do the bluebottle flies. The larvae of *L. sericata* may also be found in old wounds and sores of animals, feeding as scavengers; they are also wool maggots.

The cluster fly (*Pollenia rudis*) is common in the colder climates. The adults frequently collect in attics and other protected places in late summer and fall to hibernate. The flies are larger and darker colored than houseflies, and sluggish in habit. The larvae are parasites of earthworms.

Figure 258. A greenbottle fly (*Lucilia sericata*). (From USDA.)

Family Sarcophagidae (Flesh Flies)

Flies of this group are medium in size, usually grayish in color, and often with checkerboardlike patterns on the abdomen. The postscutellum is undeveloped. Both hypopleural and pteropleural bristles are present, and there are four notopleural bristles (see Figure 234).

The adults (Figure 259) are commonly associated with decaying organic matter and dead animals in which a number of species breed. However, some members of the family parasitize invertebrates, such as insects and snails; mammals are hosts of others. The adult females usually do not lay eggs, but deposit small larvae. This is a large family of flies with about 1000 known species which are worldwide in distribution.

Sarcophaga kellyi is one of the best known members of this family. It parasitizes grasshoppers chiefly, but a few other insects are attacked also. The flies usually deposit their larvae on the grasshoppers in flight. The females dart at flying grasshoppers and deposit their small larvae usually on the underside of the wings. When the flies are numerous, they may dart at stones or other small objects thrown into the air. The female flies also deposit their larvae on grasshopper nymphs as they hop about, and on newly molted individuals which are resting while the body wall hardens. The small maggots tunnel into the hosts and feed upon the internal organs. From one to several larvae are often observed in dissected grasshoppers. When the larvae are mature,

Figure 259. A flesh fly (*Sarcophaga securifera*). (From USDA.)

they leave the dead or dying hosts and enter the soil for pupation. Several generations may be completed in one season. Diapause takes place as mature larvae in puparia within the soil. A number of other related species are also parasites of insects.

Several species of *Sarcophaga* develop in the pitcher plant (*Sarracenia*) in which they feed on trapped insects. They are cannibalistic, and it is said only one larva ever develops in a pitcher.

Wohlfahrtia vigil is a large gray fly found in the cooler parts of North America. It is a parasite of a number of animals such as rabbits, minks, dogs, and foxes. Occasionally small children are attacked. The larvae produce superficial lesions.

The red-tailed flesh fly (*Sarcophaga haemorrhoidalis*) is a widely distributed well known species. The larvae normally feed as scavengers but may occasionally be found in wounds and the digestive tracts of mammals.

Family Muscidae (Houseflies, Stable Flies)
This large group of flies is often referred to as the housefly family because of this well known insect. Other common species of the family are the stable fly, horn fly, and the tsetse fly.

THE HOUSEFLY (*Musca domestica*). This insect is of worldwide distribution and the most common fly observed around human habitations (Figure 260). If the flies around a home were collected, probably more than 90 percent of them would prove to be the housefly. This dark gray fly is marked by four longitudinal lines on the thorax and is about ¼ inch in length. The arista of the antenna is plumose. Vein M_1 of the wing bends sharply forward and almost meets R_{4+5} at the margin, nearly closing cell R_5. Mouthparts are of the sponging type; houseflies cannot bite.

Houseflies are associated with filth. The larvae develop in the manure of horses, pigs, chickens, and cows; human excrement; garbage; and decomposing vegetable matter. The adults may feed on human excrement, sputum, exudates of sores, and other filth, and then feed upon the foods of man. Since their bodies and feeding habits are well adapted to transmit disease organisms, they may transmit a number of diseases such as typhoid fever, dysentery, cholera, and yaws. Eggs of several parasitic worms may also be transmitted by houseflies. Their sponging mouthparts are well adapted for feeding on liquid materials. Solids may be dissolved by means of saliva or regurgitated contents of the crop.

The distance flies may fly from their breeding places is important in the problem of control. It has been shown experimentally that they can travel more than 10 miles. However, flies usually go no farther than is necessary to procure food and places for egg laying. When flies are quite abundant it is reasonably certain they are breeding in the immediate neighborhood.

Houseflies usually overwinter as larvae or pupae in colder climates, but in the South some breeding may continue throughout

Figure 260. Life cycle of the housefly (*Musca domestica*), showing eggs, larvae, pupae, and adults. (Prepared by the Clemson University Cooperative Extension Service's Entomology-Plant Pathology and Agricultural Communications Sections, Federal Extension Service Cooperating.)

the winter months. This insect may reproduce with great rapidity; the females lay a large number of eggs, and the life cycle is short. The small, white, elongate eggs are laid in batches in manure or other breeding media. Each female lays about 500 eggs. Eggs hatch in 12–24 hours. The larval stage is about 7 days in duration. The mature larvae are ⅓ to ½ inch in length and are white. Before transforming to the pupal stage, the larvae seek a drier area of the breeding material. A brown puparium is then formed in which the larva pupates. The pupal stage requires 4 or 5 days. Under favorable conditions a generation may be completed in about 12 or 14 days, but the length of a generation is prolonged in cool weather. Therefore, with proper temperature and moisture conditions enormous populations of houseflies may develop in relatively short periods of time.

Elimination of breeding media is the first and most important step in fly control. The proper disposal of garbage, sewage, and other organic materials in which flies breed is mandatory. Outdoor toilets should be eliminated or made as flyproof as possible. The excreta should be covered daily with borax, waste oil, or heavy applications of lime. Manure should be removed and spread thinly over fields and pastures every 2 or 3 days. Treatment of manure with sprays to prevent fly breeding may be done, but as a whole the practice is not too satisfactory.

Regardless of preventive measures employed, there will always be some breeding of flies, and other measures must be used. Electric fly screens and fly traps may aid in reduction of populations, but the use of chemical compounds becomes necessary, particularly in and around barns. A number of insecticides are available as sprays, baits, and resin strips inside and outside of barns and in homes. Upon selection of the desired product it should be carefully used, following all directions on the printed label. Particular precautions should be taken when pesticides are used in dairy barns and homes. Some of the more commonly used compounds are dichlorvos (Vapona), lindane, malathion, methoxychlor, ronnel, trichlorfon, and pyrethrins and their combinations.

THE STABLE FLY (*Stomoxys calcitrans*). The stable fly rather closely resembles the housefly with which it is often confused (Figure 261). Its mouthparts are of the piercing-sucking type and are held bayonetlike in front of the head. The abdomen is broad and spotted. Cell R$_5$ of the wing is not closed nearly so much as in the housefly. The insect prefers to live in the open and is commonly seen in the sunshine on fences, posts, and boards. During stormy weather stable flies frequently enter houses and bite people, who think they are houseflies that have assumed biting habits. Both males and females are vicious blood suckers. Horses, mules, cows, and other animals are attacked. Such animal diseases as anthrax may be transmitted by these insects.

Figure 261. The stable fly (*Stomoxys calcitrans*). (From J. Smart, *Insects of Medical Importance,* after E. E. Austen. Copyright 1943. Used by permission of British Museum of Natural History, London.)

In cold climates the insect overwinters as larvae and pupae. Under southern conditions some breeding may continue throughout the winter months. Eggs are laid in rotting and fermenting straw. Larvae are not found in pure manure, but a mixture of manure and straw affords an ideal breeding medium. The bases of old straw stacks and piles of decomposing vegetable matter of all types are favorite breeding places. The larvae resemble those of the housefly. The length of a life cycle is about 3 weeks. As the female flies must feed on blood before eggs can be produced, they are 1–2 weeks old before the first eggs are deposited for the next generation. Eggs are laid in batches and the total number deposited by each female is about 500.

In the control of stable flies, elimination of breeding places is of prime importance. Straw should be baled and stored in a dry place or scattered thinly over the ground. Mixtures of manure and straw or wet, sodden feed around feed troughs should be spread on the land so it will dry, as neither stable flies nor houseflies breed in dry matter. Decaying vegetable matter such as lawn clippings and vegetable trimmings afford breeding quarters and should be properly disposed of. Marine plants washed ashore in heaps along certain Gulf Coast beaches afford breeding quarters. Spraying this material with a mixture of creosote and fuel oil will eliminate breeding. The same control measures as recommended for the housefly may be employed around the premises.

THE HORN FLY (*Haematobia irritans*). Injury to cattle by horn flies is similar to that of stable flies. Occasionally they attack sheep, horses, goats, dogs, and other animals. Warm, moist weather is most favorable for horn fly development, and under such conditions they may increase to huge numbers and cause irritation and much loss of blood and vitality of cattle.

The horn fly is about one-half the size of the housefly and the stable fly. Unlike these flies, it remains on the animal all the time. Throughout the warm season it may be seen on the shoulders, backs, and bellies of animals, or resting on the horns.

Horn flies breed only in fresh cow manure. Each female lays 375–400 eggs. A life cycle may be completed in 10–12 days. Winter is passed as larvae or pupae. Several compounds such as malathion, methoxychlor, and coumaphos are used as sprays for control on beef cattle. On milk animals methoxychlor and malathion are used with restrictions. Pyrethrum sprays are also applied.

Tsetse flies (*Glossina* spp.) (Figure 262) are important pests in Africa as they transmit sleeping sickness of man and nagana of cattle. The causative organisms are trypanosomes. The female flies do not lay eggs, but deposit mature larvae.

Family Anthomyiidae (Anthomyiids)

The anthomyiids are common flies and are quite similar in appearance to the Muscidae. Members of this family have cell R_5 of the

Figure 262. A tsetse fly (*Glossina palpalis*). (From J. Smart, *Insects of Medical Importance,* after E. E. Austin. Copyright 1943. Used by permission of British Museum of Natural History, London.)

wing only slightly, if at all, narrowed. Feeding habits of the larvae are diverse. Most of them develop in decaying plant material. Some feed on growing plants and others are parasites of insects.

THE SEED-CORN MAGGOT (*Hylemya platura*). The maggots feed in seeds which, as a result, either fail to sprout or produce weak plants. The seeds of corn, peas, beans, and other plants are attacked. The adult flies are grayish and about ⅕ inch in length. The insects diapause in puparia, and the adults emerge in early spring in the South. Eggs are deposited in soil in which there is an abundance of organic matter. Pupation is in the soil. The life cycle is relatively short, and 3–5 generations develop annually.

Planting sufficiently late to ensure rapid germination in well prepared seedbeds is probably the best preventive measure. Satisfactory control has been obtained by use of dieldrin, lindane, or heptachlor in seed treatment. Commercial seeds are often treated to control this and other soil insects.

THE ONION MAGGOT (*Hylemya antiqua*). The maggots tunnel and feed in the bulbs and underground stems of onions, causing serious damage. Most injury occurs when the spring seasons are wet. The onion is the only crop that suffers injury by this pest. It is found chiefly in the northern part of the United States and Canada. Damage occurs only rarely in southern climates.

Winter is passed chiefly as larvae or pupae in puparia which are found in the soil or in piles of cull onions. Some adults may survive the winter. They are grayish, bristly flies with large wings and are about ¼ inch long. Eggs are deposited around the bases of the plants. Upon hatching, the young larvae migrate down the plants and tunnel into the bulbs where they feed for 2 weeks or longer. The mature larvae are yellowish white and about ⅓ inch long. Pupation is in the soil, and 2 or 3 weeks later the adults emerge. A third generation may attack onions just prior to harvest and cause them to rot in storage.

Effective control has been provided by applications of ethion or trithion to the soil prior to planting. Malathion dusts or sprays are satisfactory for use on rows of growing plants. Cull onions, which are a source of infestation, should be destroyed or removed immediately after harvest.

THE CABBAGE MAGGOT (*Hylemya brassicae*). The biology of the cabbage maggot is similar to the two preceding insects. The maggots attack the underground parts of cabbage, cauliflower, broccoli, radishes, and turnips. When infestations are heavy the roots of the plants may be honeycombed. The insect is an important pest only in Canada and the northern United States.

Soil treatments with either diazinon or chlordane are recommended for control of the pest. The insecticides should be applied to the soil around the base of the plants when the leaves appear, with a second treatment made shortly following thinning or transplanting. In treatment of transplants the soil around each should be drenched with a water dilution of the poison.

The spinach leaf miner (*Pegomyia hyoscyami*) is a common example of a leaf miner of this family. The adult is similar in appearance to the housefly. The larvae feed between the upper and lower surfaces of the leaf, producing both linear and blotchlike mines. The use of parathion would probably provide the most

Figure 263. The lesser housefly (*Fannia canicularis*). (From J. Smart, *Insects of Medical Importance*, after E. E. Ausen and Thompsen. Copyright 1943. Used by permission of British Museum of Natural History, London.)

Figure 264. The sheep ked (*Melophagus ovinus*). (From Illinois Natural History Survey.)

satisfactory control. Diazinon, naled, and dimethoate are also suggested for use in control of the pest.

Several members of this family are often observed in homes. The two species most commonly seen are the lesser housefly (*Fannia canicularis*) (Figure 263) and the latrine fly (*Fannia scalaris*). These insects breed in filth and they could be of some importance as disseminators of disease.

THE PUPIPARA. This section is comprised of several families of rather aberrant forms of Diptera. The adults are louselike in form, flattened and leathery in appearance, and most members are wingless. All but a few species are external parasites of birds and mammals and suck the blood of their hosts. These insects do not lay eggs, but give birth to mature larvae that are ready to form their puparia—thus, the name *pupipara*.

Family Hippoboscidae (Louse Flies)
This is the only family of the group that needs to be discussed here. The most common representative is the sheep ked (*Melophagus ovinus*). The adults are wingless, about ⅕ inch long, brownish, and covered with short spinelike hairs (Figure 264). The saclike abdomen is somewhat flattened, broad, and unsegmented.

Sheep, and occasionally goats, are attacked. The presence of a few keds on animals does no material harm, but a heavy infestation produces emaciation and unthriftiness. Only two stages may be found on the animals. They are the brown seedlike puparia enmeshed in the wool, and the adults. Each female produces a total of 10–20 mature larvae with an interval of about 1 week between each. Several overlapping generations may be completed within a year. Sheep keds are obligatory parasites and die if separated from the hosts for more than a few days. A number of insecticides are effective in control of sheep keds. Pyrethrins with a synergist and rotenone may be used without restrictions. Ronnel and malathion are also recommended. These compounds, however, must be used with the suggested precautions.

Two louse flies are found on deer (*Lipoptena depressa* and *Neolipoptena ferrisi*). The adults have wings when they emerge from the pupal stage but these are shed a few days later. Several of the parasites have been observed attached to each other in chains. The first fly takes blood from the host. The second draws blood from the abdomen of the first, and so on down the chain to the last member.

Several louse flies are common parasites of birds. The pigeon fly (*Pseudolynchia canariensis*) is a common parasite of pigeons in warm climates. The adults are winged and are able to fly. *Lynchia americana* is fairly common on owls, hawks, and grouse. Other species infest quail and doves.

CHAPTER 16
ORDER SIPHONAPTERA[1]

Fleas are small, wingless, laterally compressed parasites that feed on the blood of mammals and birds. This is a small order of insects with only about 1100 known species in the world. However, the group is important as some are transmitters of disease, others are intermediate hosts of tapeworms, and most annoy man and animals by their feeding.

General characteristics of the order are:

1. Wings absent.
2. Piercing-sucking mouthparts.
3. Complete metamorphosis.
4. Body compressed laterally; legs modified for jumping.

The bodies of fleas are greatly modified for their parasitic way of life (Figure 265). They are oval and compressed in form which, combined with a hard, smooth body with backward projecting bristles and spines, permits them to slip easily through the hairs and feathers of the hosts and makes capture difficult. The legs are long and are modified for jumping which aids further in escaping their enemies and in finding their hosts.

Mouthparts are for piercing and sucking. Both males and females pierce the skin and suck the blood of the hosts. Their antennae are three-jointed, small, and are found in grooves on the sides of the head. Eyes are simple; they are sometimes absent. There are ten segments in the abdomen, the last three of which are greatly modified. Bristles on the body and the short, stout, comblike spines, ctenidia, which are often present on the head and pronotum, are of value in the taxonomy of the group.

Most species of fleas are quite active on the host and they frequently transfer from one animal to another. Considerable time may be spent off the hosts. They do not exhibit a marked degree

[1] *Siphon*, tube; *apteros*, wingless.

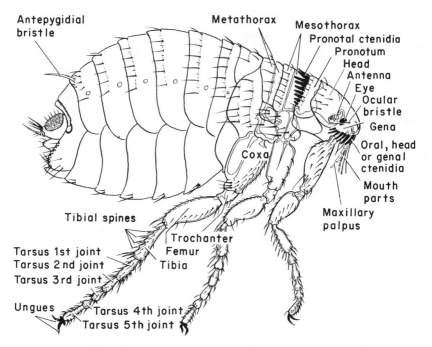

Figure 265. A female flea (*Siphonaptera*) showing characters used in identification. (Redrawn from W. B. Herms, *Medical Entomology*, 3rd ed. Copyright 1939 by The Macmillan Company. Used by permission of the publishers.)

of host specificity; the cat flea, for example, also attacks dogs, man, rabbits, squirrels, rats, poultry, and other animals.

Adult fleas are relatively long lived. Some may live for more than a year. They usually feed at least daily, but they may exist without food for long periods of time. The human flea has been observed to live for 4 months without food. It is believed that females must have blood before the development of eggs.

The eggs, which are white, rounded at the ends, and relatively large, may be laid on the hosts, the ground, or in the nests of animals. Most flea eggs are dry, and even though they may be laid among the feathers or hair of the host, they readily roll off the animal. The eggs hatch into elongate, legless larvae. Their mouthparts are for chewing, and their eyes are absent. The larval food consists of organic matter, including feces of the adult fleas and their own cast skins. When the larvae are mature they spin silken cocoons in which they pupate. As with most parasites of warm-blooded animals, some reproduction may continue throughout the year. The largest flea populations are usually developed in localities where sandy soils prevail since moisture conditions are more uniform and, consequently, are more satisfactory for the development of the larvae.

Fleas are transmitters of the bubonic form of plague (black death). Plague, which is one of the dreaded diseases of mankind, is caused by the bacillus *Pasteurella pestis*. Plague is essentially a disease of rodents, among which it is transmitted by fleas. Man becomes infected when bitten by an infected flea. The disease among wild rodents is referred to as the sylvatic plague.

The endemic or murine type of typhus fever is a flea-borne disease and is also essentially a disease of rodents. This is a mild form of typhus which must not be confused with epidemic typhus which is transmitted by body lice.

Fleas are intermediate hosts of the double-pored dog tapeworm (*Dipylidium caninum*). The fleas become infected in the larval stage when the tapeworm eggs are ingested in feeding. The primary hosts are infected by the ingestion of a flea or parts of its crushed body. Usually only dogs, cats, and certain wild animals are infected, but occasionally man is, especially children. A common tapeworm of rats and mice (*Hymenolepis diminuta*) has a number of arthropods as intermediate hosts. Among these are several species of fleas such as the rat fleas. This parasite is rarely found in man.

Family Pulicidae

The Pulicidae form a large family and contain some of the most common species such as the cat flea (*Ctenocephalides felis*) (Figure 266) and the dog flea (*C. canis*). These are pests of cats, dogs, and man, but other animals such as rats, rabbits, and poultry are also attacked. They breed in places cats and dogs and other hosts frequent, such as in sheds, homes, cellars, and lawns. Both species possess genal and pronotal combs. The length of the developmental stages from egg to adult may be as short as 2 weeks but frequently the time is much longer, depending upon weather conditions. The cat flea is much more common than the dog flea. Both species are intermediate hosts of the double-pored tapeworm (*Dipylidium caninum*).

The human flea (*Pulex irritans*) (Figure 267A) attacks man, cats, dogs, rats, rabbits, horses, and a number of other animals. Breeding places are the habitats of its hosts. When conditions are favorable, a life cycle may be completed in 3 weeks. Pronotal and genal combs are absent. The maximum length of life of the adult human flea is said to be more than 2 years.

The oriental rat flea (*Xenopsylla cheopsis*) resembles the human flea in that both pronotal and genal combs are absent. It is generally found in buildings and frequently bites man. This species is very important because it is the chief transmitter of bubonic plague. Rodents, chiefly rats, are its principal hosts. The life cycle of this flea is given as 5 weeks or longer. Adults have been reported as living for as long as a year.

Family Dolichopsyllidae

The Dolichopsyllidae is the largest family of fleas. Rodents and birds are the normal hosts. The fleas are characterized by bearing two or more rows of bristles on the abdominal tergites and by the absence of the genal comb. The northern rat flea (*Nosopsyllus fasciatus*) is the most important species. It is widely distributed in both Europe and America. Common hosts are rats, mice, skunks, and man. This species is capable of transmitting bubonic plague, but it is a weak vector.

Family Hystrichopsyllidae

The fleas of this small family are parasites mostly of rats and mice. The cosmopolitan mouse flea (*Leptopsylla segnis*) is one of the best known members. It is worldwide in distribution. Man is rarely attacked by it.

Family Tungidae

Fleas of the Tungidae remain attached on the hosts more or less permanently. The best known members are the sticktight flea and the chigoe flea.

The sticktight flea (*Echidnophaga gallinacea*) (Figure 267B) is a common pest of poultry, dogs, cats, and other animals. The adults

---

Figure 266. The cat flea (*Ctenocephalides felis*). (From Department of Entomology, Texas A&M University.)

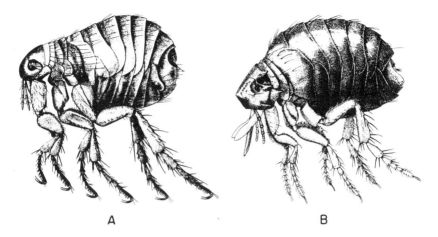

A   **B**

Figure 267. A. The human flea (*Pulex irritans*). B. The sticktight flea (*Echidnophaga gallinacea*). (From USDA.)

Figure 268. Ulcers produced on foot of man by chigoe fleas (*Tunga penetrans*). (From J. Smart, *Insects of Medical Importance,* after Manson-Bahr. Copyright 1943. Used by permission of British Museum of Natural History, London.)

often collect in masses, mostly on the head of the host, and remain attached even for weeks. A life cycle is completed in 30–60 days.

The chigoe flea (*Tunga penetrans*) is a native of tropical regions; it does not occur in the United States. The female burrows into the skin of man and animals, chiefly in the feet, and an ulcer is produced (Figure 268). These ulcers may become infected, with serious results to the host.

Control of fleas consists essentially in ridding the animals of the parasites and their eradication in breeding places. Powders containing rotenone, pyrethrum, malathion, or methoxychlor may be used to control fleas on both cats and dogs. Dichlorvos incorporated in collars is effective on these animals. Carbaryl also may be employed on dogs. Because cats may ingest poisons in cleaning themselves, care must be exercised in selecting insecticides for use on them. Fleas on rodents may be eliminated by dusting their runways and areas between the walls of buildings with malathion and carbaryl, and then poisoning the rodents. Sprays or dusts of lindane, chlordane, malathion, carbaryl, or methoxychlor will control fleas on lawns, in barns or other animal quarters, and under houses. In the home, the pests may be controlled by sprays of carbaryl or methoxychlor. Before spraying, thoroughly clean the rooms, rugs, and upholstered furniture with a vacuum cleaner. Such repellents as diethyltoluamide and dimethylphthalate will give protection against fleas. Some species have developed resistance to certain chlorinated hydrocarbon compounds. When resistance is encountered, malathion or carbaryl should be used.

CHAPTER 17
ORDER HYMENOPTERA[1]

SAWFLIES, ANTS, WASPS, BEES, AND OTHERS

The Hymenoptera are a large order of insects with more than 90,000 known species. This is thought to be the most beneficial order, inasmuch as it contains many parasites and predators of injurious insects, as well as the most important insect pollinators of plants—the bees (Figure 269). However, some destructive forms are found here, e.g., certain species of ants, sawflies, and the wheat strawworm. Within the order there is great diversity in size, form, and development.

Its members may be recognized by the following general characteristics:

1. Wings, usually present, 2 pairs, membranous; hind pair smaller; venation specialized and more or less reduced.
2. Mouthparts for chewing, or for chewing and sucking.
3. Metamorphosis complete.
4. Abdomen of female usually provided with a saw, piercing organ, or sting.

The ants, bees, and wasps are the best known members of the order. However, there is another group, composed of parasites, predators, sawflies, and others which, although less commonly known, is much larger. Instinctive behavior in its highest form is exhibited in members of this order, particularly among the social insects. These insects have been studied by naturalists since early times, and many books have been written about them, but still much about their way of life remains to be known.

The Hymenoptera are placed at the top of the list of the orders of insects by most authorities. The unusually highly developed instinctive behavior of the higher forms of the order is the chief reason for placing them in this position. In morphological aspects the order cannot be so rated. Mouthparts of Lepidoptera, Diptera,

[1] *Hymen*, membrane (or marriage); *pteron*, wing.

Figure 269. The yellow bumble-bee (*Bombus fervidus*). (Courtesy of C. O. Mohr.)

and Siphonaptera are more diverse in form. Wing venation of Diptera, Coleoptera, and other orders exhibits greater modifications. In both morphology and habits dipterous larvae are more specialized. These and other reasons may justify placing the Hymenoptera in a lower position among the orders with a complete metamorphosis.

The meaning of the word Hymenoptera is generally accepted as "membrane wings" because of the nature of the wings. But the characteristic of membranous wings is not distinctive as it is shared by a number of other orders. Perhaps the interpretation "marriage on the wing" is more appropriate because certain common forms, such as honeybees and ants, have mating flights. Normally two pairs of wings are present, but some adults are wingless. The hind wings are smaller than the front wings. The front and hind wings are held together by small hooks, hamuli, on the front margin of the hind wings which fasten into a fold on the hind margin of the front wings. The front and hind wings are thus fitted together so securely on each side that they may be mistaken for a single wing by the novice. Wing venation is specialized and complicated.

All hymenopteron insects are provided with chewing mouthparts, but in the more specialized groups they are modified also for sucking or lapping. In the more generalized forms (e.g., sawflies) the mouthparts are quite similar to those of the Orthoptera, but the mouthparts of bees exhibit marked modifications. The honeybee, for example, has retained the labrum and mandibles as structures typical of chewing mouthparts while the maxillae and labium are modified into a suctorial or lapping organ. Between these extremes of mouthpart types intermediate forms are found.

The female adults of the order usually have a well developed ovipositor. This organ is variously modified for egg deposition or a sting in the more highly developed forms. As the sting is a modified ovipositor, it is quite obvious that the drone bee and other males of the Hymenoptera are harmless.

The Hymenoptera have a complete metamorphosis. The larvae have a distinct head, chewing mouthparts, and spiracles along the sides of the abdomen. In the suborder *Symphyta* the larvae are caterpillarlike in form and bear thoracic legs and also usually abdominal prolegs. In some forms, especially internal feeders, prolegs are absent. Larvae of the suborder *Apocrita* are grublike or maggotlike and legless. Pupae are of the exarate type. Larvae of many species spin cocoons in which to pupate. Cocoons of some forms are composed of rather loose silk, somewhat like the cocoons of moths, and in others they are parchmentlike in texture.

The order Hymenoptera is divided into two suborders, the Symphyta (Chalastogastra), sawflies and horntails; and the Apocrita (Clistogastra), wasps, bees, ichneumon flies, and others. In the suborder Symphyta the abdomen is broadly joined to the thorax, the trochanter has two segments, and there are at least three basal cells in the hind wing. Most members of the Symphyta are plant feeders. In the suborder Apocrita the first segment of the abdomen known as the propodaeum is fused with the thorax, and the second segment is conspicuously constricted into a slender petiole, producing the characteristic "wasp-waisted" appearance (Figure 270). The Apocrita are further characterized by having not more than two basal cells in the hind wing and a one- or two-segmented trochanter.

Suborder Symphyta (Chalastogastra) (Sawflies and Horntails)

The more generalized members of the Hymenoptera belong in this suborder. The body build of the adults is less modified and the wing venation less reduced than with other members of the

---

Figure 270. Thorax with abdominal attachment of typical Hymenoptera, lateral view. A. A paper wasp (Vespidae). B. A digger wasp (Sphecidae). 2nd A, second abdominal segment. Cx, coxa; N_1, pronotum; N_2, mesonotum; N_3, metanotum; N_1L, pronotal lobe; P. propodaeum (first abdominal segment); Pl, pleuron; S, scutellum; Sp, spiracle; Tg, tegula.

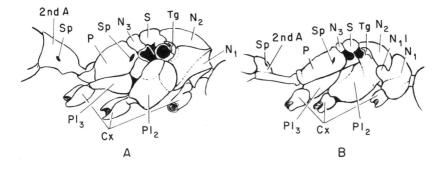

order. The mouthparts are for chewing. Antennae and eyes are well developed. The ovipositor of the females is well developed and more or less sawlike in form for the insertion of eggs in the tissues of the host plants. The larvae are phytophagous, with rare exceptions, and the majority are external feeders. Most of them are caterpillarlike and differ from lepidopterous larvae in having more than five pairs of prolegs, which do not bear crochets. Also, they usually have only one pair of ocelli while caterpillars have several pairs.

Most members of the suborder have only one generation each season, and winter is passed either as larvae or pupae in protected places. Those forms that are external feeders usually diapause in cocoons or within cells in the soil, while the internal feeders generally pass the winter in the feeding tunnels of the host plants.

Family Tenthredinidae (Sawflies)

This is a large family and most members of the Symphyta belong here. Adults are small to medium in size; the largest individuals are seldom more than ⅘ inch in length. Some are brightly colored, and the sexes of the same species may be dimorphic in color. The larvae are mostly external feeders; a few are leaf miners or form galls. Space will permit only a brief discussion of a few of the most common species.

THE PEAR SLUG (*Caliroa cerasi*). The larvae feed on the leaves of pear, plum, and cherry, and occasionally other plants. Feeding is chiefly on the upper surface of the leaves and only the parenchymatous tissue is used as food. This produces a scorched appearance of the foliage, which drops prematurely. The larvae are slimy and sluglike in appearance and are about ½ inch long when fully grown. When mature they leave the trees and form cells in the ground for pupation. Probably two generations occur each season throughout most of the insect's range in the United States. The insects diapause as prepupae in the soil. Sprays of lead arsenate readily control the pest.

THE IMPORTED CURRANTWORM (*Nematus ribesii*). The larvae of this insect are pests of the currant and gooseberry. They are found wherever the currant grows and first appear on the plants early in the spring. The greenish, black-spotted larvae feed on the leaves, and heavily infested bushes may be stripped of their foliage. When mature, cocoons are formed by the larvae either beneath rubbish or slightly underneath the surface of the soil. The adults are about ⅕ inch long and black with yellow markings on the abdomen. There are two generations each season with a partial third in the South. The pest is easily controlled with insecticides. Before the formation of fruit, lead arsenate sprays may be employed. When fruit is present on the plants, applications of rotenone or malathion are recommended.

THE GREEN LEAF WORM (*Isodyctium* spp.). These small green larvae are commonly observed during the spring on foliage of the pecan in Texas and Louisiana. The larvae are found chiefly on the underside of the leaves which they riddle with holes (Figure 271). When mature they enter the soil for pupation. There appears to be only one generation each season. The adults emerge in April, and eggs are inserted in tissues of the new growth. The adults are about ⅕ inch long and beelike in appearance. Carbaryl or malathion sprays provide effective control should control measures be justified.

THE LARCH SAWFLY (*Pristiphora erichsonii*). This is an important pest of the larch in the northern part of the United States and Canada. The larvae often defoliate trees over large areas. The pest overwinters as larvae in brown cocoons found among fallen leaves and debris. Following pupation, adults emerge in late spring or summer. Eggs are deposited in slits made in the young shoots of the plant. The larvae feed first on the edges but later devour the entire leaves. There is one full generation with possibly a partial second each season. Timely applications of stomach poisons control the pest.

Other common species of sawflies are several species of rose

Figure 271. Injury to pecan foliage by the green leafworm (*Isodyctium* sp.). (From Texas Agricultural Experiment Station.)

slugs, the birch leaf miner (*Fenusca pusilla*), and the willow saw-fly (*Pteronidea ventralis*).

Family Cimbicidae (Cimbicid Sawflies)

Adults of the Cimbicidae are large, stout, and bear clubbed anten-nae. The group is small in number of species. The most common member is the elm sawfly (*Cimbex americana*). The adults are bluish black and nearly 1 inch in length. The fully grown larvae are about 1½ inches long, yellowish white or greenish white with a black stripe down the back and with black spiracles. The larvae assume a spiral position when at rest. If disturbed, a fluid may be ejected from glands located slightly above the spiracles. This insect has only one generation annually. Winter is passed as mature larvae in cocoons found in the ground. The larvae feed on the foliage of elm, willow, and occasionally other trees.

Family Pamphiliidae (Web-Spinning Sawflies)

The adults are rather stout bodied in appearance and about ½ inch in length. The family is small in species and the biologies of only a few are known. The plum web-spinning sawfly (*Neurotoma inconspicua*) appears to be the best known member of the group. The larvae feed on the leaves of plums and cherries. They are gregarious and web the leaves together, among which they live. The mature larvae enter the soil in which cells are formed. Here they remain in the larval stage until the next spring when they pupate. Adults emerge the latter part of spring or early summer. Eggs are inserted in slits made in the leaf petioles or midribs of the leaves. Only one generation occurs each season. *Pamphilius persicum*, a leaf-rolling member of the family, feeds on the foliage of the peach.

Family Siricidae (Horntails)

This family of rather large insects is known to have only about 15 species in North America. All the larvae are wood borers.

Figure 272. The pigeon tremex (*Tremex columba*).

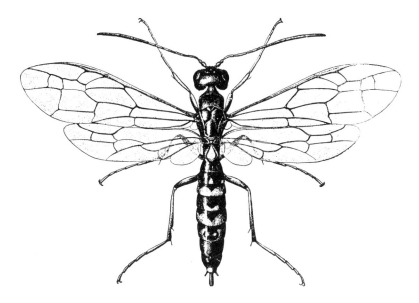

Figure 273. The wheat-stem sawfly (*Cephus cinctus*). (From USDA.)

Adults of both males and females are characterized by a horny spearlike plate borne on the dorsum of the last abdominal segment, and the females bear a long ovipositor.

The best known species is the pigeon tremex (*Tremex columba*). The adults are black and brown, and about 1½ inches in length (Figure 272). Elm, maple, apple, beech, and other trees are hosts. Eggs are laid in the wood and frequently the ovipositor becomes fastened and cannot be removed, and the trapped female dies. The larvae tunnel through the wood and as they grow, the tunnels become progressively larger. The fully grown larvae attain a length of about 1½ inches. Pupation is in thin silken cocoons within the tunnels. The insect seldom occurs in numbers large enough to cause appreciable damage.

Family Cephidae (Stem Sawflies)
The adults are slender and elongate with compressed bodies. The larvae are borers in the stems of grasses, shrubs, and other plants.

THE WHEAT STEM SAWFLY (*Cephus cinctus*). This is an insect (Figure 273) of importance to wheat in the Plains states. A related species, the European wheat sawfly (*Cephus pygmaeus*), occurs in New York and Pennsylvania. Infested wheat fields will have fallen straws suggestive of injury by hessian flies or jointworms. The adults are black with yellow rings on the abdomen. The larvae are found in the frass-filled burrows within the straws. They are wrinkled, pale yellow, and about ⅛ to ½ inch in length. Native grasses, wheat, rye, barley, timothy, and other plants are attacked.

Mature larvae overwinter in the straws near the surface of the ground. Pupation occurs in the spring and adults emerge in early summer. Eggs are deposited within the stems. The larvae tunnel downward in the stems and reach the basal parts of the plants near the ground by late summer. A groove is then cut completely around the inside of the stem, which causes breaking of the straws. A larval chamber is formed for diapausing in the base of the stem.

The most effective control measure is deeply plowing under infested stubble in the fall. Harvesting as early as possible reduces losses. Rotation with immune crops such as corn, alfalfa, and oats is helpful in reducing infestations.

The larvae of the currant-stem girdler (*Janus integer*) tunnel out the canes of the currant in feeding, and reach maturity in the fall. They overwinter within the burrows, enclosed in silken cocoons. The adults are shining black and about ½ inch in length. They emerge in the spring and the females lay their eggs in the canes. Following deposition of the egg, the female girdles the cane with the ovipositor above the puncture. This injury kills the tip of the cane, which checks growth and provides conditions more conducive for development of the larva.

Suborder Apocrita (Clistogastra) (Ichneumon Flies and Wasps)

Most members of the order Hymenoptera belong to this suborder. Its chief morphological characteristic is the constricted base of the abdomen. The thorax appears to consist of four segments. However, the fourth segment, known as the propodaeum, is the first abdominal segment. The constricted abdominal segment, which would seem to be the first, is really the second. The hind wings do not have more than two basal cells. Most of the larvae are grub-like or maggotlike in form, and legless. The form of the ovipositor varies, depending upon the function. In some members it is used for boring; in others, it is employed to place eggs within the bodies of other insects; and in some, such as bees and wasps, it is modified into a stinging organ and connected with poison glands.

The Apocrita have a wide range of feeding habits. Many larvae are parasites of other insects and so they are extremely important in helping keep in check other harmful insects. Some larvae feed on plant materials. Food of the adults consists chiefly of nectar, pollen, sap, other plant materials, and, in case of certain parasites, body fluids of the hosts. The most important pollinators, the bees, are found in this suborder.

The taxonomy of the group is quite difficult. It is divided into a number of superfamilies, many families, and subfamilies. Only some of the more important families and their members can be discussed briefly here.

Family Ichneumonidae (Ichneumon Flies)
The Ichneumonidae form one of the largest families of insects, and its members are very widely distributed. There are probably more than 6000 species in North America. Much variation is found in size, form, and markings of the adults. Most are somewhat wasp-like in appearance and many of the females have a very long ovipositor, often longer than the body. The adults are commonly observed around flowers of the composite group.

All species are parasites in the larval stage. Most groups of insects are parasitized by some member of this family, and spiders are attacked by certain forms.

Megarhyssa macrurus is the largest and probably most interesting of the ichneumons. The larvae are parasites of the larvae of horntails. The female locates in some way a tree infested with horntails and then selects a spot which is judged to be over the tunnel of a horntail larva. She then makes a derrick of her body and drills a hole into the tree with her long ovipositor. When the tunnel is reached, an egg is deposited and the ovipositor is withdrawn. Sometimes the ovipositor becomes wedged and cannot be withdrawn and the trapped insect dies. Upon hatching from the egg, the larva apparently searches out the borer and then feeds upon it. The mature larva pupates within the burrow of the horntail, and the adult emerges the next season.

Pimpla conquisitor is an important parasite of a number of lepidopterous pupae. Eggs are deposited on the larvae in the pre-pupal stage and the small larvae feed on the pupae. This insect is one of the most important parasites of the cotton leafworm (*Alabama argillacea*), and it is also an important natural enemy of the eastern tent caterpillar (*Malacosoma americanum*) as well as a number of other Lepidoptera. The larvae overwinter within the cocoons of some of the hosts. Several generations are thought to be completed each season. The genera *Glypta*, *Campoplex*, *Phobocampe*, and others too numerous to mention contain important parasites.

Family Braconidae (Braconids)
The Braconidae are another large family of parasitic insects. More than 2000 species are known from North America alone. They parasitize a wide range of insects, but chiefly aphids, and the larvae of Lepidoptera, Coleoptera, and some Diptera. The adults resemble the Ichneumonidae. The species tend to be somewhat smaller and stouter bodied than the ichneumon flies, and the wing venation of many is reduced.

Members of this family have much in common with the ichneumons in their habits; however the mode of pupation often differs. Many pupate in cocoons on the outside of the body of the host and others apart from the host with the small cocoons frequently in a mass. Polyembryony (the production of several embryos from one egg) is known to occur in several species.

The genus *Apanteles* is perhaps the most beneficial of the braconids. There are probably 200 species in North America and all are parasites of caterpillars, some of which are of much economic importance.

Apanteles glomeratus (Figure 274) is one of the best known and most important members of the genus. It is a parasite of the imported cabbageworm (*Pieris rapae*), the cabbage looper (*Trichoplusia ni*) and caterpillars of other butterflies and moths. Thirty to 40 eggs are deposited within the body of each caterpillar. The eggs hatch in 3 or 4 days and the larvae feed on the fat and lymph of the host until mature, some 8–12 days later. Then the larvae leave the body of the host and spin their small, white, silken cocoons near the host. The adults emerge 5–10 days following pupation. This insect is of European origin and was introduced into the United States in 1883.

Apanteles congregatus is a common parasite of the larvae of sphinx moths. The presence of the small white cocoons (often mistaken for eggs) on the backs of tobacco and tomato hornworms is frequently observed.

Macrocentrus ancylivorus is an important parasite of the oriental fruit moth (*Grapholitha molesta*) and the strawberry leaf roller (*Ancylis comptana*). This parasite has provided effective control of the oriental fruit moth in some sections. Eggs are laid

Figure 274. A braconid parasite (*Apantales glomeratus*) of the imported cabbageworm and other caterpillars. A. Adult. B. Empty cocoon. C. Adults emerging from cocoons (natural size). (From USDA.)

within the host caterpillar. The length of a life cycle is 25–30 days. Three generations develop annually on the East Coast. Winter is passed as larvae within the bodies of the hibernating hosts.

Microbracon mellitor parasitizes the pink bollworm (*Pectinophora gossypiella*) and other caterpillars. Before eggs are deposited, the host larva is stung and paralyzed. Eggs are deposited either on or near the host. The parasitic larva feeds only on the surface of the body of the caterpillar, sucking the body fluids from lacerations made by the mandibles. A generation of this parasite may be completed in 15–20 days with favorable conditions.

Meteorus laphygma is quite important as a parasite of the fall armyworm (*Spodoptera frugiperda*) and other cutworms in the Southwest. The eggs are inserted in the bodies of second and third instar caterpillars. Each female parasite produces about 100 eggs. Upon reaching maturity, the larvae leave the host and pupate in brown cocoons attached to the host plant of the caterpillar or some nearby object. When conditions are most favorable, a generation may be completed in 12 days. There may be as many as 18 generations annually in warm climates.

Members of the subfamily Aphidiinae parasitize only aphids. These tiny and delicate parasites are among their most important natural enemies. The most important genera of the group are *Aphidius, Lysiphlebus,* and *Praon.* Eggs are deposited within the bodies of the aphids, and the developing parasites devour the internal organs of the hosts. Prior to pupation, a hole is cut through the ventral side of the host, which is then glued to the plant so it will not drop to the ground. A cocoon is then spun in the abdomen of the aphids, with the exception of members of the genus *Praon* which spin their cocoons underneath the body of the dead hosts. The adults cut circular holes through which they emerge. The dead parasitized aphids are brownish and inflated in appearance. *Lysiphlebus testaceipes* is the most common of this group of parasites. Its life cycle is short, varying from 1 to 3 weeks, depending upon temperature.

Family Chalcididae (Chalcid Flies)

This extremely large family of insects is generally considered a superfamily and subdivided into a number of families. Most of its members are small; however some are as large as bees. The general color is metallic blue or green. Only one vein is usually present in the wings. The antennae are elbowed and contain not more than 13 segments.

Nearly all of the chalcid flies are parasites and attack mostly the egg and the larval stages of their hosts. They parasitize chiefly members of the Homoptera, Coleoptera, Lepidoptera, and Diptera. A number of species have been introduced into this country to aid in the control of certain pests. A few species of the family are phytophagous and are pests, e.g., the wheat strawworm (*Harmolita grandis*) and the wheat jointworm (*Harmolita tritici*). However, some forms, such as the fig wasps (*Blastophaga*), although phytophagous, are beneficial as pollinators. Space will permit the brief discussion of only a few members of this large and important family of insects.

Trichogramma evanescens is a common egg parasite (Figure 275) which has been used quite extensively in this country in biological control. The insect parasitizes the eggs of Lepidoptera chiefly, and those of Hymenoptera, Neuroptera, Diptera, and Coleoptera to a lesser extent. The eggs of the parasite are inserted through the chorion of the host eggs. Each female deposits 35–40 eggs. The length of a life cycle of the insect is dependent chiefly on temperature. In summer weather, a life cycle may be completed in 9–16 days. Diapause is as immature larvae within the host eggs. These tiny and frail insects are greatly influenced by weather conditions, which determine their abundance. Some beneficial results have been reported, but as a whole, their use in biological control has not been too encouraging.

Species of the genus *Euplectrus* are gregarious and feed as ectoparasites on caterpillars. *E. platyphenae* feeds on larvae of cutworms. The females deposit their eggs on the bodies of the hosts, usually in clusters of 20–30. Upon hatching, the larvae attach

Figure 275. An egg parasite (*Trichogramma evanescens*) depositing its egg within the egg of a moth. Greatly magnified. (From USDA.)

Figure 276. *Euplectrus comstocki*, an ectoparasite, feeding on the brown cotton leafworm (*Acontia dacia*). (From Department of Entomology, Texas A&M University.)

themselves in a cluster to the body of the host. Here they remain until they are ready to pupate. Pupation is within cocoons underneath the dead caterpillar. The life cycle is short. It is said a life cycle of this insect may be completed in as little as 7 days during warm weather. As many as 18–20 generations may be completed during one season in warm climates. *E. comstocki* is a related species which feeds in clusters on the cotton leafworm (*Alabama argillacea*), the brown cotton leafworm (*Acontia dacia*), the fall armyworm (*Spodoptera frugiperda*), and other caterpillars (Figure 276).

Coccophagus gurneyi is a native of Australia which was introduced into this country to aid in the control of the citrophilus mealy bug (*Pseudococcus gahani*), a citrus pest of California. Each female lays 125 or more eggs. A life cycle is completed in about 4 weeks during warm weather.

Aphelinus mali is a parasite of the woolly apple aphid (*Erisoma lanigerum*). Eggs are deposited within the abdomen of the host. One or more eggs may be deposited in the abdomen of each aphid, but only one parasite ever develops. Each female parasite lays about 100 eggs. The dead aphids appear black and swollen, and the body wall hardens. Pupation is within the abdomen of the host. The adult parasite emerges through an opening it makes in the body wall, usually in the dorsocaudal region of the abdomen. A generation is normally completed in about 1 month.

Eretmocerus serius is an important parasite of the citrus blackfly (*Aleurocanthus woglumi*). It has proved to be very effective in controlling this important pest in those regions where climatic conditions are favorable for its development. Each female lays about 200 eggs and a generation is completed in about 4 weeks. The parasite produces 2 generations while its host is producing 1.

Metaphycus lounsburyi was introduced from Africa to aid in the control of the black scale (*Saissetia oleae*). The parasite reproduces both sexually and asexually. The parthenogenetic offspring are females, and approximately one-fifth of the progeny of fertilized females are males. The length of a life cycle depends upon weather conditions and may vary from 1 to 3 months.

THE FIG WASP (*Blastophaga psenes*). The production of the smyrna fig is dependent upon the tiny fig wasp (Figure 277). Without the pollination services of this insect no fruit would be matured. The common fig plants are dioecious. The male plant is known as the caprifig and produces inedible fruit. The female plant is represented by many commercial varieties, including the smyrna fig. Only this variety requires pollination to mature its fruit. The fruit of the fig plant is a hollow receptacle, and flowers are borne on its inner surface. On the free end of the fruit is a tiny entrance to the receptacle, known as the eye.

The fig wasp develops in galls within the receptacle of the caprifig fruit which produces an abundance of pollen. The bodies of the winged females become covered with this pollen as they crawl over the stamens in leaving the fruit by way of the eye. They enter other fruit in seeking places for oviposition, including the fruit of the smyrna fig plant. The walls of the receptacle of the latter are not suitable for oviposition, but pollination is effected as the insects crawl over the pistillate flowers. The smyrna fig develops only the pistillate flowers.

For centuries it has been known by natives of Asia Minor that the suspension of caprifig fruit in the smyrna fig trees in the spring was essential in the production of a crop, although they did not understand the reasons why. The practice of distribution of caprifigs among the branches of the smyrna fig trees is known as

Figure 277. The fig wasp (*Blastophaga psenes*). A. Female. B. Male. (From USDA.)

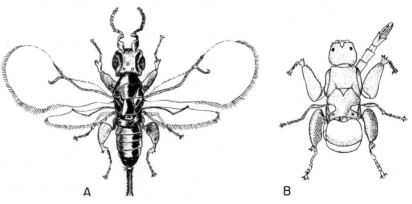

A   B

caprification. The establishment of this insect in the United States was essential for the production of this fruit here. The growing of the caprifig trees is necessary to maintain a supply of the tiny wasps. In commercial production, the caprifig fruit containing mature fig wasps is removed at the proper time and suspended by various methods among the branches of the smyrna fig plants.

THE WHEAT STRAWWORM (*Harmolita grandis*). There are two generations annually of this wheat pest, and each generation produces a different type of injury. Larvae of the first generation cause a stunted appearance of the plants in early spring and usually the crown is destroyed. The infested plants later die or are so injured that they produce no grain. The second generation causes stunting and weakening of the straw, which reduces the yield of wheat.

This widely distributed insect is chiefly a pest in the wheat growing sections west of the Mississippi River. Winter is passed in the straw or stubble as pupae. The adults emerge in the early spring. They are about ⅙ inch in length, wingless, brownish, and antlike in appearance. Eggs are deposited within the stems near the base of the small wheat plants. The larvae tunnel into the stems and eat out the developing heads. Pupation is within the plants and the adults of this generation emerge in the late spring. These adults are larger, and most of them have wings. At the time of their emergence the wheat is usually heading.

Eggs for this generation are inserted in the higher joints near the wheat head. The larvae remain in the straw or stubble through the summer and pupate in midautumn.

As the adults either are wingless or not strong fliers, crop rotation is the most satisfactory method of control. Destruction of volunteer wheat is advised. Disposal of straw aids in reducing the population of the pest.

THE WHEAT JOINTWORM (*Harmolita tritici*). This insect is probably second in importance to the hessian fly as a wheat pest in wheat growing sections east of the Mississippi River. Infested fields show broken or bent straws, suggestive of the injury caused by the hessian fly. The straws exhibit gall-like swellings in which are found the small yellowish larvae.

Winter is passed as larvae or pupae in the galls within the straws. The small, black adults (Figure 278) emerge in the spring, and the females deposit their eggs within the straws above the joints. Irritation produced by the larvae causes the straws to thicken and produces the swellings. Larval development is completed as the wheat is maturing; however, the insect remains in this stage until fall when most of the individuals transform into pupae. Only one generation is produced annually.

Plowing under the wheat stubble deeply or burning it is recommended. Rotation of crops also is of some aid in reducing infestations.

Figure 278. The adult of the wheat jointworm (*Harmolita tritici*). (From USDA.)

THE CLOVER SEED CHALCID (*Bruchophagus platyptera*). This pest is of importance in the production of alfalfa and clover seeds. The small larvae feed within the individual seeds, destroying their contents. Winter is passed, usually as larvae, within the seeds, which are scattered on the ground. The tiny adults emerge in early summer and eggs are inserted within the soft immature seeds. The larval period is fairly short, being about 2 weeks in duration. Two or 3 overlapping generations may develop each season.

This is a difficult insect to control. At the present time, chief dependence for control is on natural enemies. Destruction of chaff and screenings eliminates many immature forms. In some years it is advisable to use the first crop of clover instead of the second for seed, as the yield will be greater. When there are evidences of a heavy infestation, cutting and removing the hay before the seeds mature is advised.

Family Cynipidae (Gall Wasps)

Insects of this family are small, dark colored, with a compressed abdomen. Most members are gall makers, but some are parasites or inquilines. The inquilines live within the galls made by other species and the parasites feed on both gall makers and inquilines. Although most species of this family are always associated with galls, it must be remembered that other arthropods produce galls also, e.g., plant lice, mites, gall midges, flies, moths, and beetles. Each species of gall wasps infests a special part of its host and produces a characteristic gall (Figure 279). The galls are so definite in form that the species may be identified by them.

Eggs are inserted within the tissues of the growing plants where the maggotlike larvae develop. Pupation occurs within the larval cells. Scientists have long speculated on the phenomenon of gall formation, and it is still far from being fully understood. The galls appear to be produced in some way by the reactions of the plant tissues to the stimulus caused by the larvae.

The biologies of gall wasps are often quite involved. Alternation of physiologically and morphologically different generations is found in many species. When alternation of generations occurs, the first generation consists of agamic females which produce a gall of one type, and the second is a sexual generation which makes another type of gall. Furthermore, the individuals of the two generations have been found to be so unlike morphologically that they were thought to be different species until life history studies showed them to be the same. Both sexual and asexual reproduction in the same species may occur at the same time. In many species males are not known to occur, and all generations are similar.

Figure 279. A wool-bearing gall on leaves of live oak produced by a gall wasp (*Andricus lanigerus*). (From Texas Agricultural Experiment Station.)

Gall wasps are of little economic importance. A few of the galls have a slight commercial value in the manufacture of permanent inks, and as a source of dye and tannic acid. Only a small number of species inflict appreciable damage to plants. Most galls are found on oaks (*Quercus*); however, many other kinds of plants also serve as hosts.

A huge number of galls of varied forms and sizes are known, but none are more interesting than the "oak apples." They are formed by the deformation of the leaves caused by the developing larvae. The large oak apple formed by *Amphibolips confluens* is one of the most common forms. It ranges in size from 1 to 2 inches in diameter, and its interior consists of a spongy mass which contains a larval cell. The galls appear on leaves of red, scarlet, and black oaks in early spring. Some of the galls produce both males and females which emerge in early summer; others produce females in the fall.

The empty oak gall is produced by *Amphibolips inanis*. This gall is about 1 inch in diameter, and it is empty except for filaments which hold the larval cell in position.

The gouty oak gall is one of the better known of the stem galls. It is produced by *Callirhytis punctata*. Twigs and small limbs of red oak, water oak, and black oak are infested. The gall consists of rough woody swellings ½ to 1½ inches in diameter (Figure 280). The adult gall wasps emerge in the spring, and eggs are laid in young buds. Alternation of generations is said to occur in this species. The galls cause some damage to shade trees. Cutting out the newly formed galls is the only practical control measure that can be suggested.

Space does not permit the mention of more members of this large family of insects. It is hoped that the brief discussion of the few forms given here will provide some concept of the way of life of this remarkable family of insects.

Family Chrysididae (Cuckoo Wasps)

The cuckoo wasps can be distinguished from other hymenopterous insects by the three- or four-segmented abdomen which is strongly concave below so that it can be folded underneath the thorax. This characteristic enables the insect to roll into a ball for protection when attacked by its enemies. Members of the family are seldom more than ½ inch in length, and their color is usually metallic green or blue.

These insects are so named because they are parasitic in the nests of solitary bees and wasps. The female finds a solitary bee or wasp in the process of building its nest. While the owner is away she slips in and deposits an egg. Later the egg hatches and the larva either devours the rightful occupant of the nest or starves it by eating the stored food. A number of species belong in this family; however, their biologies are little understood.

Figure 280. A stem gall (related to the gouty oak gall) on oak caused by a gall wasp. (From Texas Agricultural Experiment Station.)

Family Pompilidae (Spider Wasps)

The spider wasps provision their nests with spiders, and this practice has suggested the common name. As other wasps have the same habits, the name is not quite distinctive. Members of this family have slender bodies and long spiny legs. Most are medium in size; however, some are quite large. In fact, the largest members of the order belong here.

Most representatives of the family nest in the ground. The wasp seeks out a spider, paralyzes it with the sting, and then digs a burrow. The paralyzed spider is then dragged into the cell prepared at the end of the burrow. Following the laying of an egg on the spider, the passageway is filled with soil. The egg hatches, and the larva feeds upon its helpless host. As biologies of the native species have not been carefully studied, they are not very well known.

Perhaps the best known and most interesting members of the family are the tarantula hawks (*Pepsis* spp.) (Figure 281) which are found in the Southwest. They provision their nests with tarantulas and trapdoor spiders. These giants of the family have

Figure 281. A tarantula hawk (*Pepsis*). (From Department of Entomology, Texas A&M University.)

steel-blue bodies, orange-colored wings, and bear a vicious-appearing sting. They are commonly observed in flight, slowly circling near the ground in search of their prey. Many pitched battles have been fought between these insects and tarantulas, and the aggressors have not always been the victors.

Family Tiphiidae (Tiphiids)

The Tiphiidae are closely related to the velvet ants, *Mutillidae*. Most species are average in size, black, somewhat hairy, and have short legs. All known members are parasites of bees, wasps, tiger beetles, and, particularly, larvae of white grubs (Scarabaeidae). Those that are parasites of the latter group are very beneficial. One species of this group, *Tiphia popilliavora* was imported to this country to help control the japanese beetle (*Popillia japonica*). The female locates the grub in the soil and burrows to its cell. She paralyzes the prey with her sting and then places an egg on the side of the abdomen between the fifth and sixth segments. The larva which hatches from the egg first feeds as an ectoparasite by puncturing the body wall and sucking out the body fluids. In the last larval stage the entire body contents of the host are devoured, and pupation is within the cell of the host. In the North only one generation is completed each year, and diapause is within the cocoon. There may be a succession of generations in warmer climates except when development is halted by dry weather.

Family Mutillidae (Velvet Ants)

This common name has been applied to these insects because of their velvety appearance and their resemblance to ants (Figure

282). Most species are black and strikingly ringed or marked with red, yellow, or orange. The females are wingless; they are capable of inflicting painful stings. The males usually possess wings and are generally larger than the females. This family consists of many species, most of which are found in the South and West.

Information on the biology of these insects is rather meager. So far as is known, all are ectoparasites in the larval stage of prepupae and pupae of wasps and bees mostly, and flies and beetles to some extent. It is said the eggs are laid on the hosts. The eggs hatch and the larvae soon devour the host insect and then spin cocoons, at least in some species, within those of the hosts.

Family Formicidae (Ants)

Because of their wide distribution and common occurrence, ants are the most familiar of all insects with the possible exception of the ubiquitous housefly. Ants are recognized by the presence of one or two nodes between the propodaeum and the gaster (swollen part of the abdomen), elbowed antennae, and the absence of wings except in the sexually mature forms.

Ants have been observed since ancient times, and many references to them are found in literature. They have been seriously studied by biologists, who have written a number of books about

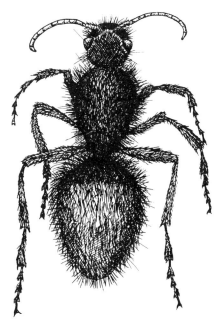

Figure 282. A velvet ant (*Dasymutilla klugii*).

them. Still, our information is quite incomplete, and myrmecology remains a most fertile field of investigation.

No solitary species of ants are known; all are social insects. A colony consists of three castes—workers, males, and females (queens). The workers are modified females. Following the mating flight, the males die and the wings of the young queens are shed. The worker caste is wanting only in certain species that are parasites in the nests of other ants.

Polymorphic forms may exist in each of the three castes. Some males are much larger than others, and some have workerlike characteristics. A somewhat similar series of forms may be found among the queens. Still more variations occur among the workers. Two distinct sizes of workers are commonly found in the colonies of many species, the larger forms designated as majors and the smaller individuals known as minors. A so-called soldier caste with very large heads and mandibles is frequently observed.

Great differences occur in the size of colonies of ants. In some of the more primitive species the number of individuals is quite small, while in the more specialized species there may be tens of thousands of individuals, with a marked division of labor among them. Considerable differences are found in nesting habits. The more common species make their nests in the ground. The number of nests of all species that may be found in the ground within a designated area is astonishingly large, and ants have some value in the improvement of the texture of the soil, as do earthworms. Colonies of other species are located in such places as under stones, in stumps, timbers of buildings, and stems of plants. A typical nest consists of a series of chambers of various forms connected by tunnels. Special cells, such as those of the wasps and bees, are not provided for the brood. The brood is kept in the chambers and may be moved from one to the other to obtain more favorable temperature and humidity conditions.

Food habits of ants differ very much. Some are carnivorous and feed on both dead and live insects, as well as other small animal life. Some species are important as predators of a number of insect pests. Others feed on plant products—seeds, bark, and bulbs. Many members of the family prefer as food sweet fluids—sap, nectar, and honeydew excreted chiefly by certain homopterous insects, mostly aphids. In some cases ants protect aphids for the honeydew they excrete. Species of the tribe Attii grow fungi on chewed up leaves, which is their only food. Workers feed the larvae, and they also lick them to obtain excreted exudates for themselves. This exchange of food materials between adults and immature insects is known as trophallaxis.

Swarms of ants are commonly observed at certain seasons. The individuals in the swarms are recently matured winged males and females. They emerge as if by signal from a number of colonies—probably from all colonies of that particular species in the immediate locality in which the males and females developed. A probable benefit in mass flights is an increase in the chances of the females mating with males of other colonies, and thus preventing too much inbreeding. The factors determining the mass flights are not known.

Mating occurs in the air. After the mating flight the males soon die, and the females proceed to establish new colonies. Some may be captured by workers of their kind and taken into established colonies; others may find their way into colonies without aid. In the usual procedure the wings of the young queen are broken off, and she makes a small cavity in the soil, underneath a stone or bark. The cavity is closed and she remains isolated here for a long period of time, probably months in some cases, while the eggs in her ovaries mature. Eggs are laid and the larvae hatching from them are fed by the young queen with food material secreted in the saliva until they are mature. The queen gathers no food, and the material which sustains her and the larvae is derived from body fat and dissolved wing muscles. The adults of the first brood are workers; they are quite small because of the limited food supply during their developmental period. They open the chamber and go forth in search of food. The care of the colony is then completely taken over by them. The adults subsequently produced are larger than those of the first brood, for they were more adequately fed in the larval stage. As the colony grows, the nest is enlarged by the addition of more chambers. After the colony becomes well established and populous, probably several years later, winged males and females are produced which again go forth on mass mating flights and establish new colonies.

Only a few of the thousands of young queens that attempt to establish new colonies succeed. Birds and predaceous insects destroy many. Adverse weather conditions cause many fatalities. Many starve because the individual female does not have sufficient food reserves. Ants are among the most successful of all insects in nature. This rigorous process of natural selection probably has materially aided in maintaining this position.

The establishment of new colonies is usually by the method described above. However, some young queens do not have the ability to establish colonies and must be adopted by workers of their own species; sometimes they are accepted by colonies of a different species. The adoption of a young female by another species helps explain the mixed colonies which at times are observed. In certain slave-making species a young queen secures adoption in a colony of aliens. She then proceeds to kill the queen of the colony and takes over her duties.

Ants are long-lived insects. The queens, in particular, live for a long time. One queen was observed to live to the ripe old age of 15 years. No other insect is known to live nearly so long in the adult stage. Their colonies may exist for many years, even as long as a generation of man.

THE CARPENTER ANTS (*Camponotus* spp.). These ants have attracted attention particularly because of their large size and their habit of making nesting tunnels in timbers. Occasionally they become pests on lawns and in homes. The common name has been applied to them because of their habit of constructing nests in rotten or decaying wood. They may be predaceous, but more often they are found feeding on dead insects. Sweets are also favorite foods, and aphids and related insects are attended for their honeydew.

The black carpenter ant (*Camponotus pennsylvanicus*) (Figure 283) and its varieties are widely distributed throughout the country. They are brownish and blackish and quite large. Their colonies are most frequently found in stumps, logs, tree trunks, telephone poles, and timbers of buildings. Some damage to telephone poles and timbers of old buildings is attributed to these ants.

Camponotus caryae and its varieties are widely distributed and occasionally become household pests. These ants are blackish and brownish with color variations between the varieties. The *discolor* variety appears to be the most common in the South. Its gaster (abdomen) is black, and the head and thorax a brownish red.

Figure 283. The carpenter ant (*Camponotus pennsylvanicus*). (Prepared by the Clemson University Cooperative Extension Service's Entomology-Plant Pathology and Agricultural Communications Sections, Federal Extension Service Cooperating.)

Sprays of chlordane or dieldrin are recommended in the control of carpenter ants. If the nests can be located, the application of chlordane dust in the entrances is suggested. These compounds are dangerous poisons and must be used with caution.

THE PHARAOH ANT (*Monomorium pharaonis*). This species is probably the best known of the house ants. Color of this ant varies from yellow to red and it is $\frac{1}{15}$ to $\frac{1}{12}$ inch in length. The species may be differentiated from the thief ant (*Solenopsis molesta*), a closely related species, by having three segments in the antennal club while the latter species has two. The insect feeds on almost everything in the house, such as sweets, proteins, fats, dead insects, and bath sponges. Fats are apparently preferred as food. The ant is reported to be predaceous, attacking bedbugs, immature stages of the boll weevil, and other insects.

Nests may be found almost everywhere. Favorite nesting places are behind baseboards, between floors, in furniture or small boxes, and outdoors in trash or under stones. Colonies are occasionally found in linen and clothing.

This insect is difficult to control. Applications of chlordane and dieldrin afford relief from the ants, but repeated applications will need be made to keep them in check.

THE THIEF ANT (*Solenopsis molesta*). The thief ant is very small; it is only $\frac{1}{20}$ to $\frac{1}{15}$ inch in length. The insect is so small that its presence may be overlooked by the housewife. The color is yellow, and the antennal club bears two segments. This is one of the more important house ants. Greasy materials are preferred as food. It is most frequently found around kitchen sinks and cupboards. Nests may be located in cracks and crevices in homes, but they are usually found outdoors in soil or rotten wood. They are often made near the nests of larger species which the insects enter through tunnels too small for the larger forms. Here they prey upon the larvae and pupae of the host ants. Seedcorn is frequently damaged by this insect. Its presence is indicated by starch grains scattered through the soil near hollowed out kernels. The same household control measures are suggested as for the pharaoh ants; however, control is difficult.

THE ARGENTINE ANT (*Iridomyrmex humilis*). Wherever this ant (Figure 284) is found it is the most annoying household pest. The insect is now found in the southern states and California. It is also known in a number of foreign countries. Whenever the pest becomes established in a neighborhood it drives out other species of ants. It infests homes and business places, and feeds on almost all kinds of food materials. Citrus and other fruits suffer injury through attacks on the blossoms, and, indirectly by the ants transporting and protecting aphids, mealybugs, and certain scale insects.

Figure 284. The Argentine ant (*Iridomyrmex humilis*). A. Wingless female. B. Worker. C. Developmental stages: a, eggs; b, young larva; c, mature larvae; d, pupa, lateral view; e, pupa, ventral view; f, pupa, dorsal view. D. Male. (From USDA.)

Workers are about ¹⁄₁₂ to ⅛ inch in length and brown with lighter colored appendages. The petiole has one segment and the inner margins of the mandibles bear about 12 denticles. Nests are established in almost any dark, moist place in lawns, gardens, or orchards. During cold weather the small colonies combine and form large central nests in piles of manure or decaying vegetation.

The best results in control and eradication are obtained through community-wide campaigns. Baits when properly distributed have proved to be efficient in combating the pest. The use of sprays of chlordane and dieldrin within the home are recommended. When nests are located they should be destroyed by treating thoroughly with chlordane sprays prepared with the wettable powders or emulsions. General infestations in gardens, yards, or other outdoor places may be treated with sprays containing suspensions of wettable chlordane powder.

THE SOUTHERN FIRE ANT (*Solenopsis xyloni*). This native species is common in the Gulf states. The workers are larger than those of the Argentine ant, yellowish red, with the smaller individuals much darker colored. This ant is capable of inflicting severe stings. Young animals are often attacked and killed in their nests. The species is omnivorous in its food habits with some preference shown for protein foods. Nests are generally found in open spaces where loose mounds or numbers of craters are formed. A related species (*Solenopsis geminata*) is found chiefly along the coast from Texas to South Carolina. Chlordane and dieldrin sprays and dusts are recommended in the control of these ants. Mirex is also recommended.

THE SLAVE-MAKING ANT (*Formica sanguinea*). This unusual ant is widespread in both Europe and North America. In this country it is found chiefly in Canada and the northern part of the United States. Nests are found in the soil, stumps, or under logs or stones. The workers raid the nests of other species (e.g., *F. fusca*) and carry those pupae that are not devoured to their own colonies. Here the pupae develop into adults and become slaves, so the colony becomes a mixture of the two species.

Formica sanguinea may exist without slaves. However, other species, such as the shining amazon (*Polyergus lucidus*), cannot carry on the normal functions of a colony without slaves to do the work. The mandibles of this species are fitted only for fighting and are not suitable for digging, collecting food, and rearing brood. The amazon queen establishes a new colony by invading a weak colony of *Formica fusca* and killing its queen. In due time, an amazon colony is established. When more slaves are needed, colonies of *F. fusca* are raided, and the pupae are carried off.

THE RED HARVESTER ANT (*Pogonomyrmex barbatus*). The barren, circular areas marking the locations of colonies of the red harvester ant are familiar sights in pastures, fields, parks, and wastelands of the Southwest. The diameter of the area the ants keep devoid of vegetation may vary from one to several yards. The height of the mound usually is only a few inches, but it may be as much as a foot. Trails lead from the nest to the foraging grounds. The nests may persist for a number of years. We once observed a colony which was thought to be more than 40 years of age. Food consists of seeds of many kinds which are stored within chambers of the nests. Sprouted seeds are not used as food and are discarded.

The workers are reddish brown and are ¼ to ½ inch in length (Figure 285). They have a vicious sting which is to be feared. The presence of nests near homes and on the grounds of parks, schools, and other public places is a considerable nuisance. Some loss is

Figure 285. Workers of the harvester ant (*Pogonomyrmex barbatus*).

caused through the collection and storage of seed within the colonies, particularly alfalfa seed. However, the most important loss is the destruction of vegetation around the nests. Frequently a number of colonies may be found in a designated area of pasture and farmland. As each nest represents the destruction of several square yards of grass or field crops, the aggregate loss is appreciable.

The red harvester ant is difficult to control. The use of one of several insecticides provides temporary control; but after a period of time, in some cases months later, ants may reappear in a number of the treated colonies. And, again, new colonies are being established each year. However, annual treatment of all nests in a designated area greatly decreases the number and prevents the establishment of all but small colonies. Early season treatment before much, if any, brood has been raised enhances the chances of destruction of the colony. Dieldrin and chlordane dusts produce the most satisfactory control. The 2 percent dieldrin dust or the 5 percent chlordane dust is applied in a circle as a continuous band about 6 inches wide 2 or 3 feet from the entrance of the nest. A teacupful of water containing 2 percent chlordane as an emulsion or a wettable powder in suspension poured into the entrance of the nest is also an effective treatment.

THE TEXAS LEAF-CUTTING ANT (*Atta texana*). This is the most destructive species of the genus in the United States. It is found in Mexico, south and east Texas, Louisiana, Oklahoma, and probably also occurs in Arkansas.

Damage caused by these ants is in stripping plants of their foliage. A number of trees, shrubs, weeds, and cultivated crops serve as hosts; however, only one species of plants is attacked at one time. Large trees may be defoliated in a relatively short time. Small shrubs and other plants may be denuded overnight. The leaf fragments are carried into the nests, cut into small pieces, and stored in special chambers. The leaves are not used as food, but are utilized as a medium upon which the ants cultivate a fungus which constitutes the only food supply.

This insect is reddish brown and its size is more variable. There are a number of castes within a colony and a marked division of labor. Each caste performs its own special duties. The large, so-called soldiers may be from ⅓ to ½ inch in length and the smallest workers, which tend the fungus gardens, are hardly larger than the pharaoh ant. This species does not sting, but it does bite with the mandibles. A number of queens may be present in a colony.

A colony of leaf-cutting ants (Figure 286) may consist of a few mounds or it may cover an area of several thousand square feet. The interior consists of a series of connected chambers which are usually about the size of squirrel nests and obovoid in conformation. These chambers may extend downward in the soil to a depth of 12–15 feet in exceptional cases. Colonies occur most frequently in sandy soils; however, they occasionally may be found in heavy soil.

During the winter months, the worker ants and the queens are concentrated near the center of the colony. With the advent of warm weather, the queens move to more distant parts of the colony and establish individual centers of activity. It is evident that control measures should be applied before the queens disperse if the best results are to be obtained. The most favorable time for applying control measures is during late winter or early spring.

The use of methyl bromide is the most effective measure for control of the leaf-cutting ant. A 1-pound can of the fumigant will destroy a colony of ordinary size. The gas is injected through a length of rubber tubing inserted in a large entrance tunnel near the center of the colony. Mirex is also used in control.

Family Vespidae (Wasps, Hornets, and Yellow Jackets)
All adult vespids are winged, and when at rest the wings of most species fold lengthwise like a fan. The lateral extensions of the

Figure 286. A colony of the Texas leaf-cutting ant (*Atta texana*). (From Department of Entomology, Texas A&M University.)

pronotum reach the tegulae and do not form rounded lobes as in the Sphecidae and the bees. These two characteristics differentiate members of this family from almost all related insects with which they may be confused. All members of the family construct nests of some type. They may be divided into two separate groups on the basis of their nesting habits, the solitary wasps in which one female makes a nest for her young, and the social wasps in which a number of individuals work together to construct a nest and rear the young.

THE SOLITARY WASPS. Most of the solitary wasps belong to the subfamily Eumeninae, and its members are commonly known as eumenids. Nesting habits are varied. Many make burrows in the ground; some in wood; others in stems of pithy plants; and some are mason wasps, constructing nests of earth. A nest may consist of one or a series of cells. Each cell is provisioned with insects, chiefly caterpillars, which have been paralyzed by the sting. Then an egg is laid and the cell is sealed. Most species have the unusual habit of suspending the egg by a slender thread from the cell walls. Adults are carnivorous and also feed on nectar.

A majority of the eumenids belong to the genus *Odynerus*. The body conformation and frequently the color markings resemble the yellow jackets, but the body is usually smaller and more slender. Many species of the genus make their burrows in level ground or on sides of cliffs and ravines. The cells are provisioned with caterpillars. Some forms construct mud turrets over the entrance to the burrows. Members of the genus *Eumenes* construct mud nests (Figure 287), which resemble tiny water jugs, on twigs of plants.

THE SOCIAL WASPS. Within a colony of social wasps are found three castes, as with the ants—the females or queens, workers, and males. The workers are females which are imperfectly developed sexually. Both workers and queens are capable of inflicting painful stings. In the common paper wasps, *Polistes*, the queens and workers are quite similar in appearance.

In temperate climates colonies of social wasps are not permanent, and the nests are abandoned at the close of the season. Males

Figure 287. Mud nest of a potter wasp (*Eumenes*) on the stem of a plant.

Figure 288. Paper wasps (*Polistes annularis*) and nest. (From USDA.)

are reared in a colony only during the latter part of the season. When the weather becomes cold in the fall the males and workers die, and the fertilized females seek overwintering quarters in sheltered places. In the spring the females emerge from diapause, begin the construction of new nests, and lay eggs. The first brood consists only of workers, which upon emergence proceed to procure food for the larvae and queens, and expand the nests. After the emergence of the first brood the sole function of the queen is egglaying.

Social wasps have predatory habits, and the larvae are fed chewed-up insects. The adults also feed on nectar, honeydew, exuded sap, and fruit juices. Another source of food of the adults is a liquid material emitted from the mouth of the larvae.

The common paper wasps belong to the genus *Polistes*, which is represented by a number of species and varieties. Their familiar nests consist of a single horizontal series of cells, not enclosed in an envelope, and supported by a short, stout peduncle (Figure 288). They are most commonly found hanging under eaves of buildings, in sheds, barns, and from branches of shrubs and trees. The nests are gray and are composed of a paperlike material made from weathered fibers of wood. This material is collected from dead trees, unpainted boards, fences, and posts, and is chewed by the mandibles into a paste with the addition of a salivary fluid. Most nests are relatively small; however, some nests of *Polistes annularis* which are approximately the size of a man's hat may be found during the latter part of the season. Wasps are beneficial because they destroy the caterpillars of many injurious insects, such as the corn earworm and the cotton leafworm.

Each section of the country has its common species of wasps. *Polistes annularis* is a black form which builds its nests outdoors in shrubs and trees. The individuals fight and sting viciously when the nest is disturbed, a fact to which any country boy can attest. *Polistes rubiginosus* constructs its nests in dark and protected places between walls and in hollow logs. *P. pallipes* is a black form with yellow markings, commonly found in the East. Its nests are located in old buildings and other sheltered places. *P. exclamens* and related species are common in the Southwest. These adults are conspicuously marked with yellow and are erroneously called yellow jackets by many. True yellow jackets belong to the genus *Vespula* and make their nests in the ground.

The bald-faced hornet (*Vespula maculata*) is a large black and white insect, which is widely distributed in North America. The oval shaped nests are often quite large and are usually found attached to limbs of trees (Figure 289). The nests are constructed of the same paperlike material as that of common wasps. They differ radically from wasp nests in being enclosed in an envelope and consist of several layers of horizontal cells. There is a single opening at the lower end of the nest; this is always guarded by

Figure 289. Nest of the bald-faced hornet (*Vespula maculata*). (Redrawn from *The Hymenoptera of Connecticut,* Bull. 22, Connecticut Geological Natural History Survey.)

special workers. As a colony increases in size, the nest is enlarged. Nests are abandoned at the end of the season. The fertilized females hibernate in barns, attics, and other sheltered places, emerge and begin new nests in the spring. Hornets are beneficial, inasmuch as the workers prey upon such insects as flies and caterpillars. The prey is masticated and fed to the larvae within the cells.

Several species of *Vespula*, e.g., *V. diabolica* and *V. maculifrons*, are known as yellow jackets. They make their nests in cavities within the ground. A favorite nesting site is where a small stump has rotted away. Hollow stumps are also utilized as sites for colonies. These black and yellow-banded insects are much smaller than the hornets and wasps, and their sting, although painful, is not nearly so severe.

Family Sphecidae (Mud Daubers, Cicada Killers, and Others)
Members of this large family can usually be distinguished from related insects by the lateral extensions of the pronotum which form rounded lobes and do not reach the tegulae, and by the hairs on the thorax which are simple and not branched or plumose. All adults bear wings which are not longitudinally folded. Nesting habits differ greatly. Some build nests in the ground, others construct nests of mud, and certain species make cells in stems of pithy plants or utilize any other suitable cavity that may be found. All species provision the cells of the nests with spiders or insects which are paralyzed by the sting. When the nests are completed, most species quickly store sufficient food for larval development, lay an egg in each cell, and seal it. This method of feeding is known as mass provisioning. However, species of *Bembix* and some others feed the larvae from day to day until they are mature. This is termed progressive provisioning. Obviously a female can produce only a few young by this type of feeding. The mature larvae spin cocoons and pupate within the cells. A number of species have been carefully studied because of their intriguing habits. The limited space in a general textbook permits only a few notes on the biologies and habits of some of the most common forms.

The organ-pipe mud daubers belong to the genus *Trypoxylon*. The adults are black, moderate in size, and are rather elongate and slender. Some of the species construct nests of mud which consist of several parallel and contiguous tubes often 3 or more inches in length (Figure 290). Each tube is divided into cells by transverse partitions. The cells are provisioned with spiders. While the nest is being constructed and provisioned, the male stands guard during the absence of the female. Other members of the genus nest in branches of plants, abandoned tunnels of beetles, and similar cavities.

The thread-waisted wasps are probably the best known members of the family. This name has been given them because of the

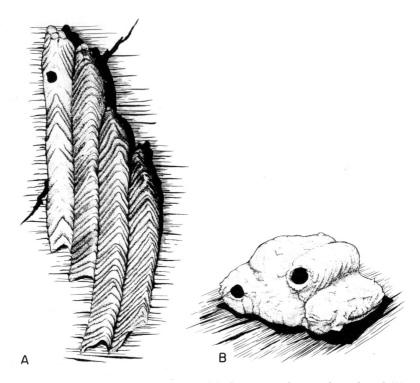

Figure 290. A. Nest of the organ-pipe mud dauber (*Trypoxylon*). (Redrawn from S. W. Frost, *General Entomology*. Copyright 1942 by the McGraw-Hill Book Co. Used with permission of McGraw-Hill Book Co.) B. Nest of yellow mud dauber (*Sceliphron cementarium*).

long petiole of the abdomen. The adults are rather large, measuring an inch or more in length. Most of them make nests in the ground, but the mud daubers that construct the nests of mud found on ceilings and walls of buildings or other protected places are more commonly observed. The adults have the peculiar habit of nervously jerking the wings at frequent intervals. They are commonly seen around damp places collecting mud in small balls and flying away to some building or other protected place where the nests are being constructed. The nests usually consist of several rows of cells about 1 inch long placed side by side. The cells are provisioned with spiders.

The two most common mud daubers are the blue mud dauber, *Chalybion californicum,* and the yellow mud dauber, *Sceliphron cementarium.* The blue mud dauber has a steel-blue body and blue wings. This species does not build its own nest but appropriates the nests of the yellow mud dauber. It brings water to the nest, softens the mud, and digs open the cells. The cells are carefully cleaned of their contents and restocked with spiders of its own. An egg is then laid in each cell, after which it is resealed. It is said this species uses the black widow spider quite extensively in provisioning its nests. The yellow mud dauber is blackish brown with yellow markings and yellow legs. At least two generations of this species are completed each season. Diapause is within cocoons in the cells.

Certain members of the genus *Ammophila* (Figure 291) are known as the tool using wasps. They make their nests in the ground and provision the cells with caterpillars. The burrows are closed with earth which is then packed by pounding with a small stone or other object held between the mandibles.

The cicada killer (*Sphecius speciosus*) is a large and striking insect 1–1½ inches in length. It is black or rusty with yellow bands on the abdomen. Adults appear in the summer when cicadas are present and prepare nests in the ground. The cells of the nests are provisioned with cicadas, one or two individuals being placed in each cell, after which an egg is laid and the cell sealed.

The sand wasps are stout bodied and of moderate size. They are most easily recognized by the elongate and triangular labrum. These wasps nest in sandy soils, and many burrows may be located in a restricted area, forming a nesting community. The adults practice progressive feeding; the larvae are supplied with food consisting chiefly of flies until they are mature. The best known species of this group in the South is the horse guard (*Bembix carolina*). This common name has been given it because of the habit of hovering around livestock in its search for flies. The adult is about 1 inch long, black with light yellow or light yellowish green markings on the abdomen. We once observed a

Figure 291. A digger wasp (*Ammophila*). (From Utah Agricultural Experiment Station.)

nesting site of this species in sandy soil about ½ acre in area, in which thousands of nests were located.

BEES

Bumblebees and honeybees are the most familiar members of this group of insects; however, they represent only a few of about 2500 species which are known to occur in North America. There are not only many species, but the individuals are numerous. Many may be observed visiting flowers on any favorable day during the warm seasons.

Although differing much in habits and size, detailed morphological characteristics of bees are so similar that no satisfactory classification is generally agreed upon. The grouping followed here is that of Comstock. In common with the *Sphecidae*, the lateral extensions of the pronotum of bees terminate in lobes which do not reach the tegulae. A basic difference between bees and most nest building Hymenoptera is that they provision their nests with pollen and honey instead of spiders and insects. Their most distinctive characteristics are morphological modifications which are correlated with the collection of this food material. A characteristic present in only a few other Hymenoptera is branched or plumose hairs on the body, especially the thorax. The branched hairs are concerned with the collection of grains of pollen when flowers are visited. Females are provided with pollen brushes, with the exception of species of *Prosopis* and parasitic bees. Pollen brushes are borne on the hind legs except in the *Megachilidae*, in which family the brush is located on the ventral side of the abdomen. Those bees which carry pollen on the hind legs have the first segment of the tarsus (metatarsus) dilated to form a pollen basket (corbicula) on the outer surface. The maxillae and labium of the mouthparts are greatly modified to form a proboscis for lapping the nectar of flowers. The structure of the proboscis exhibits considerable variation among the groups and provides a useful characteristic in classification.

Nesting habits of bees are similar to those of wasps. Most bees are solitary in habit, and nest in the ground, stems of pithy plants, or tunnel in solid wood. Some, often referred to as cuckoo bees, make no provisions for their young, but oviposit in nests of other bees where they live as parasites or inquilines. The bumblebees and honeybees comprise the social bees which live in colonies consisting of many individuals. Within their colonies are found the three castes—queens, workers, and males (drones).

Honeybees, bumblebees, and also the solitary bees are the most important insect pollinators of plants. These insects are of primary importance in the pollination of many orchard fruits and other economic plants. When the annual value of crops produced on insect-pollinated plants in this country is estimated, the importance of bees to agriculture is quite obvious.

Family Andrenidae (Andrenids)
This is a large family of solitary bees. All construct nests, with the exception of parasitic species. The length of the proboscis is quite variable, but it is always pointed at the apex. Females of the nest building species bear pollen brushes on the hind legs. Only a few genera and species can be discussed here.

ANDRENA. Some members of this genus (Figure 292) are about as large as the worker honeybee. Nests are made in ground that is more or less bare of vegetation. The bees dig vertical tunnels from which branching brood chambers are made. Although solitary in habit, the females tend to build their nests close together and form nesting communities.

HALICTUS. This common group of mining bees includes many species which are small to moderate in size; they are often of a metallic color. Their nests are made in level ground, sides of ditches, or along pathways. Nesting communities containing hundreds of bees are often observed. A nest consists of a burrow from which short, lateral burrows are excavated. Each lateral burrow terminates in a cell which is lined with clay. A mass of pollen and honey, kneaded into a rounded pellet, is placed in each cell. An egg is then deposited on the food material and the cell is sealed. Information on the biology of the group is rather limited. It appears that only fertile females overwinter. They emerge in the spring and establish nests. Some species produce one generation each season; others may have two. The first offspring reared in the spring are females. The males appear later in the season and die when the weather becomes cold. In some species, at least, several females use the same tunnel to the cells they are preparing and provisioning. The opening to this common tunnel is constricted; a guard is posted there, and only bees that are members of the group are allowed entrance.

Figure 292. A mining bee (*Andrena wilkella*). (From D. J. Borror and D. M. DeLong, *An Introduction to the Study of Insects*. Copyright 1954 by D. J. Borror and D. M. DeLong. Copyright © 1964, 1971 by Holt, Rinehart and Winston, Inc. Used by permission of the authors and Holt, Rinehart and Winston.)

ANTHOPHORA. This is a widely distributed genus and more than 80 North American species are known. The adults are of average size, robust, and hairy. Nests are usually constructed in steep banks, preferably in clay soils. Walls of adobe houses in the Southwest are favorite nesting sites. While digging the tunnels, the females make frequent trips to bring water for moistening the hard, dry soil. The wet pellets of earth removed from the tunnels are used to construct turrets over the entrances. The turrets are rough on the outside and slope outward and downward. The tunnels terminate in lateral cells. The walls of the cells are waterproofed with a cementing substance. Following the completion of the cells, a mixture of pollen and honey is placed in each, an egg is deposited, and the cell is sealed. Only one generation is completed each season. Winter is passed in the larval stage within the cells. Members of this group also are gregarious in their nesting habits, and numbers of nests may be found in a restricted area.

THE CARPENTER BEES. Two genera comprise this group, the large carpenter bees (*Xylocopa*) and the small carpenter bees (*Ceratina*). The large carpenter bees are nearly 1 inch in length and resem-

Figure 293. Nest of a carpenter bee showing arrangement of the brood cells. (From Texas Agricultural Experiment Station.)

Figure 294. Exit holes of the large carpenter bee *(Xylocopa virginica)* in the end of a log. (From Texas Agricultural Experiment Station.)

ble bumblebees in both size and appearance. The dorsum of the abdomen is rather bare, and the females do not have pollen baskets on the hind legs but brushes of hair instead. Nests are made in solid wood; the tunnels may be as much as 1 foot long. Tunnels are divided into cells with partitions made of bits of wood cemented together (Figures 293 and 294). Pollen, honey, and an egg are placed in each cell. Winter is passed as larvae within the cells. Only one generation is thought to be developed each season.

The little carpenter bees are greenish blue and about ¼ inch in length. They make their nests in stems of pithy plants such as sumac. The arrangement of the nest is similar to that of the large carpenter bees. Two generations are developed each year. Winter is passed as females in the old nests.

Family Megachilidae (Leaf-Cutter Bees and Related Forms)
Members of the family are fairly large and rather stout bodied (Figure 295). They may be differentiated from most related bees by the presence of two submarginal cells, subequal in size on the front wings, and by the females of the pollen-collecting species having the pollen brush on the ventral side of the abdomen instead of on the legs.

Some members of the family are known as leaf-cutters, because they cut out neat circular pieces of leaves with which they line the cells of their nests. The nests may be difficult to locate, but the work on leaves of plants is quite conspicuous. Nests of Megachilidae are made in natural cavities, stems of pithy plants, and the ground. Some species of the family are quite valuable as pollinators of alfalfa and other crops.

The leaf-cutters comprise the genus *Megachile*. The provisions for the brood, consisting of a mixture of honey and pollen, are placed in a leaf-lined cell. Several such cells are usually made end

Figure 295. *Megachile latimanus,* a leaf-cutter bee. (From D. J. Borror and D. M. DeLong, *An Introduction to the Study of Insects.* Copyright 1954 by D. J. Borror and D. M. DeLong. Copyright © 1964, 1971 by Holt, Rinehart and Winston, Inc. Used by permission of the authors and Holt, Rinehart and Winston.)

to end in the tunnel. Many species of the genus *Osmia* construct nests of earth which is bound together with a fluid thought to be secreted by the salivary glands. Nesting sites are almost any available cavity in wood, plant galls, stems, snail shells, and between stones. Other common genera are *Anthidium* and *Coelioxys.*

Family Bombidae (Bumblebees)

This family is comprised of the common bumblebees (*Bombus*) and certain parasitic species of the genus *Psithyrus.* Bumblebees are large to medium in size and are rather densely clothed in black and yellow hairs. The common name has been given them because of the noise made in flight.

THE BUMBLEBEES (*Bombus* spp.). About 50 species of bumblebees are known to occur in North America. All are social insects; a colony consists of three castes—queens, workers, and males. The workers are imperfectly developed females. The males are developed from unfertilized eggs. In temperate climates both males and functional females are produced only the latter part of the season. They mate, the males together with the workers die with the advent of cold weather, and the fertile females (queens) overwinter in protected places.

In the spring the queens emerge from hibernation and proceed to establish new colonies. A nesting site may be a depression in the ground, a deserted mouse's nest, a hollow log, a cavity in a rotted stump, or a place may be made in a pile of grass, weeds, or other rubbish. Having selected a nesting site, the queen prepares the nest. This is made from the finest and softest materials available, e.g., dry grass and moss. Within this heap of material a cavity is formed with an entrance to one side. Pollen and nectar are collected, mixed into a paste, and placed in the center of the floor of the cavity. A small waxen cell is constructed upon this mass of food material. The first batch of eggs is laid in the cell, which is then sealed with wax. The queen carefully guards the cell containing the eggs until they are hatched. A large waxen pot is constructed near the entrance of the nest and filled with honey to provide adequate food for use while she is on guard and during inclement weather. The eggs hatch in about 4 days, and the larvae first feed upon the mass of pollen and honey which forms their bed. Later, additional food is provided by the queen through a small hole made in the wax covering of the cell. The wax covering is enlarged as the larvae grow. The larval period is about 10 days. Then each larva spins a thin but tough cocoon in which to pupate. About 2 weeks are spent in the pupal stage. The first brood usually consists of only 5–15 individuals. The empty cocoons from which the adults emerged are utilized as receptacles for the storage of pollen and honey. Additional cells of wax are also made for this purpose. All individuals produced in the first part of the season are workers. As soon as the first brood emerges from the pupal stage, these workers assume all duties of the colony except egglaying, to which duty the queen then devotes all her time. If conditions are favorable, the colony increases in strength and at its peak may contain several hundred individuals.

The proboscis of bumblebees is longer than that of the honeybee and most solitary bees. This longer proboscis enables them to pollinate more efficiently the flowers of certain plants, such as red clover, in which the corollas are so long that the nectaries cannot be reached very well by bees with shorter proboscides. Since bumblebees are highly beneficial as pollinators, their nests should not be destroyed. Moreover, where their services are most needed in the production of seed crops, such as red clover and alfalfa, they should be encouraged to establish nests by the creation of more favorable environmental conditions.

Bees of the genus *Psithyrus* are parasites in the nests of bumblebees. The females may be recognized by the absence of pollen baskets on the hind legs. However, the males of the two genera are quite similar in appearance. These parasites have no worker caste. Eggs are laid in the nests of bumblebees, whose workers rear the brood as their own.

Family Apidae (Honeybees)
The family, as considered here, is comprised of only one genus, *Apis*. Four species are generally recognized; however, one of these

may be considered a variety. Only one species, the common honey-bee (*Apis mellifera*) (Figure 296) which was introduced by the early English and Spanish settlers, is found in North America. Several races of the honeybee are recognized and are used in commercial beekeeping. The remaining species are indigenous to specific regions, including the Malay peninsula and India. *Apis dorsata* (the giant bee of India) and *Apis florea* (the dwarf bee of India) build a single comb suspended from a limb or ledge. They are unmanageable and worthless in commercial beekeeping. *Apis indica* is similar in size and habits to the honeybee. Some authorities consider it a variety of the common honeybee.

Unlike the bumblebees, which disband at the close of the season when fertile females overwinter, the honeybees cannot overwinter, and their colonies are established on a permanent basis. Inasmuch as honeybees maintain their colonies throughout the year, which necessitates the storage of food (honey); and whereas they are the only pollinating insects which can be controlled, they are extremely valuable to man.

Man probably began keeping bees before there were any records of the human race; beekeeping, therefore, is one of the oldest agricultural pursuits. Bees were kept through the centuries for the honey and beeswax they produced. But beekeeping is today a minor branch of agriculture insofar as the monetary return from honey and wax is concerned. However, bees are very important in the pollination of many plants (Figure 297). Their worth to agriculture as pollinators has been conservatively estimated at 15 to 25 times the value of honey and beeswax they produce. Fifty or more crops are dependent upon bees for the maximum

---

Figure 296. The honeybee (*Apis mellifera*), worker, queen, and drone (male). (From USDA.)

Figure 297. Honeybee collecting nectar on alfalfa blossom; pollen is also picked up. (USDA photo by W. P. Nye.)

production of seed or fruit. Formerly there was more uncultivated land which provided more suitable places for the nesting of the native bees (bumblebees and solitary bees). In most areas there were sufficient numbers of these bees to take care of pollination needs. Since more large areas have been brought under cultivation and the habitats of the native pollinators destroyed, there are not sufficient native insect pollinators, and agriculture must depend more upon honeybees (Figure 298). Probably more than 80 percent of insect pollination of fruit and seed crops today is done by honeybees.

In nature, colonies of bees are found in hollow trees and logs, and in caves. The nests are made up of several vertical waxen combs with cells on both sides. The cells are utilized for the storage of honey and pollen, and the rearing of brood—(Figure 299).

A colony of bees is composed of three castes, a queen, workers, and males (drones). It may have a population of 30,000–60,000 individuals. The queen resembles a paper wasp with short legs and wings. She is not so robust as the drone, but her abdomen is longer and more tapering. She does not rule or direct the activities of the colony in the least. Nevertheless, perfect harmony and unity of action always exist among its individuals. The basic instinct of all is the survival of the colony as a unit.

The only function of the queen is that of egg laying. During the peak of the brood-rearing season she may lay as many as 1500–2000 eggs daily for short periods. The queen never mates

Figure 298. A modern beehive alongside an old fashioned bee gum. (From Texas Agricultural Experiment Station.)

Figure 299. A comb of brood. (From R. Grout, *The Hive and the Honey Bee.* Copyright © 1949. Used by permission of Dadant & Sons, Publishers of American Bee Journal, Hamilton, Ill.)

after she begins to lay eggs. The colony is left only when she takes her mating flights and again when she emerges with a swarm. Bees mate in the air. Queens are reared in large cells known as queen cells and are fed throughout the larval period on a highly nutritious food, royal jelly, which is a secretion of glandular origin. With rare exceptions, queens develop from fertile eggs. The developmental period of the queen brood is 16 days. The life of a queen may last several years.

Drones are reared in drone cells from infertile eggs. The developmental period of a drone brood is 24 days. The individuals are larger and more robust than the queens, but the abdomen is not so long and pointed. They have no sting and are physically disqualified for any work. Their only reason for existence is the fertilization of the young queens. As they consume large quantities of food, the workers will not tolerate their presence when the swarming season is over and the honey flow has drawn to a close. They are starved and driven out of the colonies to die.

Workers are the smallest and most populous members of the colony. They develop in the worker-size cells from fertile eggs. As development is in small cells and the larvae are not fed the highly nutritious food, royal jelly, throughout the larval stage, they develop into sexually imperfect females. Three weeks are required for the development of the worker brood.

The length of life of the adult worker depends upon the amount of work it does. It may live throughout the cold winter months, but during the honey-gathering season it expends its energy and dies in about 6 weeks. The worker is correctly named, for it does all the work both in the colony and in the field, with the exception of egg laying. The young worker bees feed and care for the queen and brood, polish the cells, secrete wax, build the combs, clean the hives, convert the nectar into honey, ventilate the hives, and act as guards. When they are about 3 weeks old they become field bees. Their duties as field bees are gathering nectar, pollen ("bee bread"), propolis (a gum from trees for sealing cracks and crevices), and supplying the colony with water.

Bees collect nectar of flowers when it is available. It then must be converted into honey. The principal sugar found in nectar is sucrose or cane sugar. Enzymes are added to the nectar and most of the sucrose is transformed into dextrose and levulose. The excess water is evaporated to less than 20 percent and the product, which is then honey, is sealed in the cells with waxen caps.

In nature, bees increase the number of colonies by swarming. During late spring or early summer when the colony becomes overcrowded, the weather warm, and some nectar available, the swarming impulse is manifested and the colony prepares for this important event. A number of queen cells are started, work slackens, and scout bees seek a new habitation. As the time approaches for the emergence of the young queens, the swarm, composed chiefly of field bees and the old queen, emerges from the colony and clusters on some convenient object such as the limb of a tree (Figure 300). Soon afterward the cluster is broken, and the bees fly away to establish a new colony.

Bees have a means of communication by which they can transmit information of new sources of nectar, pollen or water, and also

Figure 300. A swarm of bees clustered on a limb. (From American Bee Journal.)

indicate directions and distances. This is done by the returning worker bees by means of characteristic dances or movements on the combs. Many other social insects have communication systems also, but not much exact information is known about them.

CHAPTER 18
SOME ECOLOGICAL ASPECTS AND INSECT BEHAVIOR

A comprehensive presentation of the ecology and behavior of insects is not possible in a general text, but much pertinent and useful information on their environmental relationships, their interrelationships, and behavior can be summarized here. Ecology is a valuable aid in studies of insect control, behavior, taxonomy, and distribution.

In any environment every animal and plant has its influences upon others. Some of these relationships may be direct and simple, or indirect and quite involved. *Ecology* is the study of the total relationships of all animals and plants in their environment, involving the organic as well as the inorganic. This is a very complex science and no plant or animal, or any biotic unit, with all of the interactions and influences of such factors as temperature, water, sunlight, soils, and involved chemical processes, is fully understood. When research is conducted by an ecologist on an insect or a group of insects, many factors may be included in the study. However, as a rule, only the key factors which have a major influence on insects are considered.

The North American continent is roughly divided into a number of biological zones (*biomes*) such as the semidesert region of the Southwest, the prairies of the Midwest, the subtropical areas of the southern tips of Florida and Texas, and the timbered regions of the East and the North, and elsewhere. Within any biome a number of smaller units can be observed. For example, within a forested region, open areas are found. There may be bodies of water, swamps, and hills. Transitional areas may be between these. These are biological units of natural areas known as *communities*.

A community is considered by some as an assemblage of species within a habitat (Figure 301), while others would stress the ecological interrelationships of the species here. A *habitat* is an area decided upon rather arbitrarily by the investigator. It would seem to possess certain uniform qualities of topography, vegetation, and other characteristics which are thought to be important. Per-

Figure 301. A typical habitat of the cotton fleahopper (*Psallus seriatus*). A favorite host plant (*Croton capitata*) in the foreground. (From Texas Agricultural Experiment Station.)

haps a more logical approach would be to consider all places where the animal may live. Probably a place to live would be a more satisfactory term than habitat.

Some may prefer to consider the animal and its environment as a unit known as an ecosystem. An *ecosystem* may be defined as a self-containing habitat in which living organisms and the physicochemical environment interact in an exchange of energy and matter to form a continuing cycle. An ecosystem is so involved it would probably defy analysis, and this approach would hardly be of aid in understanding the distribution and abundance of different animals in nature. It is perhaps more logical to approach the problem from the viewpoint of the environment of the individual. Artificial agricultural ecosystems of man, known as *agroecosystems*, are of special interest to the entomologist. They usually consist of monocultures of plants, of several varieties and ages, fertilized and often irrigated, and are frequently very unstable. That is, they may have huge populations of different insects which are not held in reasonable limits by natural control factors. This often results in great economic damage to agricultural crops.

Conversely, in natural ecosystems outbreaks of pests do occur, but with less frequency.

Within each community are found dominant forms of plant and animal life. Although they also usually occur in other areas, there are locations where each species is best adapted. Some animals are herbivorous; others are carnivorous or scavengers. There are present disease organisms, parasites, and predators. All make up a web of relationships which is combined into one biological unit. Within this community, the place or status of each species is termed its *niche*.

The natural distribution of an animal is not just a matter of chance, but is the result of the effects of complex ecological factors upon it. Insects living within a region have become adapted to conditions over a long period, or upon migration into the area found the environmental factors suitable for their way of life. Some species which are absent may never have occurred there, or because the environment was so harsh migrated elsewhere or became extinct.

There are two approaches to the study of ecology. Animals and plants may be studied as a whole, with a combination of all environmental factors, together with biological activities and interrelationships within communities. The approach from this viewpoint is known as *synecology*. *Autecology* is the study of an individual species with all its life activities and its responses to everything else within the community.

To acquire some basic understanding of the distribution and abundance of insect life in nature, it is necessary that the components of the environment be divided and subdivided so that they may be studied separately as much as possible to determine their individual effects upon insect populations. Because of the interaction of all factors, it is almost impossible to separate them completely.

The ecological factors of the environment may be considered in four major categories: (1) weather; (2) food; (3) a place to live or habitat; and (4) biotic factors.

WEATHER

Weather affects everything within a community in a direct or indirect way. It consists of conditions which are present from day to day and not annual averages (climate). The principal components are temperature, humidity, light, and air currents. All may have an influence on development or behavior of insects and other organisms. Because there is an interaction of these factors, the effects of one may depend upon the others. Weather determines the availability of food, which largely determines survival. Direct influences of the weather factors are rates of development and increase. It is an important factor affecting the dispersal and diapause of insects and may influence behavior in many other ways.

TEMPERATURE

Insects are cold blooded animals, and the temperature of their bodies is approximately the same as that of the environment. It fluctuates with the immediate surrounding temperatures. They are so physiologically adjusted that they can withstand temperatures not normal in their geographical range. A few species of social insects, particularly the honeybee, are able to exert an influence on the temperature of their colonies. When the temperature becomes too high, bees fan to produce air currents within the hive. Also, water is brought in and is deposited in empty cells of combs on the top bars of the frames so that evaporation may aid in lowering the temperature. In cold weather bees cluster, and heat is produced by the oxidation of food that is consumed. A large colony with ample stores may withstand quite low temperatures.

The extremes of temperature at which insects may live extend over a wide range. Certain dipterous larvae may live at a temperature of 120° F in hot springs. But the upper zone of fatal temperatures of most insects with an exposure for any appreciable length of time is somewhat lower. No insect can survive for even a short time at a temperature range of 140–150° F.

The range of the lower zone of fatal temperatures is much more indefinite. Much depends upon the origin of the particular species. Insects of tropical origin succumb to the effects of cold more readily than those native to temperate climates. All stages of the cotton leafworm, *Alabama argillacea* (a tropical insect), are killed when the temperature drops to slightly below the freezing mark. The fall armyworm, *Spodoptera frugiperda*, does not survive the winter further north than the Gulf Coast region of the United States. Numerous other examples may be cited. However, some insects may survive temperatures as low as −50° F. Insects native to climates with cold winter weather will almost invariably have at least one stage of the life cycle that is capable of entering into a state of dormancy or diapause, which is sufficiently resistant to low temperatures to enable the species to survive.

An insect cannot survive when the water in its tissues freezes. The lethal range of freezing temperatures may be as high as 27–30° F. If a group of insects is cooled below this temperature range, some will freeze and others will not. The water within the tissues of those that survive is in a supercooled state. There is considerable variation in the tendency for the water in the tissues to supercool. The water is mixed with colloids and is finely divided. Small crystals of ice may be formed in isolated spots. From these spots the formation of ice may spread throughout the body.

Early or late freezes may be as detrimental to insects as extremely low temperatures in midwinter. A freeze may occur before an insect has entered diapause or after diapause is broken and it has entered a susceptible state. Alternating cold and warm periods may also be destructive to many insects.

The optimum temperature range for insects depends upon the species and where it is found. Insects inhabiting cold climates have a lower range of optimum temperatures than those in warmer conditions. Optimum ranges for the developmental stages of the same species may also differ. In general the optimum range of temperature for most insects would probably be between 65 and 85° F.

A species near either the upper or the lower zone of fatal temperatures may survive for an indefinite period, but growth and reproduction would be curtailed. Most insects become inactive at temperatures of 40–60° F. Little insect damage occurs at temperatures below 40° F. Temperatures of freezing or slightly lower will prevent all insect damage to stored food products and clothing.

The temperature range for egg production and oviposition is often about the same as that for the development of the immature stages, but not necessarily so. The fecundity of an insect may be greatly influenced by factors other than temperature, such as food, moisture, and the number of other animals in the environment. The age of the female also influences the rate of egg production.

The influence of moisture is much involved in the study of the effects of high temperatures on insects. High temperatures in nature are not likely to be lethal unless the weather is dry. Under natural conditions the loss of water may be more hazardous to many insects than the heat.

MOISTURE

Moisture is of major importance, yet its effects are not as critical as that of temperature. The combination of the two has a marked effect on the biology and distribution of insect life. They are so interrelated it is difficult to separate the influences of the two.

This discussion is chiefly concerned with terrestrial forms so it is better to consider moisture here as humidity in the atmosphere, aside from water for drinking, in food, and in flooding and in water-logged soils. Excess moisture may increase chances for the incidence of fungus and bacterial diseases. Terrestrial insects may be found living in environments ranging from those saturated with atmospheric water to arid conditions. Aside from water obtained in drinking and in moist foods, insects feeding on dry materials may maintain the water balance in their bodies by water of metabolism. Ticks and some insects can absorb water through the cuticle.

Certain wood borers, which normally complete their life cycles in 1 or 2 years in living trees, do not mature for as long as 20 years when the trees have been converted into building materials or furniture. This is thought to be due to the lack of water and nutrition. The rice weevil does not develop in wheat with less than 10 percent moisture and will select grain with a high water content.

Adequate moisture is essential to the maturation and laying of eggs. With many insects, speed of development is most rapid in an atmosphere saturated with moisture. With some, development ceases and they may not survive a long exposure to dry air.

A striking example of the effects of temperature and humidity on insect activity may be observed particularly in hot, dry weather. When temperature is high in midday, insect activity is almost at a standstill. Most activity occurs in early forenoon and late afternoon when the temperature is lower and humidity is higher.

AIR CURRENTS

Winds are of great importance in dissemination of insect life. Air currents lift a great diversity of insect life often hundreds of feet in the air, and gentle winds aid in their dispersal flights. Hurricanes for instance have played an important role in the spread of the pink bollworm (*Pectinophora gossypiella*) in the Cotton Belt of the southwestern United States. The cotton leafworm (*Alabama argillacea*) drifts into the cotton-growing region each season from the tropics. The fall armyworm (*Spodoptera frugiperda*) spreads northward each season from warmer climates. The potato leafhopper (*Empoasca fabae*) overwinters in the Gulf states and migrates northward each season. These are a few known examples. Air currents appear to be a much greater factor in dissemination of insects than is generally realized.

DIAPAUSE

Diapause is so involved with temperature, humidity, food, and particularly light that it must be considered along with these factors. Diapause is characterized by a period of suspended activity and morphological development which commonly occurs in many insects during cold or dry seasons. Physiological development may continue during this period in preparation for the resumption of activity. Diapause must be differentiated from a state of quiesence which is due directly to unfavorable conditions; normal activity is resumed as soon as these are ameliorated. Before entering diapause, immature forms frequently grow more slowly. In both immature stages and adults a reduction in water content and an increase in fat body reserves occurs in comparison with nondiapausing individuals of the same species. In several insects diapause has been shown to be an endocrine deficiency syndrome of the corpora allata.

With many insects diapause is an inherited characteristic set in action by an internal biological "clock" which may be "set" by certain environmental components, and may occur well in advance of unfavorable conditions. An unfavorable condition such as low temperature, too, may be necessary as a stimulus to break diapause. If some conditions remain unfavorable, diapause may continue for a long time, even for several years. Diapause may be more intense in some insects than in others. It accurately synchronizes seasonal activities of insects so that food and other requirements for growth and reproduction are present when they emerge. In the final analysis diapause enables an insect to exploit its environment to the fullest.

Some insects develop only one generation annually. With exceptions, diapause occurs in all individuals and is independent of outside stimuli. This is known as obligatory diapause. With other species there may be several generations free of diapause, with the incidence of diapause increasing in the last generations of the year. This is facultative diapause. Some species have both facultative and obligatory diapause in their populations.

Temperature, length of day, humidity, and type of food vary with the seasons, the latitude, and the elevation. The light hours (photoperiod) along with these other factors and their involved interactions provide the stimuli which set off the "clock," bringing on diapause. The relative importance of these factors may vary with the species and the region. However, the photoperiod usually appears to be the more dominant factor with many insects. There are often several biological races of the same species, and their response to the diapause stimuli may not be exactly the same. Also, the response may be different in populations inhabiting other geographical regions. The importance of temperature in inducing diapause is fully recognized, but it may not be the only or the chief factor. Autumnal temperatures may be even higher when diapause is induced than in the spring when diapause is broken and activity is resumed. Experimentation has shown photoperiodism to be the added stimulus to "trigger" the induction of diapause in many insects. For example, more bollworms (*Heliothis zea*) may enter diapause at lower than at higher temperatures, but the shorter daylight hours have proved to be the major factor in producing the change. Also, exposure of parents to long days tends to augment the incidence of diapause in their progeny, especially when the progeny are held under short day conditions.

The quality of food appears to be a major factor in the determination of diapause as in the pink bollworm (*Pectinophora gossypiella*) under tropical conditions. But in temperate climates, its influence is overshadowed by the photoperiod.

So the photoperiod provides stimuli which function in general more effectively as a biological "clock" than those stimuli provided by temperature, food, moisture, and other components of the environment. Responses to the photoperiod may at times be somewhat obscure and involved, but as a whole they keep insect activities in step with the seasons. The more accurate the stimuli in predicting conditions, the more valuable they are to insect life.

Photoperiod control of diapause requires both light and dark periods of a certain duration. Longer light hours tend to prevent and shorter periods promote diapause. Conversely, longer light hours tend to break diapause. There are exceptions; some insects are known to enter diapause on a lengthening day. Other components such as the quality of food may be the predominant factors in these cases.

The photoperiod seems to be the major factor in regulating the reproductive life of aphids. They normally reproduce parthenogenetically but when the photoperiod shortens in the fall, sexual males and females are produced. They mate and the females lay overwintering eggs. Here again temperature plays an important role. This may not occur at the lower latitudes in warmer climates. Deterioration of food may also be involved.

Biological clocks not only regulate seasonal cycles of living organisms but seem to be involved in the rhythmic daily activities as well. The implication has been that an organism is passive and the physical environment determines the activities. Butterflies are active during the day, moths at night, and crickets chirp after nightfall. This is quite true. But recent laboratory studies suggest that organisms do not just act in response to their environment but have internally accurate "clocks" on which the environment acts to keep the time measuring system accurate.

Diapause is controlled by hormones. Sources of hormones are the brain, subesophageal ganglion, and the prothoracic glands. The latter two sources appear to be controlled by the brain either directly or in an indirect manner. Just how the brain responds to those external stimuli which affect diapause is not very well understood, particularly when the response is delayed for some time after the stimulus is received.

LIGHT

In addition to the major role played by light in the incidence of diapause, it is important in the other phases of insect life in both a direct and indirect way. The stimulus may guide insects to those places where conditions such as food, temperature, and moisture are more favorable. It has a role in the diurnal rhythm of insects. Mating of insects is greatly influenced by light. There is considerable variation in the time and conditions of mating of different insects. The virgin queen honeybee flies from its colony on its mating flight around midday in warm, clear weather. The mating flights of ants and termites occur in warm, moist weather, particularly following rain when the soil is soft. Colonies of ants of the same species may tend to swarm at the same time. The swarming and mating of mayflies occur at twilight. The same conditions have been observed in certain species of midges. Insects tend to develop more slowly in the dark. Those developing in wood or in the soil tend to have longer life cycles than those exposed to light.

Man does not have as wide range of color perception as do insects which may respond to wavelengths of 2500–7000 Angstrom units. They are generally most strongly attracted to the ultraviolet range of 3650 Ångstrom units. Wavelengths of 5500 and 7000 units (yellow and red) are the least attractive.

Each species has its optimum range of light intensity as well as its optimum range of temperature. Insects which prefer light of low intensity are known as nocturnal insects, those of medium intensity as crepuscular, and those of higher intensity are diurnal or day-active insects.

Honeybees can detect and react to polarized light. Bees which have found a source of food are not only able to return to the location but also to communicate to other bees of the colony the location of this source of food. They appear to register the angle made by a line from the colony to the sun and another line to the food. They then keep the sun at this angle to their line of flight. They can do this even on cloudy days because of their sensitivity to polarized light. Other insects such as some ants and certain caterpillars (*Malacosoma*), also respond to polarized light.

Research and observations have indicated that moonlight has an influence on the activities of nocturnal insects. Moths of the bollworm, tobacco budworm, and cabbage looper are captured in fewer numbers in ultraviolet light traps when the moon is full. The number of all insects captured in this period is also less. Egg deposition of these moths is the highest in the new moon period.

FOOD

Food is a determining factor in the distribution and abundance of insect life. Man has changed the food supply for many insects through the introduction of new crops, the production of crops on an unprecedented scale, and by unwittingly bringing in new pests. In so doing he creates artificial ecosystems (agroecosystems). Potential pests abound in the insect world and become damaging whenever the right crop, planted in monoculture, is presented to them by man. Sometimes the geographic range of a plant may be greater than the extent to which some insect can live because of temperature or other factors, but other insects will replace it. If different foods are required of a species, suitable hosts for both larvae and adults of those with a complete metamorphosis must be located.

An acute shortage of food for some species often occurs over extensive areas. However, in a natural population consisting of many species with such variable food habits and with so many factors limiting their numbers, there is ample food most of the time for most species. It is to be remembered that of the vast assemblage of species of insects, most exist in nature in relatively small numbers.

Insects, such as cockroaches, feed upon almost any organic compound, so they may be termed omnivorous or polyphagous feeders. Those that feed only on plant materials are herbivorous. Some, such as the screwworm or oxwarble, are carnivorous. There is much specialization as to hosts. Those with a very limited number of hosts, such as the boll weevil, are oligophagous. Others which confine their feeding to only one species are monophagous. Insects that are general feeders and those with their food restricted to several hosts are more able to survive than those restricted to one host. Both the most serious pests and most beneficial parasites usually are those that feed on a small group of hosts.

Insects that feed on other live insects are entomophagous. Those which live on decaying organic matter are saprophagous. Fungi feeders are mycetophagous. If the food of certain insects consists of microorganisms such as protozoa, bacteria, and yeasts, they are termed microphagous feeders.

Oftentimes fields of crops may be completely destroyed by hordes of insects. When all available food has been exhausted, those immature forms which have not obtained the minimum amount of food necessary for development die. Considerable variation in the size of the adults of the same species is observed. This is caused by lack of sufficient food in the smaller individuals. When the food supply is exhausted or deteriorating, the insects may be seen crawling or flying in search of other sources. The crawling or migration of armyworms and chinch bugs are common examples. Large numbers of winged forms of aphids in many common species, such as the turnip aphid and the cotton aphid, are frequently observed. These fly in search of other food. Many make seasonal migrations to alternate hosts as does the poplar gall aphid. When the food supply is exhausted, the monophagous feeder suffers most. The oligophagous and omnivorous feeders naturally have a better opportunity of locating other food and surviving.

Transference to related plants may be rather easy, but the changeover to more distantly related varieties is very difficult, restricted, or impossible. In time strains may develop and become fully adapted to their new hosts. When a new crop is first introduced, it may be virtually free of pests, but eventually some of the native insects will begin feeding upon the crop and serious pests may develop.

A PLACE TO LIVE (HABITAT)

In higher animals a single complex of factors which are favorable provides a place in which to live from the time of birth to death. Most insects, however, must be adapted to live in two or more different habitats, particularly during the different stages of the life cycle. The conditions under which they may be found are often quite dissimilar. Also, modifications of the body structures are required, and the nature of the sense organs must be changed to better equip the insect for life in another place.

TERRESTRIAL MEDIUM

The physical conditions under which terrestrial insects live are most varied. The term terrestrial does not mean much more than the fact that these insects do not live in water. Some live on the soil, in the soil, on plants and animals, and also within plants and animals. Others may be cave dwellers; the dragonfly spends much of its time as an aerial insect. Cave dwellers and parasitic insects live under the most uniform conditions. Insects living within the bodies of animals, and to a less suitable degree within the tissues of plants, have the most desirable living conditions. Such living quarters afford an abundance of food, uniform conditions of temperature and humidity, and considerable protection from natural enemies. This may result in a degradation of the sense organs but in a specialization for locomotion and respiration. Obtaining sufficient food for existence may be a problem with cave dwellers. Degeneration in visual perception may result, but other sensory organs may be more developed.

Activity of subterranean insects is greatly curtailed. Excess water, fungi, and bacteria may be destructive, but they are shielded from an excessive amount of dessication and the temperature is quite constant. The texture of the soil is important and determines the types of insect found. Loose soils are best suited for many beetles, lepidopterous larvae, and ants. The Texas leaf-cutting ant is found in Norfolk type of sands from Mexico through south and east Texas, and into Louisiana and Oklahoma. Drainage and texture of this type of soil is most suitable for the construction of its nests and maintenance of its colonies. Certain insects require hard, compact soils. The rate of evaporation and the moisture content of a soil type also influence the insect population. Subterranean insects tend to adjust to temperature and humidity conditions in the soil by varying the depths at which they are living. In changing the texture of the soil through cultivation, man may cause an increase in insect populations, as in case of the pale western cutworm. Drainage aids in the control of horseflies as the larvae live in mud and water. Conversely, increasing the soil moisture by irrigation has influenced the spread of the western corn rootworm (*Diabrotica virgifera*) and various species of wetland wireworms.

Unlike subterranean, cave, and parasitic insects, those which live on or above the ground are subjected to wide variations of weather conditions and food supply. The presence of vegetation may provide food, some shelter and protection from natural enemies, and also aid in the maintenance of more uniform temperature and humidity conditions. In desert or semidesert regions where vegetation is sparse, insects are exposed to extreme variations of temperature, humidity, and light. They are aided in existing under these conditions by thick body walls, long legs which lift the body off the ground, and by burrowing into the soil. Also, they may crawl upon plants to escape the high ground temperature. Some may be active only at night or enter into an aestivate diapause during the hottest and driest periods of the year.

AQUATIC MEDIUM

It is quite obvious that aquatic insects are subjected to conditions decidedly different from the terrestrial forms. Oxygen is the important factor with them, as most respire through the body walls or by means of tracheal gills. In contrast, moisture and evaporation are the critical factors with terrestrial insects. Both physiological and morphological modifications are required of insects which live in aquatic environments.

The elimination of excess carbon dioxide and the addition of an adequate supply of oxygen to the water (aeration) are important in determining the abundance and types of aquatic insect life. Of the two gases, oxygen is the more important. Any agency which brings more water in contact with the air increases the oxygen content. Wave action in ponds and lakes is the chief factor in aeration. The volume and rate of run off of water influences its oxygen content. Swift currents and rapids aerate water. Rainfall adds much oxygen to bodies of water. Temperature is a factor; the higher the temperature the less gas is soluble in water.

Surface tension supports the weight of water striders, and mosquito larvae hang from the surface film. Some dipterous larvae and bugs respire through extensible respiratory tubes which are thrust through the surface film. Some bugs and beetles envelop themselves in a bubble or film of air and come to the surface only when necessary to replenish the oxygen supply. Aeration requirements differ for those insects which obtain their oxygen from the water. Nymphs of dragonflies may be found in poorly aerated water, while blackfly larvae and certain midge larvae prefer swiftly running streams.

Aquatic vegetation may be a source of food, and a place to hide and deposit eggs. Most lake and pond insects are found near the shore and on the bottom, and rarely in open water.

Although aeration is the chief factor in restricting aquatic species, temperature is also important. There are definite temperature ranges for various insects. Some species may develop at relatively low temperatures while others live normally under much warmer conditions. The same general relationships exist between temperature and growth as with terrestrial species.

BIOTIC FACTORS

Insects are as deeply affected by biotic factors as by the physical components of the environment. Their behavior, body conformation, mouthparts, locomotor organs, and the development of the sense organs and nervous system have been modified as much by biotic as by physical factors. Organs for protection, mating, production of sound, care of immature forms, and pollination of plants are developed only for life with other living things.

The goal of any living organism is the reproduction and perpetuation of the species. Its success is determined by its inherited capacity for survival and by all the involved interactions upon it of the physical, chemical, and biotic factors of the environment. An insect's adjustment to and maintenance of its niche in nature is greatly aided by the plasticity of its genetic composition. This means there are differences in individuals and those that survive the adversities of environmental conditions may leave behind progeny. This genetic plasticity is one of the important factors which has enabled insects to survive through the geological ages and to adapt themselves to live in almost all conceivable environments.

In addition to food and weather, which are discussed above, some of the salient factors which are involved in the struggle for the maintenance of their existence and their niches in the living world are reproduction, protection and shelter, intrarelationships, and interrelationships with other animals and plants. In a general discussion of these topics, much of their habits, behavior, instincts, and relationships may be learned.

CAPACITY FOR INCREASE

Every species of insects has an innate capacity for population increase. This involves the maximal rate of reproduction under most favorable conditions with the optimum moisture and temperature, ample food, and space, as well as the correct number of individuals of its kind at ideal levels, and with the exclusion of all other organisms. This rate of increase is never attained by any means. The actual rate of increase of the population of a species is not under conditions of overpopulation or underpopulation but at some point between the two. In small populations the chances of the females mating are smaller and they may be older when fertilized, which results in fewer eggs being laid. The death rate is relatively higher in small populations because of predatism of other animals. It is possible that the random loss of genes in small populations may occur which may result in chance fixation of harmful genotypes. This may be a factor which helps explain why small populations or colonies of some animals fail to increase or may even disappear. An individual has a much greater chance of survival, not necessarily in a huge overcrowded population, but in a somewhat smaller population. Social insects obtain a measure of security because of their numbers and organization. Other insects may obtain similar benefits from the organized activity of an unorganized population.

Extremely large populations suffer from lack of food and

overcrowding; and with an abundance of food, parasites and predators flourish. Too, with weather conditions favorable for disease organisms, outbreaks can occur which may virtually wipe out entire populations.

The reproductive capacity of insects is great. The ability to build up large populations in a relatively short period when conditions permit is a very important factor in the success of the group. Those which are the most defenseless, preyed upon ruthlessly by natural enemies, ravaged by diseases and mitigated against most harshly by weather appear to have the highest reproductive capacity, which is an essential compensating factor.

The capacity for reproduction is determined by the number of eggs laid or young produced, the length of a life cycle, the number of generations annually, and by special reproductive provisions. Most insects are quite prolific. An individual female bollworm moth may lay as many as 3000 eggs. The San Jose scale produces about 400 young. The queen honeybee may lay 1500–2000 eggs daily during the height of the brood-rearing season. These are rather extreme cases; however, quite a number of insects may lay this many eggs or produce this many young. When the eggs are protected, as in tissues of plants, there is a tendency to lay a fewer number. Probably the average number of eggs laid by all insects would be between 100 and 200. Perhaps the average number of generations annually would be 2 or 3. Yet by taking the first offspring of each generation, it is possible for the cotton aphid (*Aphis gossypii*) to produce a maximum of 51 generations under greenhouse conditions. Those insects which develop in the soil or in wood have longer life cycles. The length of the life cycle of most May beetles is commonly 2 years in the southern states and 3 in the North. The periodical cicada has a life cycle requiring 17 years in the northeastern states. The more common wood borers, such as the round-headed borers, have a life cycle of 1–2 years, yet the length of the life cycle may be extended over a period of years under adverse conditions.

Some special methods of reproduction are *parthenogenesis* and *polyembryony*. Parthenogenesis is the common method of reproduction of aphids in the summer months and throughout the year in warm climates. It also is known to occur in some Diptera, Hymenoptera, and other groups. *Paedogenesis* is an unusual form of parthenogenesis. In this case the larvae, and on rare occasions the pupae, give birth to living young. Paedogenesis occurs chiefly in the Cecidomyiidae. In polyembryony hundreds of individuals may be produced from a single egg which in its development divides into a number of embryos. *Platygaster hiemalis* is a well known example of this mode of reproduction; it is a parasite of the hessian fly. (See Figure 239B.) These reproductive methods eliminate the hazards of the egg stage, and the males are eliminated as well in parthenogenesis, resulting in a great increase in the population in usually a very short time.

PROTECTION

Among insects a great diversity of protective measures have been perfected as a safeguard against weather and natural enemies. Any protection afforded eggs is a factor in reproduction. Some are hardly afforded any protection at all, while others are well protected. Eggs deposited on the surface of plants are subjected to great hazards. This may be compensated at least in part by the greater fecundity of some species. The Miridae and Membracidae, for example, oviposit in the tissues of plants. The Chrysopidae place their eggs on stalks in an attempt to protect them against their enemies.

A variety of structures and other protective measures are found among the active stages of insects. The value of the exoskeleton needs no mention. In addition, the body may bear spines, bristles, scales, and hairs which may provide further protection in some way. The hairs of some caterpillars are hollow and filled with a nettling or poisonous substance which is toxic or at least irritating to animals which brush against them. The fluids of blister beetles are toxic. Stinkbugs and some related insects secrete odors which are repellent. Bombardier beetles discharge an irritative smokelike substance at their attackers. Caterpillars of moths spin silken cocoons in which to pupate. Some larvae, such as bagworms and casemaking clothes moths, live in silken cases. Many aphids secrete a waxy substance for protection, particularly against an excess of moisture. Social insects, such as hornets, build paper nests. The honeybees construct waxen combs. Ants may construct earthen mounds to obtain proper moisture and temperature conditions. Larvae of tortoise beetles make themselves appear as repulsive as possible by the collection of excrement and cast skins on the dorsal surface of their bodies.

There are those insects with stings which may take the offensive when their colonies are threatened. The best known examples are the honeybees and wasps. Many ants inflict serious pain and discomfort through their bites and stings. The sting of the red harvester ant and the fire ant are certainly to be avoided. The bite of some hemipterous insects, such as the assassin bugs, may be as painful as the sting of most Hymenoptera.

Size may be of value in protection. Very small insects may be overlooked by large predators or they may hide more readily. Very large forms may appear too formidable and the grotesque appearance of others may succeed in frightening away some enemies.

Camouflage is a common means of protection. The walking stick (Phasmidae) resembles a twig or a stem of grass so well that it may not be detected until it moves. The color of plant-feeding insects may blend well with their hosts. Some insects mimic others for protection. The viceroy butterfly, which is edible to birds, mimics an inedible species, the monarch. Some flies mimic wasps or bees. Other insects are camouflaged for aggressive purposes. Many insects which have a bad taste to birds and other enemies, such as the harlequin bug, advertise this fact by their gaudy markings. Wasps are frequently marked by bright colors as a warning to their enemies.

The environment in which an insect is found may afford protection, as in the case of subterranean forms and those which feed in the tissues of plants and the bodies of animals. Some, such as ants, move their young when disturbed. Others, such as snout beetles and leaf beetles, feign death. Certainly running, jumping, flying, swimming, and hiding are the most common of all protective measures. The period of activity of an insect may afford some protection against certain enemies, although they may be exposing themselves to others.

COMPETITION

Most competition between insects of the same species is for food and mates. The most striking form of competition is cannibalism, which is commonly observed among aphid lions, robber flies, beetles, and others of predatory habits. Infrequently a plant feeder, such as the corn earworm, is cannibalistic. When the larvae are in close proximity they attack and devour each other. Overcrowding to the point of starvation frequently occurs among phytophagous insects, such as plant lice, which reproduce rapidly. They cannot disperse very rapidly, nor do they have any means of eliminating each other.

PARENTAL CARE

Insects may be grouped as free feeding, solitary, and social in habit. The vast majority of insects are free feeding or free living. With them, there is no provision made for the young, other than that the females may deposit the eggs on or near the food supply. Most solitary insects are either solitary wasps or solitary bees. Nests are constructed and mass provisioning is practiced. There is no caste system and little or no parental care other than providing a mass of food in which eggs are laid. Carpenter bees provide their nests with pollen and honey. The cells of mud daubers are provisioned with spiders. The cicada killers place cicadas in the cells of their nests. The preparation of a nest and mass feeding provides considerable security for the young and greatly increases the chances for survival and the perpetuation of its species.

A step forward in parental care is progressive feeding in which the adults provide food to the young as needed from time to time. The sand wasps prey on flies with which their larvae are fed until they are mature. Ambrosia beetles grow a fungus on the walls of their tunnels which they collect, chew up, and plug the entrance to each larval cell. As the larvae eat out these plugs, more is supplied.

SOCIAL INSECTS

Although insects of the same species may be the most severe of competitors, yet among them may be found the most perfect examples of communal life in the animal kingdom. Individuals of the same species living together in organized groups with a division of labor are known as social insects and their communities as colonies. Several characteristics are held in common by social insects: more or less elaborate nests are constructed; there is a relatively large population; and cooperation, division of labor, generally progressive feeding, care of young, and trophyllaxis are practiced; swarming occurs with some species.

Social insects are most commonly found among those with complete metamorphosis, such as ants, honeybees, bumblebees, and paper wasps. However, the social habit may be found among others with gradual metamorphosis, particularly Dermaptera (earwigs) and Isoptera (termites).

Some insects, such as ants, honeybees, and termites, establish permanent colonies in which swarming occurs. Others, such as bumblebees and paper wasps, have annual colonies and do not swarm in temperate climates. They overwinter as fertile females which establish new colonies the next season.

The number of individuals in a colony of social insects may range from a relatively few to hundreds of thousands. Nests of the paper wasp, *Polistes*, may have 50 or fewer individuals. A population of 200–300 bumblebees would be a strong colony. Forty-five thousand honeybees would represent a strong colony. The South American leaf-cutting ant (*Atta sexdens*) whose colonies consist of numbers of mounds over a large area, have populations estimated by some to be in excess of one-half million. Some tropical species of termites have populations estimated as being even larger.

In the organization of a colony of social insects, such as ants, a caste system with a division of labor is necessary. There are three general castes, the sexually developed females or queens, the males, and the workers. Only one mature queen is usually found in a colony, although young queens may be reared for emergencies and for establishment of new colonies.

CASTES

The caste system appears to be more highly developed in the Isoptera (termites) than in any other group of social insects. Each caste includes members of both sexes. A number of castes are recognized, but not all of these are found in the colony of any one species. Those present in the colonies of the more common species are primary queens and kings, complimental queens and kings, workers, and soldiers. In some species there is a special soldier caste known as nasuti, the individuals of which have an elongated projection or snout on the head. The primary queens and kings have fully developed wings which are broken off after swarming. The complimental queens and kings have wing buds which never develop. The relationship of the queens and kings is on a permanent basis and repeated matings occur. Both males and females are found in the worker castes. Under certain circumstances, workers may lay eggs. With paper wasps the usual castes are present.

The males and females of ants usually have wings and the workers are always wingless. Following the mating flight, the males die and the young queens shed their wings. The worker caste is wanting only in those species which are parasites of other ants. Polymorphic forms may exist, particularly among the workers. The larger individuals are termed majors and the smaller are the minors. A so-called soldier caste with large heads and mandibles is frequently observed. Bumblebees and honeybees have the usual castes of queens (fertile females), males, and workers.

TROPHYLLAXIS

Progressive feeding developed from mass feeding, and from the former trophyllaxis developed. Trophyllaxis is the exchange of food materials between insects. Ants commonly feed each other. Upon returning to the colony, workers may be solicited for food by those that remain and in return regurgitated food may be offered. Food exchange also may take place between adults and the young. A substance secreted by the young of both ants and termites is eagerly sought by the adult workers. Similar habits are found in paper wasps, but not in all social insects. Because workers obtain a very desirable food material from the young, they work hard to enlarge the nests and bring in more food so as to have more young. Thus the care, solicitude, and protection given the young may not be altruism at all but a matter of obtaining a desirable food. Trophyllaxis occurs among some solitary wasps and may also be found among individuals of different species.

COMMENSALISM

Commensalism is defined as two or more species living together in an association in which one or more may be benefited and none harmed. Trophyllaxis is found among commensals but not among all by any means, as this involves an exchange of food material. Excellent examples of trophyllaxis among commensals are found in a number of beetles of the families of Staphylinidae and Pselaphidae and their relationships with ants. Several factors besides food account for the association of the different species, such as protection from natural enemies and more favorable living quarters.

Some insects are carried on the bodies of other insects which are usually larger; this is *phoresy*. The triungulin stage of the larva of a blister beetle is carried unwittingly on the bodies of certain solitary bees to their nests where they later consume the brood. Eggs of the human botfly are laid on flies, mosquitoes, and ticks. When these parasites feed, the larvae hatch and bore into the body of the host.

CAPTIVES

It is rather common for ants to hold other insects in captivity. The slave-making ants (*Formica sanguinea*) raid the nests of other species and carry pupae to their own colonies. Here the pupae develop into adults and become slaves of the colony. The shining amazon (*Polyergus lucidus*) may not exist without slaves. The amazon queen establishes a new colony by entering a weak colony of *Formica fusca* and killing its queen. In time an amazon colony is established. As more slaves are needed, colonies of *F. fusca* are raided and the pupae are carried off.

The honeydew excreted by aphids and some other insects are fed upon by ants. Various degrees of relationships have developed between these insects and aphids. In most instances no significant definite biological relationships exist but in others definite relationships do exist. The best known of these relationships is between the cornfield ant (*Lasius alienus americanus*) and the cornroot aphid (*Anuraphis maidi-radicis*). These aphids are dependent on ants for care and protection and in turn the ants obtain their food from the aphids. Some ants build shelters or pens in which to keep the aphids as captives.

FOOD STORAGE

If a colony of social insects is to exist on a permanent basis, some provisions must be made for an adequate food supply. The leaf-cutting ants (*Atta*) grow a fungus for food; others may store food. The storage of honey and pollen by the honeybees is well known. The harvester ants store seeds in chambers of their nests. An unique method of storage is found in the nests of honey ants. They have no methods of making cells for storage, so a caste, known as repletes, serves as living honey jugs. The workers bring in honeydew when it is available and feed it to members of this caste. They engorge great quantities of this food and their abdomens may become distended to the size of small peas. When the food is needed, it is regurgitated and fed back to the members of the colony.

NATURAL ENEMIES

Birds, Fishes, and Mammals

Even though insects are quite small, they are present in such huge numbers that their weight comprises a not-inconsequential amount of the combined weight of all land animals. They are a source of food of some domestic animals. Mammals such as armadillos, skunks, raccoons, moles, ground squirrels, and others destroy a number of insects. Some species of snakes, toads, and lizards feed to a great extent on insects. Toads in particular eat many insects.

Much of the food of land birds is composed of insects. Some of the more common insectivorous birds are swallows, nighthawks, flycatchers, cuckoos, bluebirds, and mockingbirds.

Freshwater fishes feed heavily on insects. Even though some may not feed upon insects in the adult stage, they do so during the younger periods of their lives. Some of the more important insectivorous fish are crappie, black bass, catfish, perch, and some sunfish. Although many species serve as fish food, the most important in the freshwater lakes and streams are bloodworms (family Chironomidae), mayfly nymphs (order Ephemerophera) and caddisworms (order Trichoptera).

Mammals and birds in turn are severely attacked by and suffer greatly from arthropod parasites. Nearly every bird has an infestation of mites and lice. They are also attacked by fleas, ticks, mosquitoes, and others. Among mammals are such pests as cattle grubs, ticks, screwworms, mosquitoes, stable flies, blackflies, and hosts of others.

Of greater importance are diseases borne by insects and other arthropods. Mention need be made only of such diseases of man as malaria, yellow fever, and typhoid fever. Common diseases of domestic animals are Texas fever and encephalitis. Insects are likewise important vectors of plant diseases.

Entomogenous Parasites and Predators

The role of mammals, birds, and fishes is of some value in helping keep insects, with their enormous reproductive capacity, in balance with other forms of life. But the insects themselves are of much greater value. Their most important enemies are entomogenous parasites and predators. Parasites are living organisms which live in or on other living organisms, known as their hosts, and from which their food is obtained. The hosts are usually larger and are not destroyed directly by the feeding of the parasites but may live for some time before succumbing to the attacks. Predators are larger than their prey, which they kill and devour outright.

All species of insects and all stages of their development are subject to parasitism. The parasite of a given host, such as an armyworm, is known as a primary parasite. Its parasite is a secondary parasite. There are also tertiary parasites. All parasites of a primary parasite are called hyperparasites. The most important families of parasites belong to the order Hymenoptera, namely the

Braconidae, Chalcididae, and Ichneumonidae. The Tachinidae of the order Diptera is also a very important family. The species of these entomogenous parasites number in the many thousands. For example, there are more than 6000 species of Ichneumonidae in North America. All species are parasitic in their larval stage. Insect predators are of less importance; the better known groups are members of the orders Odonata and Neuroptera, the Carabidae and the Coccinellidae of the Coleoptera, and the Syrphidae of the Diptera.

A third group of insects are the scavengers which feed upon waste materials. They play an important role in speeding up the reduction of dead animal and plant material of all types into earth mold. This humus aids in conserving the fertility of the soil which makes possible more plant and animal life. Large numbers of insects feed as scavengers, but some have mixed food habits. For example, termites may attack the roots and stems of living plants, and the larvae of some Scarabaeidae may feed as scavengers and the adults live on living plant materials. Termites constitute one group of nature's scavengers, converting logs, branches, stumps, and other plant materials to humus. Wood borers of many species are among the more common feeders on dead wood products. Cockroaches, dermestids, and the larvae of many species of flies are scavengers. However, the service rendered in the reduction of some materials may be nullified manyfold by destruction of valuable products and in particular by diseases of both plants and animals.

DISEASES OF INSECTS

Insects, as do other groups of animals, have diseases of their kind. Infestations of chinch bugs are frequently eliminated by fungus diseases. Grasshoppers and houseflies for instance are frequently attacked by fungi. Bacterial and virus diseases frequently wipe out large populations of insects, especially certain species of caterpillars. Protozoan diseases are present, but are of less importance.

INSECT AND PLANT ASSOCIATIONS

Plants are the source of food for most insects. All parts of plants are attacked by some type of an insect—foliage, buds, flowers, fruit, limbs, trunk, bark, and roots. Also, certain parts of plants, such as leaves, fuzz, and bark are utilized in construction of nests and cocoons. Too, hollow trunks and stems may become the abode of a number of insects. Insects have become adapted in a number of ways for their plant associations; mouthparts are modified for feeding, legs for clinging or collection of food, and senses are highly developed for the location of the hosts. Conversely, plants have developed means which aid in their protection by physical, chemical, and physiological characteristics.

Insects are important in transmission of plant diseases. Homopterous insects such as leafhoppers and aphids are common vectors of many viruses and bacterial wilt diseases. Some chewing insects may also transmit plant diseases such as the Dutch elm diseases and blue stain of Norway pine which are carried by various bark beetles.

Not all relationships between plants and insects have been injurious to plants. Insects are invaluable in pollination of plants. Most, but not all, plants are cross pollinated. Wind and insects are the chief factors in cross pollination. Bees, wasps, ants, butterflies, moths, flies, beetles, and thrips all render valuable service in pollination of plants. Wild bees and honeybees are the most valuable pollinators. The services of insects are necessary in the production of many cultivated crops, such as clovers, alfalfa, apples, pears, plums, and certain vegetables.

In pollination of some plants remarkable biological relationships have developed between the plant and the insect. For example, the yucca (p. 246) and the smyrna fig (p. 382) are completely dependent upon certain species for pollination. Another interesting relationship is between the blue flag (*Iris versicolar*) and the bumblebee. The structure of the flower is admirably modified so that the visitations will effect cross pollination. However, both plant and the insect may survive without the other. Flowers of some plants may be open only at those periods when their most effective pollinators are active. Pollen masses of milkweeds are so formed that they are caught on the legs of insect visitors and carried to other flowers. Also, the bodies of insects are often modified for their association with flowers. Pollen-collecting species may have pollen baskets (*corbiculae*) on their legs. Body hairs may be dense and branched to collect the pollen grains. Many have elongate tongues to reach the nectar in flowers with long corollas.

Interesting examples of mutualism between insects and plants are found. Some species of bacteria and fungi are found in the alimentary tract or fat bodies of insects such as cockroaches, beetles, and flies. In return for a protected place in which to live, the organisms aid in the digestion and assimilation of food. In tropical regions some ants may protect certain species of plants from leaf-feeding insects and even larger animals in return for the nectar secreted by extrafloral glands or to obtain honeydew secreted by aphids, scale insects, and mealybugs.

There are cases in which the plants are benefited and the insects are the victims. A number of plants trap insects. The pitcher plant is one of the best known examples. A hollow receptacle, the pitcher, is formed by petioles and leaves. Glands secrete substances which attract insects into the pitcher where they are trapped by sticky hairs pointing downward. They fall into a liquid in the bottom of the pitcher where they are digested and the food absorbed by the plant. Another interesting example is the Venus's-flytrap. The leaves have flattened terminal lobes which are semicircular with edges armed with numerous spines, forming a trap. When an insect alights, it closes. Fluids from gland openings digest the food, which is absorbed by the plant. The sundew has specialized leaves with sticky hairs which catch the insects. Also, there are some aquatic plants which trap insects.

INSTINCTS, REFLEXES, AND HABITS

The term instinct is difficult to define. It is often used vaguely and without much meaning. Through instinct, an insect may live a rather complex life and make detailed preparations for the next generation without foreknowledge, experience, or intelligence. For example, a mud dauber emerges from its earthen cell and follows a pattern of life exactly like its forbears. It constructs a nest the same as others of its species, and in the way they have been constructed for innumerable generations. This nest may be provisioned with spiders which are stung and paralyzed in the same manner, without a single deviation in detail in the procedure. All of this is accomplished without any training or experience whatever.

Instincts are more complex than tropisms. They may be thought of as complexes of tropisms. Instinctive action is made up of a coordination of reflexes. Some of the stimuli are from without and others are from within the insect. Instincts cannot be inherited, but the tendency to produce instinctive reactions is an inherited characteristic. There is no tendency for inheritance of habits. These habits are acquired through repeated acts. They are the result of learning and become reflex through frequent repetitions.

There are several characteristics of instincts. They are always performed in the same manner and the performance is almost perfect, with no previous learning. They all have a useful purpose. The separate acts must be performed in regular sequence; if variations occur, failure or disaster may result. Although instincts exhibit great inflexibility, they may still show some slight variation or modification.

The highest behavioral achievements among invertebrates are found in insects, particularly in the ants, bees, and wasps (Hymenoptera). The remarks made herein are made particularly with reference to those insects. Some insect behavior may rival that of mammals so much that it has been suggested by some that insects have reasoning power and intelligence. But it has been quite clearly shown that insects are largely creatures of instinct operating strictly in a mechanical fashion in accordance with stimuli they receive. However, among the higher forms, there is a plasticity of behavior.

Developments making such behavior possible are complex sense organs, marked modifications, particularly in the mouthparts and legs, and a brain sufficiently developed to organize the information received and to direct the manipulation of the appendages.

The senses of sight, smell, and touch are quite well developed. The compound eyes are the best or among the best visual organs in the invertebrates. Although inferior to the vertebrate eyes in some characteristics, the compound eye with its many facets is superior in the perception of motion. The sense of smell is very acute and the tactile senses are developed to a high degree. With these sense organs, insects are enabled to live successfully in their environment, and engage in rather involved relationships with one another. Also, complex nests may be built and food provided as with the mud dauber. Paper wasps make their nests from wood fiber. Honeybees secrete wax with which their combs are fashioned. A tropical ant makes its nests by fastening leaves together with silken strands as the adults cannot secrete silk and the larvae can. The larvae are held within the jaws of the adults and weaved back and forth between the edges of leaves to tie them together. Intimate associations with other species have evolved. Highly organized social units have been developed with a caste system.

Insects recognize their home and are able to return to it from a distance. In fact, their power of orientation and their faculty for recognizing landmarks may rival that of mammals. Ants may follow chemical trails or be orientated by landmarks, the sun, or polarized light. Bees and wasps make use of landmarks or navigate by the position of the sun and polarized light. Within the hive, a field bee, through the peculiar dances performed, is able to transmit to others both the distance and the direction of the food.

Insects are capable of learning. Honeybees readily learn to go to dishes setting on paper of a given color when that color is associated with food. Ants and cockroaches readily learn mazes that are not too involved.

The Peckhams described how a wasp (*Pomphilus*) brought a large spider almost to its nest. Upon examination of the nest, she was impressed with the idea the nest was too small. After further examination, she proceeded to make the nest larger. This act would indicate some intelligent ability, but careful study and closer observation would indicate these actions may be in the final analysis tropic reactions.

Learning is an important component among many ants, bees, and wasps, but for all insects its role is minor. After all, insects are animals of instinct. In insects the height of instinctive behavior is probably reached. The limitations of the brain would probably limit higher learning processes. In a study of ants preserved in Baltic amber, Wheeler found they had practically the same structure and social life 50 million years ago as they have today. This would indicate little or no evolutionary progress in this vast span of time.

CHAPTER 19
INSECT CONTROL

NATURAL CONTROL

In broadest terms, insect control includes the many factors which kill, repel, and interfere with feeding, propagation, and dispersal of insects in every way. Insect control is divided into two groups— natural control factors and artificial control measures. Natural control includes all factors which operate independently of man. Artificial control includes mechanical and physical control measures, cultural control, use of chemical compounds, and other measures applied or influenced by man.

The interactions of the many factors within a community of animals and plants under natural conditions usually keep within reasonable limits the populations of insects. But balance in nature is a dynamic and not a static condition. Damaging outbreaks do occur, but less frequently in natural systems than in an ecosystem created by man. The denudation of forests by caterpillars and the destruction of valuable timber by bark beetles and other insects, all under natural conditions, is quite well known. The outbreaks of grasshoppers in the early days of the Great Plains region is history. Somewhere outbreaks of insects under natural conditions are occurring all of the time.

Most of the basic factors of natural control have been discussed already in Chapter 18. In summary, the natural control factors that act as checks on the distribution and activities of insect populations include (1) weather—temperature, humidity, light, and air currents, (2) physical factors, and (3) biotic factors.

Weather is the most important factor in keeping insect populations in check, inasmuch as temperature, humidity, and light affect either directly or indirectly every phase of an insect's life. However, when an attempt is made to evaluate definitely the effects of any one factor, it is most difficult to do because of the interactions of all of the other factors in the insect's habitat. In general, a warm, humid habitat is favorable and extremes of temperature are destructive to insect life. Cold winter weather, especially when early and late freezes occur, destroys many insects. This weather condition is especially effective against insects of tropical origin. Conversely, hot, dry weather results in a decrease in populations of most insects. Relatively few insects have become adapted to living under very arid conditions.

Hard, driving rains are very destructive to such small insects as aphids. Conversely, a heavy blanket of snow may protect over-wintering forms against low temperatures. Again, high humidity under warm conditions fosters the development of disease organisms.

Intensity of light influences such activities of insects as dispersion, mating, and oviposition. The desired light intensity varies with the species; also, the tendency of insects is to develop more rapidly in the presence of light. Wind and air currents are important in insect dissemination. The air, as a means of dissemination, is being better understood and appreciated as flyways for insects.

The physical and chemical nature of the soil along with climatic factors determine the types of plant life. This in turn limits the indigenous species of animals to be found here. Food is the determining factor in the distribution and abundance of all insect life. When the food supply is exhausted, the insects may die or, if possible, migrate elsewhere. Too, the physical nature of the soil has a direct bearing upon insects as many spend all or part of their lives in the ground. Oceans, seas, and mountain ranges are rather effective barriers.

Every insect has its natural enemies, such as entomogenous parasites and predators, birds, fishes, mammals, and reptiles. Of these, the insect parasites and predators are of much more importance (Figure 302). Of the many thousands of species, a number

---

Figure 302. An important aphid parasite (*Lysiphlebus testaceipes*) despositing an egg in its host. (From USDA.)

Figure 303. *Tiphia popilliavora,* an introduced parasite of the japanese beetle grub. (From USDA.)

are quite prolific and may increase to large populations when conditions are favorable. As are other groups of animals, insects are susceptible to certain diseases. Fungi, bacteria, and viruses frequently wipe out large populations of insects. Protozoan diseases are present, but are of less importance.

ARTIFICIAL CONTROL
BIOLOGICAL CONTROL

Biological control is the elimination or control of undesirable insects and other pests by use of their natural enemies. This may be accomplished by introductions, artificial rearing, or protection of those natural enemies indigenous to the ecosystem. The natural factors which may be used most advantageously are parasitic and predaceous insects, bacteria, viruses, protozoa, and fungi.

A majority of our most important pests of agricultural crops are of foreign origin and have been brought into this country through channels of commerce. Today the opportunities for a pest to be introduced are increased because of the huge amount of intercontinental trade and the speed of transportation (Figure 303). When once established in a new country, an introduced pest is usually more destructive than in its original home. The natural enemies are not ordinarily brought with the pest, and the new food supply may be more desirable and more abundant. With introduced pests, the goal has been to import their natural enemies and establish them where the pest is found in an attempt to reduce their damage to the same level as in the native habitat. Often this level is not reached. Many importations of insect parasites and predators have been made, but most have failed to become established. There are many problems attendant upon the introduction and establishment of a parasite or a predator. Still, there have been a number of successes. More than 100 pests in different parts of the world have been controlled through use of parasites and predators. California alone has recorded 18 successes.

The first intentional importation of a parasite in the United States was *Apanteles* (Figure 304) *glomeratus,* a natural enemy of the imported cabbage worm, in 1884. However, the introduction of the Australian lady beetle (*Rhodolia cardinalis*) to control the cottony-cushion scale (*Icerya purchasi*) in 1888 was really the beginning of sustained efforts to control insects biologically.

Populations of natural enemies of pests may be increased by the collection and distribution of those in nature or by mass production and release of the insects. Convergent lady beetles (*Hippodamia convergens*) are collected in quantity when they congregate in huge numbers to diapause in the mountains of California. They are sold to gardeners and farmers, primarily to be distributed for aphid control. The good accomplished is questionable, but this principle of collection and redistribution may be applied satisfactorily to other insects. Mass rearing of the egg parasite (*Trichogramma*) has been done for a number of years but their release for control of a number of pests has not been very successful. The mealybug destroyer (*Cryptolaemus montrouzieri*) may be produced

Figure 304. Cocoons of the braconid parasite (*Apantales congregatus*) on the back of the tobacco hornworm (*Manduca sexta*). (Prepared by Clemson University Cooperative Extension Service's Entomology-Plant Pathology and Agricultural Communications Sections, Federal Extension Service Cooperating.)

in great numbers in insectaries. The screwworm fly (*Cochliomyia hominivorax*) is mass produced by the millions in the sterile-release program of eradication and control of this important pest.

It is possible to make use of native parasites in control of some pests. If a parasite is not present and an insect host such as the woolly apple aphid (*Erisoma lanigrum*) is established, the colonization and establishment of its parasite (*Aphelinus mali*) usually results in satisfactory control.

The oriental fruit moth (*Grapholitha molesta*) is of foreign origin. *Macrocentrus ancylivorus* is a native parasite of the strawberry leaf-roller which adapted itself to this new host. The parasite's effective range has been greatly extended by a large-scale colonization program. Other examples may be given.

Although microbial organisms are very important in the natural control of many pests, their use in biological control has lagged behind that of parasites and predators. Several successes have been achieved in this field. *Bacillus popilliae* is widely used in control of japanese beetle grubs in the northeastern states. *Borrelina campeoles,* a polyhedral virus, is effective in control of the alfalfa caterpillar, and *Bacillus thuringiensis* is used for the control of various lepidopterous larvae.

Biological Control of Weeds

The outstanding example of the control of a plant by biological means is the control of the cactus (*Opuntia inerimis*) in Australia. At one time this imported plant had taken over 50 or 60 million acres of land. The imported moth borer (*Cactoblastis cactorum*) established itself readily on the cactus and brought it under control. Another example of weed control is that of the Klamath weed in California. The introduction of a beetle (*Chrysomela gemellata*) resulted in the control of the weed over many thousands of acres. Importation of a flea beetle (*Agasicles*) for the control of the alligator weed is showing promising results.

STERILIZATION

Sexual sterilization by radiation has been employed successfully in several cases. Through release of sterile screwworm flies in large numbers, the pest has been practically eliminated in the United States (Figure 305). These flies are mass reared by the millions in cheap meat and are sterilized by exposure to gamma radiation. The sterile males compete with the normal males in mating with the normal females and thus eliminate reproduction. Screwworms caused a loss of as much as $124,000,000 in 1 year before this program was put into effect.

The eradication of the melon fly (*Dacus cucurbitae*) on Rota, a South Pacific island, was accomplished by the integration of sterile-insect releases and a bait spray. The oriental fruit fly (*D. dorsalis*) was eliminated also from the island of Guam by the

Figure 305. Insect container designed for the aerial release of sterile screwworm flies. (From USDA.)

release of sterile insects. Practical techniques have not been developed for control of other species.

For the sterile-release method to be successful, the insects must be reared in greater numbers than occur in nature. This means that millions of individuals must be reared, and the rearing medium and techniques need to be cheap and simple. Much detailed research is essential before control can even be attempted. It is doubtful that this method will be practicable in the control of most established and prolific pests and those of minor importance (Figure 306).

In addition to the use of sterilization by exposure to gamma rays, chemosterilants and the crossing of genetically incompatible strains are being investigated. The goal in the use of the chemosterilants is to sterilize the insects in a natural population by exposing them to chemical compounds. These compounds may reduce or completely eliminate the reproductive capacity of an animal. Either or both sexes may be affected, and the effect may be permanent or temporary. A number of compounds have varying degrees of effectiveness as chemosterilants. The most satisfactory method of use and its effects upon other animal life, including man, must be carefully determined. Much research needs to be conducted before the feasibility of using chemosterilants can be determined. The crossing of genetically incompatible strains from other geographical areas may produce sterility in the offspring. Research in this field has produced some positive results in experimentation with certain species of mosquitoes and moths.

CULTURAL CONTROL

Cultural control involves the use of farm and ranch practices in such a way as to eliminate, or at least reduce, populations of injurious pests. A thorough knowledge of the pest and the plant or animal hosts is required for the development of these measures. The practices are usually based on some weak point or points in the seasonal history, environment, or host relationships of the insect. After research has determined an effective practice, then farm modifications may be made to prevent, destroy, or slow down the rate of reproduction of a pest. When these methods are desirable, farm practices may be readily adapted. But if the methods are poor agronomic practices, then the decision must be made if their use is feasible. Cultural control should be practiced over a large area for the best results because some pests migrate from adjacent areas. These are the cheapest of all control measures and are essential in any integrated control program.

Sanitation Measures
Much may be accomplished by the removal of breeding and overwintering places, and food of insects. Destruction or utilization of

Figure 306. Research technician using a radioactive insecticide for studying metabolism of insecticides by insects. (From Department of Entomology, Texas A&M University. Courtesy of Dr. F. W. Plapp.)

crop residues is often a cheap and a very effective means of control of a number of pests. Even in the home, sanitation measures are quite important. If the kitchen is kept scrupulously clean, with foods enclosed in tight containers and food wastes removed every night, cockroaches and ants will not be such a problem. Disposal of discarded woolen and other materials together with good housekeeping will aid materially in elimination of carpet beetles, clothes moths, and silverfish. Houseflies breed in moist, decaying organic matter. Removal of such wastes and scattering it thinly over the soil materially aid in the elimination of breeding places.

The destruction of the diapausing larvae of a dreaded pest of cotton, the pink bollworm (*Pectinophora gossypiella*) is an outstanding example of cultural control. Control measures for the pest are based on (1) planting and harvesting dates; (2) shredding the stalks and later turning under this residue to a depth of 6 inches; and (3) destruction of larvae in gin trash by mechanical means. When these steps are taken on a sectional basis, damaging infestations are practically eliminated.

Destruction or removal of crop residues on truck farms aids materially in control of many pests such as harlequin bugs, squash bugs, cabbage worms, and certain species of aphids. Decaying and dropped fruits in orchards should be destroyed because they may harbor harmful pests such as fruit flies of citrus, plum curculio of stone fruits, and codling moth of apples. These are only a few examples of pests of crops which may be controlled at least in part by removal or destruction of crop residues.

Fence and turn rows may be the source of some pests. However, they may also harbor beneficial insect predators and parasites as well as birds and valuable plant pollinators. These habitats need to be studied to determine what cleanup measures are advisable from an economic viewpoint. A large trash pile may harbor enough stinkbugs, squash bugs or a number of other overwintering insects to start an infestation in a field. Weeds may be alternate hosts of many injurious pests.

Much food may be conserved through improved storage and sanitation. Storage facilities should be designed and constructed for the use for which they are intended. Good housekeeping is essential. Bins of all types must be thoroughly cleaned before being reused. Waste grain and products of all kinds which may harbor pests should never be allowed to accumulate. Broken packages should be removed. Processing machinery needs frequent cleaning and all trash and garbage should be removed daily.

In silviculture, techniques have been developed for slash removal in control of several species of bark beetles. Collecting and destroying branches of shade and nut trees severed by twig girdlers during the dormant season may effect satisfactory control of this pest.

Cultivation

Cultivation aids in reducing infestations of a number of insects but it should be compatible with approved agronomic practices to be most effective. Tillage influences the natural texture of the soil, which has much to do with activities of insect life. Clean culture may eliminate alternate host plants, for example, of the garden webworm (*Loxostege similalis*). Plowing when crops are not growing may accomplish much, but erosion from wind and rain must be considered. Cultivation at this time may destroy volunteer plants and crop remnants upon which a number of pests may feed and reproduce. Also, many larvae and pupae in the soil may be destroyed. For example, fall and winter plowing destroys many overwintering pupae of the corn earworm, and both larvae and pupae of cutworms. Fall and spring plowing is beneficial in destruction of the European corn borer. When grasshopper eggs are oviposited in stubble, plowing destroys many of them. Past successes would indicate that much profitable research could be done on development of and improvement of control measures of this type.

Crop Rotation

Crop rotation is often quite effective, particularly against those insects whose powers of migration are limited, or which have restricted hosts and long life cycles. The adult of the northern corn rootworm lays its eggs in the fall in cornfields, and corn roots are the primary food of the larvae. Since the larvae cannot migrate, rotation is an effective means of control. The white grub has a life cycle usually of 2 or 3 years, and certain legume crops are not suitable hosts. Consequently, rotation of corn with legumes reduces the population considerably. The winter grain mite (*Penthaleus major*) may be controlled effectively by not planting small grains successively in the same field for more than 2 years. Even though most insects can migrate readily, rotation with crops other than their hosts causes them to go to other fields where the infestations may be lighter and later. Here the results of the rotation may not be too effective, but they are of some value.

Time of Planting and Harvesting

The time of planting a crop may help eliminate a pest. In some crops early planting is desired and in others delayed planting is necessary. As an example, planting reasonably early, use of early maturing varieties of cotton, and destruction of the stalks as soon as harvesting is completed, materially reduces the number of boll weevils to emerge the next season, if conducted on a community-wide basis. If hessian fly resistant varieties of wheat are not used, a safe seeding date is recommended. Adults of the hessian fly (*Mayetiola destructor*) live for only a few days. The planting of winter wheat should be delayed until after most of this generation has emerged. In those areas of the United States infested with hessian flies, dates are established for the sowing of winter wheat which will allow the plants to make satisfactory growth and still avoid heavy infestations of the pest. Early planting aids materially in reducing losses due to the sorghum webworm and the sorghum midge. To this list of examples many more may be added which aid materially in reducing insect losses.

Time of harvesting also may be important. Usually the earlier the crop is harvested the more satisfactory as this reduces damage by insect and weather. Cotton farmers try to mature and harvest the crop before a large buildup of such insects as pink bollworm and boll weevil occurs, and then destroy the crop residues. If the wheat-stem sawfly is a problem, harvesting as early as possible reduces losses of grain. Strip harvesting of alfalfa reduces infestations of lygus bugs in adjacent fields of cotton and other crops. Cutting timber from late summer to early winter is the most appropriate time to reduce damage from wood borers.

There are certain ranch practices of value to the stockman. Castration and dehorning should be done during the fly-free season. Also, it is desirable to have calves dropped at this time. Even though the screwworm fly is practically no longer a problem in the Southwest, there are other myiasis producing flies. Also, other species, such as houseflies, may disseminate infections. Removal of stock from areas infested with blackflies and horseflies is sometimes advisable.

Cultural Control of Aquatic Insects

Some of the most important pests of man and animals are aquatic insects. These include such groups as mosquitoes, midges, blackflies, and horseflies. Through proper management of water, populations may be kept at a minimum or at least in some cases prevented from increasing. Considerable progress has been made in the field, and the recommendations made are being followed by water and soil agencies. There are a great diversity of individual problems and pests to be dealt with, and programs must be modified for each. The water management field may be divided into irrigation, drainage, and water impoundment.

PHYSICAL MEASURES

Although physical measures are the oldest of all insect control measures, many are basically sound and are still in use today. Some are outdated but are still used in some parts of the world, and others may have a place in the home and garden. Newer and refined approaches are being developed for some, making them more effective.

Temperature and Humidity

High and low temperatures may be used effectively in insect control. Also, a knowledge of the physiological effects of temperature changes is of value. Insects cannot survive long at a temperature of 140° F. Drying and heating grain in the sun has been practiced in tropical regions for centuries. Natives in tropical Africa may kill pink bollworms in cottonseed by spreading them in thin layers in the sun. Artificial heat may also be employed in control of insects in stored food, grains, dry foods, and under special conditions in certain fruits and other plant materials. Heat sterilization of greenhouse soil has been a common practice for a long time. Clothing, fiber, lumber, and other products are also heat treated. There are possibilities in the use of radiofrequency energy, particularly for control of insects in stored grain. This means of control is still in the experimental stage, and practical methods have not been developed.

Low temperatures are very effective in reducing losses of many insects. Those species incapable of diapausing may be completely destroyed. Activities of others may be checked for long periods. Even cool weather will check development and keep infestations low by increasing the length of the life cycles and reducing the number of generations. When temperatures are extremely low in northern climates and at high altitudes, opening up flour mills and exposing them to the weather is an excellent control measure. Transferring wheat in an elevator from one bin to another in cold weather results in its being chilled sufficiently to check weevil damage. Cold storage vaults for furs and food materials definitely prevent insects from feeding.

Insects can survive under a wide range of moisture conditions, but no single species can exist under all variations of humidity. Each species of insects has its optimum range of moisture conditions and may not survive under opposite conditions unless in a particular stage of its life cycle. For example, the pink bollworm may survive as a diapausing larva under adversely dry condition. Drying of breeding or feeding media may be used quite advantageously. Dry food products with sufficiently low moisture content may prevent infestation of pests. Stored grain should not contain more than 12 percent moisture to minimize insect damage. Subterranean termites must have a humid environment in which to live. Keeping conditions dry as possible under buildings aids materially in preventing their damage.

Light Traps

Ways in which light traps may be used in combating insects are:

1. Survey traps to determine the spread and range of recently introduced pests.
2. Survey traps to determine the seasonal appearance and abundance of a pest.
3. To evaluate the effectiveness of a control measure.
4. To control insects themselves.

The black light fluorescent lamp is most commonly used in light traps. These lights emit most of their energy in the near ultraviolet range which has the greatest attractiveness to most photo-positive insects.

The use of light traps in mills and warehouses may be quite beneficial in the detection and even control of pests of products milled or stored there. The attempts to utilize light traps in control of field crop pests in this country extends back for many years, with desultory results. Perhaps with the improved light traps and improved methods, their use may aid in control of some pests.

Insects are often attracted in large numbers to light in outdoor areas and around places of business where they become great nuisances. Yellow lights, which attracts few insects, should be installed for the areas to be illuminated and black light placed some distance from the area to draw the insects away.

MECHANICAL CONTROL MEASURES

The simplest of control measures is hand picking. Squash bugs may be picked off of a few plants or Colorado potato beetles picked from a small planting of potatoes in the home garden. Bagworms may be hand picked from a small tree or shrub. Screening is the most valuable of all mechanical control measures which helps keep out mosquitoes, flies, and other insects. The mosquito net is a similar control device. A few small plants may be protected by paper or tin collars.

To this list of mechanical control measures may be added digging wood borers out of trees with a knife, swatting flies, crushing armyworms, jarring and shaking pests off of plants on sheets, and using traps. Metal shields for protection against termites may be effective if carefully installed; however, they cannot be relied upon altogether.

A problem of importance is insect infestation of dried food products. In general the only practicable method of protection of these products is by means of insect resistant containers. Certainly metal and glass containers afford protection, but food packaged in paper, fiberboard, and plastic materials are not. Some of the susceptible packaging materials are used for economic reasons. However, specially constructed bags are being manufactured and are being used for some products.

HOST RESISTANCE

An important phase in insect control is the use of both plants and animals that exhibit at least some degree of resistance to certain species of arthropods and the breeding and development of these lines. The factors involved in resistance are quite complex in their relationships. The general classification of these components is (1) host preference, (2) antibiosis, and (3) tolerance. Host preference by the pest involves type of food, protection, and oviposition. Color, physical nature of the surface chemical stimuli, and other factors may be involved here. In antibiosis the feeding upon the host by the pest results in effects harmful to the arthropod. These include death in the early stages of development, lowered reproduction capacity of the females, smallness in size, and abnormalities in the life cycle. Tolerance refers to the ability of the host to grow satisfactorily, repair the injury, and reproduce its kind in spite of the attacks of its arthropod enemies.

The earliest recognition of insect resistance in a variety of plants was in the winter Majetin variety of apples which is resistant to the woolly apple aphid. Grafting the susceptible varieties of the European grapes to resistant American rootstock controlled the grape phylloxera (*Phylloxera vitifoliae*). Varieties of wheat have been developed which are resistant to the hessian fly. Resistance to the spotted alfalfa aphid, *Therioaphis maculata*, have been found in varieties of alfalfa. Great progress has been made in the development of strains of corn resistant to the European corn borer. Earliness is an important factor in the production of cotton under boll weevil conditions. The imported Brahman cow is known to be more resistant to arthropod pests than the European breeds. Its desirable qualities have now been used in the production of another breed. English breeds of sheep are less susceptible to attacks of wool maggots than the Spanish-type breeds in Australia. These are a few examples of resistance of plants and animals to their pests. Numbers of others may be found in the literature.

LEGAL CONTROL

Early experiences with imported pests, particularly with the San Jose scale in the United States and the grape phylloxera in Europe, aroused people to the necessity of quarantine laws. In 1877 four states enacted legislation for protection against certain pests. The first federal law concerning pests of animals was passed in 1884. The Federal Insect Pest Act of 1905 enabled the federal government for the first time to regulate the importation and movement of products which may spread insect pests. However, not until the passage of the Plant Quarantine Act of 1912 did the government have federal laws adequate to prevent the introduction of insects and plant diseases from foreign countries. At the same time domestic quarantines were established.

As a large part of the insect damage in this country today is caused by introduced pests, the purpose of foreign quarantine measures is to prevent the entrance of others. Although they may not be wholly successful, quarantines do prevent the entry of most pests and may delay the introduction of others for many years. The goal of domestic quarantines is to prevent the spread of certain pests already here. Such measures may not always stop the dispersal of the pests, but will check their spread and may prevent infestations in some parts of the country for many years.

Regulations are also in force for eradication of new pests when feasible and the application of control measures for established ones. These include cleanup measures, planting and plowup dates of crops, and the application of insecticides.

For the protection of the public, both federal and state pesticide laws have been enacted. Most state laws are similar to the federal statutes. Federal regulations pertaining to insecticides and fungicides were first initiated under the Insecticide Act of 1910. The act provided means to prevent misbranding and adulteration of those products marketed in interstate commerce. It was superseded in 1947 by the Federal Insecticide, Fungicide and Rodenticide Act. This act expands the protection formerly afforded the public in the act of 1910. All products subject to the act are required to be registered with the U.S. Department of Agriculture before they may be marketed in channels of interstate commerce. Furthermore, each product is required to bear a label which includes the name of the product, name and address of the manufacturer, brand name or trademark, net contents, and proper ingredient statement. Products highly toxic must bear a poison label in red and the skull and crossbones, and an antidote is required of such compounds. Adequate directions and necessary precautions must be provided. The product is guaranteed by the manufacturer to comply with the act. Claims for the pesticide must be in conformity with the registration, and proof must be supplied before registration can be effected. False or misleading statements may lead to court action. There is also legislation regulating the work of pest control operators and the use of hazardous insecticides.

If there is a residue on raw agricultural products, the food is adulterated unless it is declared safe, being exempt from tolerance or within the tolerance set by the Pesticide Chemical Amendment of 1954 (Miller Bill) to the 1938 Food, Drug and Cosmetic Act and the Food Additive Amendment of 1958 (Delaney Bill). Tolerances are given in parts per million for the various pesticides and are subject to modification. A considerable safety factor is provided in establishing these tolerances.

INSECTICIDES

Man has made use of various substances for insect control for thousands of years. Some of the earliest references date back to the Chinese, Greeks, and Romans. People in those early days knew about the use of sulfur, arsenic, asphaltic materials, and oils in insect control. The slow development and use of chemicals in control of insects was due mostly to the lack of basic knowledge of insects. People at that time relied chiefly on witchcraft and superstitions to avert insect damage; some of these practices persist even today. The discovery of the insecticidal properties of paris green in 1867 is accepted as the beginning of modern use of insecticides in the United States. By the 1920s the use of insecticides had reached the point that regulations were passed establishing tolerances on fruit for arsenic and later for lead.

The discovery of DDT as an insecticide in 1939 revolutionized insect control. The early use of this compound demonstrated the great potential of insect control by means of synthesized chemical compounds. Many more compounds were developed and have been used, but many problems have developed. Modern industrialized society has brought on many problems in pollution. The use of pesticides is only one facet of the general problem (Figure 307).

In the past 20 years of general use of these chemical compounds, crop yields have increased more than 50 percent. The quality of food products has also been much improved. Not all of this can be attributed to the use of insecticides, but they have been a major factor. Arthropod vectors of causative organisms of about 30 known diseases may be reduced or eradicated by means of insecticides. Among these diseases are malaria, bubonic plague, encephalitis, and typhus fever. Globally there were once about 200 million cases of malaria with 2 million fatalities annually. Today the disease has been brought under virtual control throughout the world.

Some pests have been controlled by biological means. Quarantine and eradication have been of much aid. Cultural practices have suppressed many and helped in control of other insects. Sterilization by radiation was a breakthrough in another field of insect control. There is little doubt that other pests will be controlled or suppressed by these or similar methods. But there are still many widespread pests of importance which it seems doubt-

Figure 307. Spraying for control of cotton insects with an airplane. (From Texas Agricultural Experiment Station.)

ful can be adequately or economically controlled by these methods. Despite the problems involved in their use, insecticides will need to be used within the foreseeable future. The greater demands for food and the hope of escape from diseases makes it imperative that they be employed. More efficient and safer insecticides are needed. The present insecticides should be more efficiently and carefully applied in pest control programs.

A broad spectrum of insect life is destroyed in addition to the target insects when insecticides, particularly those of a general nature, are used. Many of the insects are of no direct economic importance, but unfortunately beneficial entomogenous parasites and predators as well as other natural enemies are killed. However, if the destruction of natural enemies is not too widespread, they may build back rather rapidly as most of the highly beneficial forms have a high capacity for reproduction. Some plant systemic insecticides are less destructive to most beneficial forms.

The development of resistance to insecticides is not new. It was first noted in 1908 when the San Jose scale showed resistance to lime-sulfur. More than 200 species of insects and arachnids are known now to have developed resistance to certain insecticides. Repeated applications of a poison may result in resistant strains through selection. In most cases resistance to organophosphates and carbamates usually involves the increased ability to detoxify an insecticide and/or to decrease its absorption after exposure. The mechanism of resistance to the chlorinated hydrocarbons has proved to be more involved. While detoxification may be a factor, frequently the involvement of other yet unidentified mechanisms may be implicated.

Hazards to Man and Wildlife

The human body may contain at least a trace of all materials absorbed. Thus it is possible for minute quantities of such elements as lead, arsenic, and mercury to be stored, as these elements are widespread in nature and traces may occur in food materials under natural conditions. Lead is an excellent example of a cumulative poison. Although its compounds may undergo chemical changes, their toxicity is never completely lost. In contrast with these heavy metals, synthetic insecticides are capable of being broken down and eliminated. Most of them are metabolized and eliminated rather rapidly. The chief exception to these are certain chlorinated hydrocarbon insecticides, particularly DDT. However, they are broken down and eliminated, but slowly. They are degraded also in both plants and soil but their degradation is slow and traces may occur in food and may be absorbed into our bodies.

Particularly when they are indiscriminately used, insecticides may kill some birds, mammals, and fish. DDT and some related compounds are especially harmful. Fish are susceptible to substances of many kinds, and a number of insecticides are also toxic to them. Although a fish may not have enough of the toxicant in its body to kill it, it may be eaten and the insecticide passed on to other animals in a biological food chain which may result in the buildup of the insecticide and the death, for example, of some fish-eating birds.

Since World War II, many insecticides have been developed and used in such large quantities that many persons have become concerned about their long-range effect upon human beings. There is hardly any other group of chemicals which has been as extensively studied and their toxicology and pharmacology so well known. Much of this information has been obtained from results on experimental animals. Whether this data will apply to human beings is largely unknown. But the information obtained from experiments on test animals is reassuring. Available data on humans is also equally reassuring. According to vital statistics, only 5 percent of all poison deaths in the United States are caused by pesticides. Three-fourths of the fatalities from pesticides have been caused by accidental or deliberate ingestion. There are no deaths on record from residues of food. Practically all deaths resulting from the newer poisons are caused by the organophosphorus compounds and the chlorinated hydrocarbons. Although three times more of the latter have been used, the former is responsible for four times the number of deaths. This is because of the differences in the acute toxicity of the two groups.

There is concern not only with the toxicity of a product but also with the hazards involved in its use under practical conditions. The dilution and the formulation of the pesticide are important factors to consider when the hazard factors are studied. When a very toxic pesticide is employed at a very diluted figure, the hazards are greatly reduced.

A knowledge of the relative toxicity of insecticides is quite necessary for their study and use. Owing to the multiplicity of factors involved, this information may not be quite exact, but it does establish reasonably well the toxicity of a compound in relation to other products. The most satisfactory criterion for acute toxicity of liquid and solid insecticides is the median lethal dose (LD_{50}) determined on rats and other test animals. This is the amount of the toxicant dose required to kill 50 percent of the test animals in a single dosage; it is expressed in milligrams per kilogram of body weight (see Table 1).

In fumigants the LD_{50} is most satisfactorily expressed as vapor concentration on the basis of milligrams per liter and multiplied by length of the exposure. But it is generally given in parts per million (ppm) which will produce a given response in a stated time. Chronic toxicity of insecticides is usually determined by feeding test animals a measured quantity of a toxicant in their diet and determining the maximum level which does not produce harmful symptoms or death.

Insecticides may be grouped for study in different ways. The

Table 1. Acute Oral and Dermal LD_{50} Values of Insecticides for White Rats (unless otherwise stated)

Insecticide	Oral LD_{50} (mg/kg)		Dermal LD_{50} (mg/kg)	
	Males	Females	Males	Females
Chlorinated Hydrocarbon Insecticides				
Aldrin	39	60	98	98
Benzene hexachloride	1,250[a]	—	—	—
Chlordane	335	430	840	690
Chlorobenzilate	1,040	1,220	—	>5,000
DDT	113	118	—	2,510
Dichloropropane–dichloropropene	140[a]	—	2,100[a, b]	—
Dicofol	1,100	1,000	1,230	1,000
Dieldrin	46	46	90	60
Endosulfan	43	18	130	74
Endrin	17.8	7.5	18	15
Ethylene dibromide	146	117	300[a, b, c]	—
Ethylene dichloride	770[a]	—	3,890[a, b]	—
Heptachlor	100	162	195	250
Kepone	125	125	>2,000	>2,000
Lindane	88	91	1,000	900
Methoxychlor	5,000	5,000	—	>6,000
Mirex	740	600	>2,000	>2,000
Paradichlorobenzene	1,000	1,000	—	—
Perthane	4,000	4,000	—	—
Strobane	200[a]	—	>5,000[a, b]	—
TDE	>4,000	>4,000	>4,000[a, b]	—
Telone	250–500[a]	—	—	—
Toxaphene	90	80	1,075	780
Organic Phosphate Insecticides				
Abate	8,600	13,000	>4,000	>4,000
Azinphosmethyl	13	11	220	220
Azodrin	17.5	20	126	112
Bidrin	22[a]	—	225[a, b]	—
Carbophenothion	30	10	54	27
Ciodrin	125[a]	—	385[a, b]	—
Coumaphos	41	15.5	860	—
Demeton	6.2	2.5	14	8.2
Diazinon	108	76	900	455
Dichlorvos	80	56	107	75
Dimethoate	215	—	400	610
Dioxathion	43	23	235	63
Disulfoton	6.8	2.3	15	6
EPN	36	7.7	230	25
Ethion	65	27	245	62
Fenthion	215	245	330	330
Malathion	1,375	1,000	>4,444	>4,444
Methyl parathion	14	24	67	67

Source: Data from *U.S. Dept. Agr. Handbook* **331,** 1968.
[a] Sex not indicated.
[b] Value for rabbits.
[c] Approximate LD_{50}.
[d] Value for guinea pigs.
[e] Value for dogs.

Table 1 *(Continued)*

Insecticide	Oral LD$_{50}$ (mg/kg)		Dermal LD$_{50}$ (mg/kg)	
	Males	Females	Males	Females
Organic Phosphate Insecticides (Continued)				
Methyl Trithion	98	120	215	190
Mevinphos	6.1	3.7	4.7	4.2
Naled	250	—	800	—
Nemacide	270	—	—	—
Parathion	13	3.6	21	6.8
Phorate	2.3	1.1	6.2	2.5
Phosphamidon	23.5	23.5	143	107
Ronnel	1,250	2,630	—	>5,000
Ruelene	635	460	—	—
TEPP	1.05	—	2.4	—
Trichlorfon	630	560	>2,000	>2,000
Carbamate Insecticides				
Carbaryl	850	500	>4,000	>4,000
Zineb	>5,000	>5,000	>2,500	>2,500
Other Insecticides				
Binapacryl	63	58	810	720
Calcium arsenate	—	298	—	2,400
Cryolite	200[a]	—	—	—
DN–111	330[a]	—	>1,000[a, d]	—
Lead arsenate	—	1,050	—	>2,400
Metaldehyde	ca. 1,000[a, e]	—	—	—
Morestan	1,800	1,100	>2,000	>2,000
Napthalene	2,400	2,400	>2,500	>2,500
Nicotine sulfate	—	83	—	285
Ovex	2,050[a]	—	—	—
Paris green	—	100	—	2,400
Pyrethrins	>1,500[a]	—	>1,880	—
Rotenone	50–75[a]	—	>940[a, b]	—
Ryania	1,200[a]	—	>4,000[a, b]	—
Tetradifon	>14,700[a]	—	>10,000[a, b]	—

older method of grouping them is on the basis of mode of entering the insect's body—stomach poisons, contact poisons, and fumigants. Most of the synthetic poisons may enter the insect in more than one way and it is advisable to study their chemical classification or their origin. Also, it is practical to generalize information for specific groups. Approximately 400 materials are listed for insecticidal purposes. Probably less than 10 percent of those currently used are inorganic compounds. Only a relatively few of these products will be briefly discussed. Some of these are in the process of elimination and the future of others is problematical.

Inorganic Insecticides

The inorganic insecticides were once very important. This class includes arsenicals, fluorine compounds, sulfur, and some of its compounds. Their usage has been practically replaced by synthetic organic compounds because of residue problems, mammalian toxicity, insect resistance, and inefficiency. However, they were satisfactory for control of a number of pests and the problem of insect resistance was not as widespread. The acid form of *lead arsenate* ($PbHAsO_4$) was once widely used to protect fruit, shade, and forest trees, ornamental plants, and truck crops from injury by chewing insects.

Although *calcium arsenate* had other uses, it was employed primarily for the control of the boll weevil and other chewing insects attacking cotton. It is not the standardized product as lead arsenate. *Paris green* is copper acetoarsenite $(CH_3COO)_2Cu \cdot 3Cu (AsO_2)_2$. It is the oldest of the arsenicals employed in this country in the control of many pests, but presently it is no longer being used. This stomach poison is highly toxic to mammals and is also very phytotoxic. *Sodium arsenite* is highly soluble and is a very toxic compound. Its most important use in the past was as the active killing agent in arsenical cattle dips employed in the eradication of the cattle tick in the South.

Two fluorine compounds may be mentioned. *Sodium fluoride* (NaF) was once widely used to control cockroaches and poultry lice. *Cryolite* (sodium aluminum fluoride, Na_3SiF_6) has had a limited use for the control of some crop pests.

For insecticidal purposes *sulfur* is primarily a contact poison, but it also has fumigation properties. It may be used both as a dust and a wettable powder. It has been used for the control of spider mites, chiggers, and as a fungicide. Sulfur, as commonly used, is not toxic other than being irritating to the eyes. *Lime-sulfur* has had a wide usage as a dormant spray for the control of the San Jose scale, and also as a foliage spray for control of mites. It also possesses fungicidal properties. There are several related compounds of lime-sulfur which have had some usage.

Plant Poisons

Nicotine ($C_{10}H_{14}N_2$) is the principal alkaloid found in tobacco. Its chief use has been for the control of soft-bodied sucking insects. It may act as a contact poison, fumigant, or a stomach poison. Either dusts or sprays may be used. The acute toxicity of the product is high.

Rotenone, associated with several related compounds, occurs in the roots of certain leguminous plants which grow in the tropics. Derris (*Derris elliptica*) and cube (*Lonchocarpus* spp.) are the commercial sources of this insecticide. This product acts as both a stomach and a contact poison, but chiefly as the latter. It may be employed in the control of a number of vegetable pests and some animal parasites. It is a relatively safe insecticide and is exempt from tolerances, but it does not have the efficacy of synthetic pesticides used for the same purposes.

Pyrethrum is derived from the flowers of *Pyrethrum cinerariae-folium*. The insecticidal properties are due to four esters; namely, pyrethrin I, pyrethrin II, cinerin I, and cinerin II. These unstable esters are hydrolyzed by alkali and decomposed by light. Pyrethrum is usually used with synergists, as piperonyl butoxide. It remains a prominent economic insecticide because of its rapid action and low mammalian toxicity.

Allethrin is a synthetic pyrethrinlike compound. It is employed in the control of the housefly and other pests. Much research is being done in the development of this group of compounds.

Oils

Oils of some type are old insecticides, and man has used them through the centuries. Numerous types and formulations have been employed in pest control, and increased use is quite possible. They possess only slight health hazards and no pest resistance has ever been observed. Fuel oil fractions are employed in mosquito control and are used as solvents for other insecticides.

Oil of the kerosene fraction is usually used in household sprays as a solvent and cotoxicant with other pesticides. However, hydrocarbon aromatic fractions seem to have become more desirable for this use.

Plant life is susceptible to injury from oil sprays and when they are employed on shrubs and trees, care must be exercised to select the proper spray. Also, the proper dilution and correct application are important. Specifications of spray oils are based on (1) distillation range, (2) gravity, (3) percentage of carbon atoms in the paraffinic structure, (4) percentage of unsulfonated residue, and (5) viscosity. Oil sprays are used for the control of scale insects, mealybugs, aphids, certain mites, and others. They are usually applied as emulsions at 1–4 percent concentrations.

Thiocyanates, Dinitrophenols, and Others

There are several *thiocyanates* of commercial value such as the *lethane* compounds. They are contact insecticides acting on the nervous system. They are not highly toxic, but recommended precautions in their use should be followed.

The *dinitrophenols* kill as both contact and stomach poisons, and are miticides, ovicides, and aphidicides. They are phytotoxic and also toxic to mammals. The group is of limited use. Among the *sulfones, sulfonates, sulfides,* and *sulfites* are a number of compounds which are found to be successful as contact acaricides in varying degrees. These are such compounds as *Aramite* and *Morsetan* which are effective against eggs, larvae, and adults of spider mites. Others such as *ovex, chlorobenzilate,* and *tetradifon* destroy only the eggs and larvae. There may be plant injury problems associated with the use of these products and pests may develop resistance to them.

Chlorinated Hydrocarbons

DDT and the other chlorinated hydrocarbons are effective against a wide spectrum of insect life both as contact and stomach poisons. They have little or no value as plant or animal systemics. They have proven to be of great value in the fields of plant protection and improving the health of both man and his animals.

The long-term residual properties of chlorinated hydrocarbons have greatly reduced their employment. DDT is prohibited in a number of states and the uses of all are being restricted. The future of these compounds is in doubt. These poisons act on the nervous system, producing hyperactivity, tremors, paralysis, and death. Their use has several objectionable features: (1) a buildup of residues in plants, animals, and soils; (2) toxicity to beneficial insects, fish, and birds; (3) accumulation in biological food chains; and (4) the development of insect resistance. They are being largely replaced by the organophosphorus compounds and the carbamate insecticides. The halogenated hydrocarbons employed as fumigants are discussed later.

DDT ($C_{14}H_9Cl_5$) is the oldest and best known of this group of compounds, but it appears to be in the process of elimination. It is readily soluble in a wide range of organic solvents. The product is decomposed by alkaline compounds, but it is otherwise quite stable. It has had a wide usage for control of many insects, and much good has been accomplished in holding in check insect vectors of malaria, typhus, and other diseases. The acute toxicity is low and it is a relatively safe compound to handle.

Methoxychlor ($C_{16}H_{15}Cl_3O_2$) is a compound related to DDT. It is used against about the same group of insects, but in general it is less effective. Its toxicity to warm-blooded animals is quite low and it is readily metabolized. However, it is quite toxic to fish. Because of its low mammalian toxicity, it is recommended for a wide range of insects. It is insoluble in water but quite soluble in aromatic hydrocarbons. TDE or DDD is a chemically related compound.

Toxaphene ($C_{10}H_{10}Cl_8$) is a chlorinated terpene. It is a yellow, waxy, solid insoluble in water but readily soluble in a number of organic solvents, including petroleum oils. It does not have as much residual action, but it is more acutely toxic to mammals than DDT. The chronic toxicity, however, is low and it is eliminated from the fatty tissues of the animal's body without a large buildup. Toxaphene is effective in control of grasshoppers, various cotton and legume insects, webworms, and cutworms.

Strobane is a related compound made by chlorinating a mixture of pinene and camphene, and it has uses similar to toxaphene.

Benzene hexachloride ($C_6H_6Cl_6$) is made up of at least six isomers. The insecticidal properties are due mostly to the gamma isomer which in its purified form is known as *lindane*. The pesticide is insoluble in water, is broken down by alkalies, and is soluble in a number of organic solvents. The product acts as a stomach poison, contact poison, and as a fumigant. It does not have the residual characteristics of DDT. BHC is effective in controlling many insects but its use is restricted as it may impart a musty odor and flavor to many foods. The refined isomer, *lindane*, is practically free of the musty odor and does not accumulate in the fat of animals to any marked degree since it is metabolized quite rapidly. Although BHC and its purified isomer are effective against a wide range of insects, their use has been largely superseded by other products.

The *cyclodienes* are a group of chemically related compounds. They are *aldrin* ($C_{12}H_8Cl_6$), *dieldrin* ($C_{12}H_8Cl_6O$), *chlordane* ($C_{10}H_6Cl_8$), *heptachlor* ($C_{10}H_5Cl_7$), and *endrin*, which is an isomeric compound of dieldrin. These compounds are insoluble in water but soluble in organic solvents. Their acute toxicity is greater than that of DDT. Endrin particularly is highly toxic, ranging in toxicity along with the more toxic phosphorus compounds. These compounds are effective in the control of a wide range of insects and most are persistent insecticides. All are successful as soil insecticides. They are being replaced in a number of instances by other compounds. Some of the many satisfactory uses of these compounds are listed here. Chlordane is used for control of termites and household insects. It has had a wide use in control of such pests as grasshoppers, chiggers, ticks, and harvester ants. Aldrin has been an efficient insecticide in controlling grasshoppers and cotton insects. The acute toxicity to man and animals is high. Dieldrin, a highly toxic product, will control a wide variety of pests such as cockroaches, ants, fruit pests, termites, and some cotton pests. Endrin is efficient in controlling a wide variety of field and vegetable pests. Heptachlor has been used to control grasshoppers, termites, and cotton insects.

Dicofol (Kelthane) is a white, crystalline solid insoluble in water but soluble in organic solvents. This is an acaricide with long lasting residual effectiveness.

Carbamates

A number of compounds of this group have been tested as insecticides and to a lesser extent as acaricides. An outstanding insecticide, *carbaryl* (Sevin) ($C_{12}H_{11}NO_2$), was introduced several years ago and has become of major importance. Carbaryl is effective in controlling a wide range of pests of field, vegetable and fruit crops, and poultry and livestock. It is only slightly soluble in water, but is quite soluble in most organic solvents. It has only reasonable residual effectiveness and does not produce toxic residues in animals, but is very toxic to honeybees. It kills insects similar to the way phosphorus compounds do, as a cholinesterase inhibitor, having contact and stomach poison action.

Organophosphorus Insecticides

Some 45 compounds of this versatile group of pesticides are presently in use. They have a wide range of effectiveness against insects and arachnids, acting as contact poisons, stomach poisons, and fumigants. Also among them are several excellent systemic poisons. They act as cholinesterase inhibitors. Many are so dangerously poisonous to man and animals that they should be applied only by trained applicators. However, others are quite safe for use by the public, with the usual precautions. Phosphorus compounds have the advantage over the chlorinated hydrocarbons in that they are largely eliminated very rapidly from animal tissues. Some have a very short residual effectiveness, such as TEPP, while others have a prolonged action, such as azinphosmethyl (Guthion) and diazinon.

Parathion ($C_{10}H_{14}NO_5PS$) is a brown to yellow liquid with the odor of garlic. It is slightly soluble in water and petroleum oils, but miscible in common organic solvents. Hydrolysis is rapid in alkaline solution. It kills insects and mites as a contact and a stomach poison, and also acts to some extent as a fumigant. The pesticide is highly effective in the control of a wide range of insects and mites of the field, vegetable, and fruit crops. This product should never be used around the home and on livestock because it is so highly toxic. It should be applied only by a trained applicator who should wear recommended clothing and equipment and follow all safety rules in its use. The residual effectiveness is relatively short and food crops are safe for consumption in 7–21 days following application.

Methyl parathion ($C_8H_{10}NO_5PS$) has chemical characteristics similar to those of parathion, but the rate of hydrolysis by alkali is much higher. It is recommended for use on field crop pests such as the greenbug on small grains and a number of cotton pests. The product is not quite so toxic to mammals as parathion, and is less stable. The same precautions are recommended in its use as for the latter.

Technical *malathion* ($C_{10}H_{19}O_6PS_2$) is a dark-brown liquid with the odor of garlic. It is slightly water soluble, of very limited solubility in petroleum oils, but miscible with most organic solvents. The residue on crops disappears rather rapidly. Since it is not as toxic as most other organophosphorus compounds, it has wide usage. Malathion is recommended for a number of diverse pests of field crops, vegetables, fruits, livestock, stored products, and of the home.

Malathion is one of the few insecticides which may be used on dairy cattle in fly control. Two ounces of a 4 percent dust may be sprinkled on the neck, flanks, and back at intervals of 3 weeks. Sprays and dips must not be used on these animals. A 0.5 percent spray may be applied on beef cattle for fly, louse, and tick control; on sheep and goats for lice, keds, and ticks; and on swine for lice. It also may be used in baits inside and outside of barns for fly control. Sprays and dips for lice, ticks, and fleas on cats and dogs are used at concentrations of 0.25–0.50 percent of the toxicant. Household sprays for control of cockroaches and other pests are in common use. Such sprays are used in combination with other insecticides such as chlordane and pyrethrum. Because of odor, the most completely deodorized products are employed here.

Technical *diazinon* ($C_{12}H_{21}N_2O_3PS$) is a brown liquid. It is only slightly soluble in water but miscible in alcohol, xylene, acetone, and soluble in petroleum oils. The insecticide has considerable residual effectiveness. It is employed in the control of a number of pests of vegetables, fruits, cotton, and flies in and around barns.

The technical grade of *dioxathion* (Delnav) ($C_{12}H_{26}O_6P_2S_4$) is a brown liquid insoluble in water but soluble in a number of organic solvents. It is stable in water emulsions, but is hydrolyzed by heating and by alkali. Tolerances have been established for use of the insecticide on meat animals, grapes, and citrus. Chief uses at this time are for control of lice and ticks on beef cattle, fleece-worms, keds, and ticks on sheep and goats. It is also employed as a spray against fleas, lice, and ticks on dogs and for treatment of premises infested with fleas and ticks.

Trichlorfon (*Dylox, Dipterex,* or *Neguvon*) ($C_4H_8Cl_3O_4P$) is a white or pale yellow crystalline solid, soluble in water, ether, chloroform, and benzene but insoluble in petroleum oils, and it is unstable to alkali. It is recommended for use in combating certain pests of alfalfa, sugar beets, and cotton, and for poison baits in housefly control. It is one of the products recommended in cattle grub control.

SYSTEMIC PHOSPHORUS INSECTICIDES. The technical grade of *demeton* (*Systox*) ($C_8H_{19}O_3PS_2$) is a light yellow oily liquid with a distinct mercaptan odor. The product is slightly soluble in water but soluble in most of the organic solvents. This is a systemic poison with contact and some fumigating action. It is prepared as an emulsifiable concentrate, and also combined with activated charcoal for seed and soil treatment. This dangerously toxic insecticide is widely used in aphid and phytophagous mite control.

It is too toxic for use around home and livestock. It should be applied only by a trained operator who must wear recommended clothing and equipment. It is a dangerous cholinesterase inhibitor.

Among other plant systemics are products such as *phorate* or *Thimet,* and *disulfoton.* Phorate and disulfoton are employed in seed treatments to protect the young plants from aphids, mites, and thrips.

There are two grades of *ronnel* ($C_8H_8Cl_3O_3PS$); Trolene is the drug grade and Korlan the technical form. This insecticide is practically insoluble in water, but readily soluble in most organic solvents. Formulations of wettable powders, emulsions, smears, and feed additives are in use. The uses of this systemic and contact insecticide include control of pests of livestock and houseflies. It must not be applied on dairy cattle. In cattle grub control, ronnel (*Trolene*) is administered as a mineral mix or feed additive. In the control of other pests of livestock such as horn flies, lice, and screwworms, a spray of the Korlan grade is generally used. A smear of Korlan is recommended also in screwworm control. Houseflies both inside and outside of barns may be controlled with a spray. This insecticide is of low acute toxicity to mammals.

Technical *coumaphos* (Co-Ral) ($C_{14}H_{16}ClO_5PS$) is composed of brownish crystals which are practically insoluble in water, with slight solubility in light petroleum, but readily soluble in most of the common organic solvents. This is a systemic poison which also has contact action. It is widely recommended for control of animal pests, particularly cattle grubs, lice, ticks, keds, screwworms, poultry mites, and horn flies. As with ronnel, the product cannot be used on dairy cattle.

Ruelene ($C_{12}H_{19}ClNO_3P$) is an effective systemic insecticide for control of cattle grubs. It also provides control for lice and horn flies when employed as an emulsifiable concentrate spray or a ready mixed pour-on.

Trichlorfon (Neguvon) ($C_{10}H_{16}NO_5PS_2$) is another product with systemic properties used for control of cattle grubs as an emulsifiable concentrate spray or ready mixed pour-on.

Fumigants

Hydrocyanic acid or *hydrogen cyanide* (HCN) is a colorless gas with the odor of peach kernels. It is soluble in water, alcohol, and ether. The gas is slightly lighter than air and is not flammable at concentrations generally employed.

Hydrocyanic acid has been widely employed in fumigating warehouses, mills, households, ships, and citrus trees, but it is of less importance today. This gas is one of the most poisonous substances known. It should be applied only by a trained applicator wearing an approved gas mask. The oral lethal dose for man is 50 milligrams, or about 0.8 milligrams per kilogram body weight. Inhalation in high concentrations causes death immediately. A concentration of one part in 500 is fatal. Also, in high concentration the gas is absorbed through the skin, so gas masks do not completely protect the applicator.

The commercial grade of *carbon disulfide* (CS_2) is a slightly yellow liquid with a disagreeable odor due to the presence of impurities. The liquid volatilizes readily when a large surface is exposed, forming a gas heavier than air; it has excellent penetrating properties. It is an efficient fumigant for the protection of bulk grain from insect damage and has been widely used in the past. The fumigant is highly flammable and is explosive when mixed with air in a wide range of proportions. Lighted cigarettes, sparks from electric switches, and static electricity may ignite it. Also, the gas may be ignited without the presence of a flame at 297° F or above. Because of attendant hazards, a nonflammable mixture of one part of carbon disulfide and four parts of carbon tetrachloride is recommended for use on stored grain. The recommended dosages vary with the type of bin and also the kind of grain which is being fumigated. Germination of grain may be affected if the seed is not reasonably dry or if the fumigant is applied directly upon it. This fumigant is exempt from tolerances for common grains. Vapors are poisonous to mammals and recommended precautions should be followed.

Ethylene dichloride ($C_2H_4Cl_2$) is a colorless liquid with the odor of chloroform. The liquid has about the same specific gravity as carbon disulfide, and the fumigant has good penetrating properties.

This is an effective stored-grain fumigant. If the grain is reasonably dry there is little danger of affecting its germination. As the product has flammable and explosive properties, a mixture of three volumes of it with one volume of carbon tetrachloride is used to eliminate these hazards. The fumigant is exempt from tolerances when used on wheat, corn, barley, rye, and similar grains. It is of low mammalian toxicity.

Ethylene dibromide ($C_2H_4Br_2$) is a nonflammable and stable product. It is marketed in solution in an inert solvent for use in soils and mixed with carbon tetrachloride for warehouse and mill fumigation. Its recommended uses are as a grain fumigant, and against certain soil insects and nematodes. In its effect on the germination of seed, it is moderately safe if the grain is reasonably dry. Skin irritation and blisters may be produced on prolonged contact.

Methyl bromide (CH_3BR) is an important fumigant in commercial work. The product is a gas at ordinary temperatures, and is 3.3 times heavier than air. At temperatures of 40.1° F or lower, it is a colorless, odorless, and volatile liquid. The fumigant is marketed in cans or cylinders of various capacities. Small amounts of chloropicrin may be added as a warning agent.

Methyl bromide is widely employed in the fumigation of many products—milled flour and feed, dairy products, dried fruits, beans, sweet potatoes, Irish potatoes, fresh vegetables of many kinds, and nursery stock. It also may be used in the fumigation of bulk grain where the bins are equipped with aeration systems. This gas provides satisfactory control for the leaf-cutting ant. The compound is also an efficient soil fumigant for nematodes, wireworms, and other pests. Germination of seed may be impaired by this fumigant.

Since a tight enclosure is essential for successful fumigation, the use of an atmospheric fumigation vault is usually recommended. The gas should be introduced into the chamber from the outside. The fumigant is toxic to human beings, and the safe upper limit is set at 17 parts per million. In the air above this concentration, respirators should be worn. Only experienced operators should use the fumigant. A wide range of tolerances has been established for the product.

Phosphine (hydrogen phosphide) (PH_3) is of importance as a fumigant for grains in storage, seed, and processed foods. It is generated from dry tablets containing aluminum phosphide and ammonium carbonate which in combination with moisture in the air releases phosphine. Phosphine in itself is flammable, but sufficient ammonia and carbon dioxide is released to prevent combustion. There are no toxicological effects from the use of the product following routine aeration.

Paradichlorobenzene ($C_6H_4Cl_2$) is a white crystalline substance which has the appearance of ice cream salt. Upon exposure it volatilizes slowly into a gas 5.1 times heavier than air. The chemical has a characteristic though not unpleasant odor. Paradichlorobenzene is used in peach tree boror control. Applications should be made in the fall in the form of a ring around the tree base, and then covered with soil. Considerable quantities of the crystals have been employed in the control of clothes moths and carpet beetles by simply sprinkling the layers of stored clothing or fabrics.

Naphthalene ($C_{10}H_8$) is a white crystalline substance available as flakes or as the familiar "moth balls." The product volatilizes slowly, forming a gas with a characteristic pungent odor. Naphthalene is employed chiefly in the protection of fabrics from the depredations of clothes moths and carpet beetles. The dosage is the same as that of paradichlorobenzene. The flake form is the more efficient.

Several *soil fumigants* are commercially available for control of nematodes and certain soil inhabiting insects. The best known products are *D-D mixtures* (composed of *dichloropropane* and *dichloropropene*), *ethylene dibromide*, and *methyl bromide*. Fumigation of the soil with these compounds is expensive, but the cost is not prohibitive for seedbeds, small home gardens, and certain truck crops where the income per acre is large.

The soil should be well prepared and free from clods and debris. It should be neither too dry nor too wet, but suitable for cultivation, and the soil temperature should not be below 50° F. The operator should follow the recommendations of the manufacturer in the application and the proper dosages of these fumigants.

JOINT ACTION OF INSECTICIDES

Joint action refers to the response obtained when two or more insecticides are applied in combination. Studies of this phenomenon have increased during the past 10 years with the introduction of many different insecticides and mixtures of insecticides on the market.

Several types of joint action of insecticides have been defined by research workers. The two most common classifications of joint action include:

1. Similar joint action occurs when the poisons act independ-

ently but similarly. The poisons applied separately produce a common response and produce the same response when applied jointly. Equivalent amounts of one poison may be substituted for the other in the mixture without altering the toxicity.

2. Synergistic action takes place when the application of a mixture of compounds produces a total response greater than the sum of the components used separately.

Results of studies on joint action have had important bearings on insect control. In many cases the addition of relatively nontoxic materials such as *piperonyl butoxide* to pyrethrum has increased its effectiveness greatly. An outstanding case of synergism is the mixture of the *cyclodiene* type compounds (such as toxaphene) with DDT, which has extended the usefulness of the cyclodienes for control of resistant boll weevils. Some persons believe that the use of insecticide mixtures which exhibit independent joint action may tend to prevent the development of insecticide resistance in insects.

ATTRACTANTS

In nature insects respond to odors from foods, prey, oviposition sites, and to sex attractants. Attempts have been made to use attractive odors of various kinds to lure insects into traps or to poison baits. Some success has been attained in this field. Ammonia is attractive to many insects. When mixed with glycerine and sodium hydroxide it has been used to attract the walnut husk fly. Protein hydrolysates are attractive to fruit flies, particularly as bait. Metaldehyde is used as an attractant in snail and slug baits. A mixture of geraniol and eugenol is employed in trapping japanese beetles. Methyl eugenol is effective in baits and traps for the male of the oriental fruit fly, *Dacus dorsalis*. The male of the melon fly *Dacus cucurbitae* is attracted to anisyl acetone. Compounds known as Siglure and Medlure are strongly attractive to the mediterranean fruit fly. Fermenting sugars and syrups have long been used as attractants. Other attractants are essential oils such as anthol and isamyl salicylate.

Of considerable interest are the insect sex attractants known as *pheromones*. Extracts of the female gypsy moth have been used in bait traps. The chemical compound is an ester known as gyptol. The pheromone of the silkworm moth has also been identified. The occurrence of sex attractants has been demonstrated in a large number of female and male insects. Research is being done on the application of these attractants in control of certain insects. The use of juvenile and molting hormones and their analogs in control programs is also being investigated.

REPELLENTS

Any substance, not necessarily poisonous, that protects plants or animals by rendering them unattractive or offensive to insects is known as a repellent. The oldest of repellents are lime dust, ashes, smoke, and oils. Other old repellents are lime, Bordeaux mixture, creosote, and pine tar oil. To these may be added some of the essential oils, the use of which dates back for many years. Low concentrations of pyrethrum and sulfur are largely repellents. In fact, most insecticides have some repellent characteristics. Butyl propylene, glycol, and dibutyl succinate are suitable for use on livestock. Dimethylphthalate is a repellent for mosquitoes, chiggers, and ticks. Diethyltoluamide (deet) is one of the best insect repellents developed. It affords relief against a number of pests and has persistent qualities. Other materials are dimethylcarbate and indalone.

INTEGRATED INSECT PEST MANAGEMENT

Natural, biological, chemical, cultural, and other control measures of insects have been briefly presented. Entomologists have long stressed, among other things, cultural practices, and in particular their use in conjunction with insecticides. But only in recent years has a conscious and deliberate attempt been made to bring together all control measures into a harmonious and a more satisfactory program. This has been brought on by the problems which have arisen from the widespread use of the synthetic organic insecticides. Progressively less use of cultural and other practices and greater dependence upon chemical compounds have produced in many cases a monosystem of pest control.

Yields of crops have been greatly increased and a high quality of food produced. Also, means have been provided for the elimination of pestiferous and disease bearing insects. But after a period the continuous use of these insecticides has produced serious ecological disturbances in the agroecosystems. The insect parasites and predators were killed, particularly when wide-spectrum insecticides, such as DDT, with a long residual effectiveness were employed. With their natural checks greatly reduced, other insects of minor importance became major pests. A somewhat similar problem may be developing in the use of herbicides. A primary weed may be controlled, but it may be succeeded by a secondary weed which may become of major importance.

From the professional viewpoint of the entomologists, the most serious problem arising from the long and continuous use of insecticides has been in the development of resistance in many species of insects. Changing the type of insecticides has helped, but in time some insects have become resistant to them and also their combinations. Supplemental control measures for such pests must be developed.

Environmental pollution is of concern. The widespread use of insecticides has killed birds, fishes, and other forms of wildlife. Suggestions have been made that the use of all pesticides be eliminated. But this is not presently feasible with the greater demand for more food and the need for protection from pestiferous and disease-bearing arthropods. Conversely, producers desire the destruction of every injurious insect within a crop unit. This, too, is hardly practicable. Scientists in agriculture face pressures from all sides. All groups need to reach a compromise and develop a comprehensive program of insect control.

Insecticides of a more selective nature and with less residual effectiveness need to be employed. More careful supervision may be necessary, and only those applications essential for the production of satisfactory yields of crops should be made. The public may need to accept some foods with slight insect damage, and also the presence of some pestiferous insects.

The goal of some is the eradication of all injurious insects; this is not possible. In isolated cases eradication of an arthropod may be effected, as the cattle tick in the South. However, the vast assemblage of insect life, together with most of the pests, will always be an important part of the ecosystem in which man lives.

Some progress in integrated pest management has been made. There will be constant improvements. The most successful program requires the cooperative services of agronomists, ecologists, entomologists, plant and animal breeders, conservationists, and economists. The ecology of agroecosystems needs careful study. The insects within each ecological unit should be identified and their interrelationships understood as much as is reasonably possible. The population dynamics of the harmful species, together with their most important natural enemies, need to be carefully determined. Given this background information, the available means of insect control then may be used most effectively. Close cooperation among all groups and careful supervision of programs are essential to success.

CHAPTER 20
COLLECTING, MOUNTING, AND PRESERVING INSECTS

WHAT AND WHERE TO COLLECT

There is no better way to learn about insects than by making a collection. Much information will be acquired which will never be found in textbooks. Observations on habits, host relationships, and life histories of insects will be remembered long after the dull, dry facts of textbooks are forgotten. Working with live specimens, killing and mounting them, creates much more interest than studying museum specimens and looking at pictures. Furthermore, mounting and arranging specimens in a collection increases one's knowledge and understanding of the classification of insects.

Making insect collections takes one outdoors in the fields and forests, and along streams, which is excellent recreation. The student should begin by making a general collection. After a knowledge of the most common insects has been acquired he probably will restrict his collecting to insects of certain taxonomic groups. Some very fine collections have been built up by nonprofessionals, and much information of value has been added to the science.

Hardly a place in nature exists that does not harbor an insect of some kind. Even though insects may be collected in any season, they are naturally most abundant in warm, moist weather, particularly in the spring and early summer. Also, collecting may be excellent in the fall when conditions are favorable. As many species are present for only a limited period, collecting should be done throughout the year if the greatest variety of insects is desired.

Every insect has its preferred habitat and hosts, and collections should be made in as many places as possible. Flowers afford the best places for collecting nectar and pollen feeders, such as butterflies, bees, many wasps, and certain flies. Collections should be made on all kinds of plants, for all are host to some type of insect which may be found feeding on the leaves, fruit, stems, trunks, or roots. Rotten logs, loose bark, and debris of all types harbor many diverse forms. Many insects are found in aquatic environments. Some live in the water, others on the surface. Certain species are found on aquatic plants or along the shoreline. Animals and their refuse attract many species. Homes and other buildings, stored products, such as grain and foods, yield many specimens. Large numbers of different insects are attracted to lights under favorable weather conditions, and they may be collected around street lights, screens of lighted homes, or in light traps installed for the purpose.

Better specimens are frequently obtained by collecting the immature stages and rearing the adults. This practice entails more work and time; but one is compensated, not only in better specimens, but also in learning more about the biology of the insects and marks of recognition of the developmental stages.

COLLECTING EQUIPMENT

Only a few inexpensive pieces of equipment are needed to make an insect collection. The most important items are an insect net, killing bottle, insect pins, and storage boxes. Other equipment and supplies are desirable, and these will be mentioned later in the discussion. All items may be purchased from entomological supply houses, but most of the equipment may be made.

NETS

An insect net consists of a handle fitted with a wire hoop to which a cloth bag is attached (Figure 308). Two general types of nets are used, the heavier sweeping net and the lighter aerial or

Figure 308. An insect net.

butterfly net. The sweeping net needs to be of sturdier construction and the bag of more substantial material (muslin or light canvas). The aerial net is used in collecting such wary insects as butterflies, dragonflies, and wasps. It should be of light weight and provided with a porous bag of some material such as fine netting or marquisette. The length of a bag should be about twice the diameter of the hoop.

If the net is to be homemade, a handle should be selected that is light in weight, strong, and about 3 or 4 feet in length. On one end of the handle grooves are cut on opposite sides to receive the bent wire of the hoop (Figure 309). One groove should be made about 3½ inches long and the other 2½ inches with a small hole drilled through the handle at the end of each. If the bags are not going to be changed, the joint may be securely wrapped with small wire. If bags are to be changed occasionally, the handle should be provided with a metal ferrule which can be pushed up to secure the joint. If one is not at hand, a ferrule may be obtained from a tinsmith. The hoop should be made from a 4-foot length of stiff wire (20 gauge). When the ends are bent for attachment to the handle the diameter of the hoop will be slightly more than 12 inches.

KILLING BOTTLES

When an insect is collected, it should be killed as quickly as possible in a killing bottle to avoid damaging the specimen. Any wide-

Figure 309. Details of a homemade hoop and handle of a net. A. End of handle with grooves terminating in small holes in which ends of wire hoop fit. B. Hoop of stiff wire. C. Wire-wrapped joint. D. Joint fitted with ferrule to hold net in place.

Plaster of paris

Dry plaster of paris

Sodium cyanide or potassium cyanide

Cardboard

Cellucotton

Calcium cyanide

Figure 310. Killing bottles.

mouthed glass jar or vial is satisfactory for making a killing bottle (Figure 310). It should be provided with a tightly fitting cork or screw cap. A collector needs several bottles of different sizes for different types of insects.

Several chemicals are available for use as killing agents in the bottles; ethyl acetate and cyanide are the most satisfactory. Chloroform and carbon tetrachloride may be used as substitute killing agents when the other compounds are not available. Regardless of the killing agent used, the bottle should be clearly labeled POISON. It is advisable to tape glass bottles to reduce breakage hazards.

Ethyl acetate is readily available and bottles prepared with it are comparatively safe. The compound does not kill so quickly as cyanide, but insects do not recover from its effects as they may do when cyanide is used. Also, specimens can be kept longer in ethyl acetate bottles than in cyanide bottles without becoming brittle and discolored.

An ethyl acetate killing bottle is easily made. About ½ inch of a mixture of plaster of Paris and water is poured in the bottom of the bottle. The plaster of Paris is allowed to set and dry completely. Drying may be hastened by setting the bottle in an oven. When the plaster of Paris is thoroughly dry it is saturated with ethyl acetate. The bottle is then ready for use and will remain effective for months if kept tightly closed. When the bottle loses its effectiveness it may be dried and recharged.

Cyanide has been the compound most widely used in making killing bottles. Any one of three forms—calcium cyanide, sodium cyanide, or potassium cyanide—may be used. Calcium cyanide is the most satisfactory. The granular form of calcium cyanide is placed in the bottom of the bottle or vial and covered with a plug of cellucotton which is tamped firmly in place. A piece of cardboard, perforated with a few pinholes, is cut to fit tightly in the bottle or vial on top of the cellucotton. The bottle is then ready for immediate use. If sodium cyanide or potassium cyanide is used, the bottom of a perfectly dry bottle is covered with the powdered or granular cyanide. On top of the cyanide is added about $1/2$ inch of dry plaster of Paris or a fine grade of sawdust, which is then covered with a wet layer of plaster of Paris, $1/4$ to $1/2$ inch thick. The plaster of Paris must set and dry before the bottle is closed.

Cyanide is a deadly poison and must be handled with extreme care. Bottles containing cyanide must be conspicuously labeled and kept away from those who are not aware of its deadliness. When a bottle is broken or is no longer to be used, it should be carefully disposed of, preferably by burying.

Best results are obtained from a killing bottle through proper use. The bottle should be kept closed and not opened except to put in and take out specimens. Moisture often condenses on the inside of the bottle. This should be wiped out periodically and a few pieces of absorbent paper, such as cleansing tissue, should be kept in the bottle and frequently replaced. A separate bottle should be kept for moths and butterflies, as scales from their wings stick to other specimens and spoil their appearance. Insects that die slowly, e.g., beetles, also should be kept in a special bottle and never placed with fragile specimens. Killing bottles should never be overloaded with specimens. Insects in cyanide bottles should be removed as soon as they are dead. If they remain in a cyanide bottle too long they tend to discolor, and when removed they soon become brittle.

OTHER COLLECTING ITEMS

An aspirator is useful in collecting small insects. Probably the simplest form is the vial type (Figure 311). Insects are drawn through a tube into the vial by sucking on the mouthpiece. A cloth covers the inner end of the mouthpiece tube to prevent insects from being drawn into the mouth of the collector.

Small insects in trash are most easily collected by use of sifters of various types. The material should be sifted on a cloth background where movements of the tiny insects will reveal their presence. The insects may be picked up with an aspirator or a wet camel's hair brush.

Large numbers of small insects may be collected by means of a separator which is commonly known as a Berlese funnel. Basically, the separator consists of a sieve, for holding the litter or trash, which fits into the top of a funnel. The insects move downward through the sieve as the litter dries, and drop through the funnel

Figure 311. Aspirator for collecting small insects.

into a killing bottle or a jar containing a preserving fluid. The drying of the litter may be hastened by placing a light bulb or some other source of low heat above the sieve.

Light traps of several types have been made, and used in surveys to determine the distribution and abundance of certain insects. A large number of different insects may be collected in these traps. A convenient way of collecting at a light is to hang a white cloth, such as a sheet, so that the light shines against it. The insects are captured as they collect on the white background or at its base.

Baits of different kinds are useful in collecting insects. "Sugaring" for moths is commonly practiced. A sugary solution is mopped or painted on logs, tree trunks, and stumps to attract the insects. Several mixtures are used for "sugaring," but a fermenting mixture is probably the most satisfactory. The bait is applied before dark and should be visited at intervals during the night.

Other collector's items include a dip net for aquatic insects, forceps, camel's hair brushes, a strong knife, hatchet, vials of preserving fluid, boxes for temporary storage of specimens, and some type of knapsack for carrying the equipment.

MOUNTING AND PRESERVING INSECTS

After specimens are collected they must be preserved for future study. Larvae and other soft-bodied forms may be preserved in 80 percent alcohol or 4 percent formaldehyde. Most hard-bodied insects are mounted on pins. With proper care they will keep indefinitely. Those too small to pin may be mounted on "minuten" pins, card points, or microscope slides.

RELAXING JARS

It is advisable to mount insects soon after they are collected, but this is not always possible. When specimens dry they become

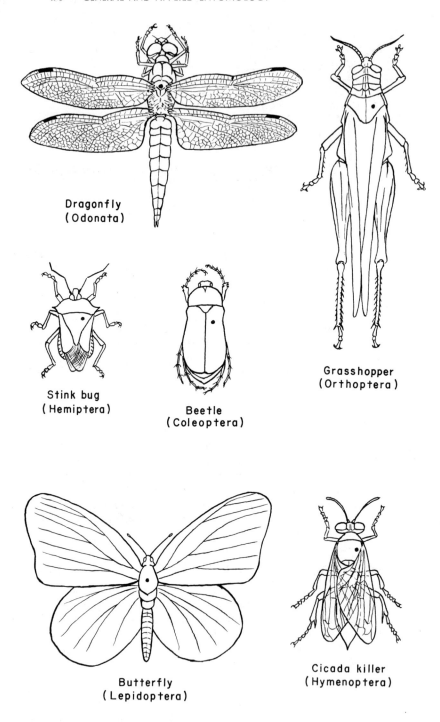

Dragonfly
(Odonata)

Stink bug
(Hemiptera)

Beetle
(Coleoptera)

Grasshopper
(Orthoptera)

Butterfly
(Lepidoptera)

Cicada killer
(Hymenoptera)

Figure 312. Correct pinning methods for common groups of insects.

brittle and may be damaged in pinning. They must be relaxed before they can be pinned. Any wide-mouthed jar with a tightly fitting cover can be made into a relaxing jar. The bottom of the jar is covered with wet sand or sawdust. A few drops of carbolic acid are added to prevent molds. A piece of cardboard is cut to fit into the jar on top of the sand or sawdust. Insects in open boxes are placed in the jar which is then tightly covered. Usually specimens are sufficiently relaxed to be mounted after 1 or 2 days.

PINNING INSECTS

Insect pins may be obtained from any entomological supply house. Common pins cannot be used as they are too short and thick, and soon rust. Insect pins are made in several sizes. For most purposes sizes 2 and 3 are satisfactory.

Insects are pinned vertically through the body. The place where the pin is inserted depends upon the type of insect (Figure 312). The following rules are followed in pinning the different groups of insects.

1. Orthoptera (grasshoppers, crickets, etc.). Pin through the back of the pronotum, slightly to the right of the middle line.
2. Hemiptera (stinkbugs, etc.). Pin through the scutellum, slightly to the right of the middle line.
3. Coleoptera (beetles). Pin through the right elytron (wing cover) about midway on the body.
4. Lepidoptera (butterflies and moths). Insert the pin between the base of the front wings.
5. Diptera (flies) and Hymenoptera (bees, wasps, etc.). Pin through the thorax, slightly to the right of the midline.
6. Odonata (dragonflies and damselflies). Pin through the middle of the thorax. To conserve space in the collection they may be pinned horizontally through the thorax.

A collection should appear neat, with the specimens uniformly mounted about an inch above the point of the pin. Labels on the pin should be uniformly arranged also (Figure 313A). This is most easily obtained by using a pinning block, a block of wood with three steps (Figure 313B). In each step a small hole is drilled. Beginning with the first (lowest) step, the holes are $3/8$, $5/8$, and 1 inch deep, respectively.

SPREADING BOARDS

Some insects, such as moths and butterflies, are usually mounted with their wings spread. Spreading boards are used for this purpose and are important collector's items. Different sizes and types may be purchased or made at home. Figure 314 shows the general type of construction and average dimensions. Soft wood top pieces should be used to facilitate the insertion of pins.

Certain rules are followed in spreading the wings of insects. The front wings of moths and butterflies should be spread with the rear margin at a right angle with the body. The front margin of the hind wings should be under the rear margin of the front wings. Strips of paper are pinned across the wings to hold them in position until the specimens are dried. In spreading the wings of dragonflies, damselflies, grasshoppers, and most other insects, the front margin of the hind wings should be at a right angle with the body and the front wings pulled forward sufficiently so the wings do not touch.

LABELING SPECIMENS

Unless a specimen in a collection is accompanied by a label bearing certain essential information, it is of little scientific value. A

Figure 313. A. Illustrations showing correct positions of insects and labels on pins. B. A pinning block used to adjust both specimens and labels to correct position on pin.

Figure 314. A spreading board with average dimensions.

label should always give the date and locality of the insect's capture. Additional information giving the name or initials of the collector and the hosts or habitat of the insect is desirable. One or two labels may be used (Figure 315). If only one label is used it should bear the locality, date, and name or initials of the collector. When two labels are used, the first should give information on locality and date, and the second the name of the collector and hosts or habitat.

Labels should be of uniform size, about ¾ inch long and ¼ inch wide and made from stiff paper. Lettering may be done by hand, printed, or obtained partly printed from entomological supply houses. A very satisfactory plan for obtaining supplies of labels is to type a number on plain white paper. This paper is photographed and prints made. The labels may be cut from the prints as they are used. Identification labels are usually plain white or bordered, about ½ by 1¼ inches in size, and pinned against the bottom of the box.

INSECT BOXES

Boxes for housing pinned specimens should have the bottom lined with a soft material such as cork or balsa wood, and they need to be as pestproof as possible. The best known type is the

College Station College Station College Station
195 Tex   195 Tex   195 Tex
College Station College Station College Station
195 Tex   195 Tex   195 Tex
College Station College Station College Station
195 Tex   195 Tex   195 Tex
College Station College Station College Station
195 Tex   195 Tex   195 Tex
College Station College Station College Station
195 Tex   195 Tex   195 Tex
College Station College Station College Station
195 Tex   195 Tex   195 Tex
College Station College Station College Station
195 Tex   195 Tex   195 Tex
College Station College Station College Station
195 Tex   195 Tex   195 Tex
College Station College Station College Station
195 Tex   195 Tex   195 Tex
College Station College Station College Station
195 Tex   195 Tex   195 Tex

A   B

Figure 315. Samples of printed labels. A. Strips of printed labels giving locality and space for date. B. Identification labels providing space for scientific name, the name of the describer of the species, and name of person identifying the insect.

Schmitt box which is readily obtained from supply houses. Cigar boxes are most frequently used by the beginner. Also, heavy cardboard boxes are satisfactory for temporary use. The collection needs to be checked frequently for museum pests.

Large collections in institutions are frequently housed in cabinets which contain glass-top drawers. The drawers are fitted with trays of different sizes which facilitate rearrangement without having to shift individual specimens.

RIKER MOUNTS

Riker mounts are convenient for display and teaching purposes. A Riker mount is a shallow cardboard box about 1 inch deep, filled with cotton and with a glass top. The insects are placed on the cotton background and are held in position by the glass cover. Various sizes of Riker mounts may be purchased or made. The size most commonly used is 8 inches wide and 12 inches long.

Riker mounts are easily made. All the items needed are a supply of cardboard boxes (such as hose boxes), window-pane glass, glass cutter, cotton, and tape. The top of the lid of the box is cut out, leaving a margin about ¼ inch wide. A piece of glass is cut to fit in the top and secured with tape along its edges. Covering the sides of the Riker mount increases its durability and improves the appearance. Black tape makes a better appearing mount. The mount may be filled with cotton of any type which is covered with a layer of medicated cotton to improve the appearance and provide a smooth surface. The cover is secured by pins pushed into the mount through the sides and ends.

PROTECTING COLLECTIONS FROM PESTS

Insect collections are attacked by dermestid larvae, ants, and other pests. If precautions are not taken, the collections may soon be reduced to fragments and powder. Naphthalene (flakes or balls) is most commonly used in the protection of collections. This compound is a satisfactory repellent, but it will not kill the pests once the collection has become infested. If an infestation has developed it is necessary to use a fumigant, such as paradichlorobenzene (PDB), carbon tetrachloride, carbon disulfide, or ethylene dichloride.

GLOSSARY

Abdomen, the third or posterior division of an insect's body

Accessory cell, a wing cell usually not present; a closed cell in wings of many Lepidoptera between branches of the radius

Accessory vein, a secondary longitudinal vein in an insect wing

Acetylcholine, a substance in many parts of the body of animals which is important in the function of nerves

Acuminate, tapering to a point

Adfrontal areas, two narrow oblique plates on head of lepidopterous larvae

Aedeagus, penis or intromittent organ of male insects

Aestivation, dormancy in summer, or during a hot, dry season

Agamic, reproducing without mating

Agroecosystem, an artificial agricultural ecosystem of man

Ametabolous, insect development without metamorphosis

Androconia, scent scales found on some male butterflies

Annulate, ringlike; with ringed divisions or segments

Antecoxal piece, a metasternal sclerite in front of the hind coxae

Antenna (pl. *antennae*), a paired segmented appendage located on the head; commonly known as a feeler

Antenodal, preceding or before the nodus

Antibiosis, the feeding upon the host by another, resulting in harmful effects to the latter

Aorta, the nonchambered dorsal blood vessel opening into the head region

Apposition eye, an eye of day-flying insects which absorbs oblique rays of light in the pigmented walls of the ommatidia

Apposition image, in diurnal insects an image built up in eyes by apposed points of light falling side by side and not overlapping

Aptera, insects which are wingless

Apterygota, a subclass of primitively wingless insects

Arista, a large bristle on antenna of certain Diptera, usually dorsally located

Arthropoda, a phylum of animals consisting of insects and related forms

Asexual, independent of sexual processes

Autecology, the study of individual species with all their life activities and responses to everything else within a community

Axon, a nerve fiber

Basement membrane, thin, noncellular membrane forming the inner lining of the hypodermis of the body wall

Beak, a jointed, protruding mouthpart structure of a sucking insect

Bilateral, with equal or symmetrical sides

Binomial, pertaining to two names; the zoological system of nomenclature consisting of a generic and a specific name

Biome, a biological zone

Biotic, pertaining to the plants and animals of a given habitat

Book lung, a respiratory sac containing leaflike plates (found in spiders)

Bucca, the mouth in adult Diptera

Bursa copulatrix, copulatory pouch of the female in some orders of insects

Calypters, a pair of scales at the base of the wings above the halteres

Campodeiform, pertaining to larvae resembling certain members of the Thysanura; i.e., the body elongate and flattened with the legs, antennae, and cerci well developed

Capitate, with a head, a type of antenna terminating in a knoblike process

Capitulum, a false head anteriorly borne (in ticks)

Caraboid, resembling a carabid larva

Cardiac valve, a valve at the junction of the proventriculus and ventriculus

Cardo, basal segment of the maxilla

Carina, a ridge or keel

Caterpillar, the larva of a butterfly or moth

Caudal, pertaining to the anal end of the body

Cecum (pl. *ceca*), a blind sac, one of a group of appendages opening into the anterior region of the ventriculus

Cephalad, pertaining to the anterior end of the body

Cephalothorax, the combined head and thorax of Crustacea and Arachnida

Cercus, a generally paired appendage at the end of the abdomen, usually slender and segmented

Chaetotaxy, arrangement and nomenclature of setae on the exoskeleton of an insect, particularly in Diptera

Chelicerae (sing. *Chelicera*), anterior paired appendages in Arachnida, representing modified second antennae of the Crustacea

Chitin, a nitrogenous compound occurring in the cuticula of Arthropoda

Cholinesterase, enzyme or enzymes which break down or hydrolyzes acetylcholine

Chordotonal, pertaining to organs for the perception of sound

Chorion, shell of an insect egg

Chrysalis (pl. *chrysalids* or *chrysalides*), the pupa of a butterfly

Class, a division of the animal kingdom between the phylum and the order in rank

Clavate, clubbed, thickened gradually toward the tip, e.g., a clavate antenna

Clavus, triangular or oblong anal area of the front wing in Hemiptera and Homoptera

Closed cell, a cell bounded on all sides by veins

Clypeus, the sclerite between the frons and the labrum

Coarctate larva, a larva resembling the puparium of Diptera; the diapausing stage of a blister beetle larva

Cocoon, a silken covering constructed for protection of the pupa

Coelom, body cavity

Colleterial glands, glandular structures accessory to the oviducts

Collophore, a ventral tube on the first abdominal segment of Collembola

Colon, that part of the alimentary canal between the ileum and rectum

Commensalism, one or more species living together and in association, with one or both benefited and neither harmed

Commissure, the nerve cord connecting two ganglia

Community, animals or plants of a natural area or habitat

Compound eye, an aggregation of visual elements (ommatidia), each represented externally by a facet

Corbicula (pl. *corbiculae*), the pollen basket on the hind tibia of bees

Corpora allata, generally paired small endocrine glands behind the brain

Corpora cardiaca, structures on either side of the aorta behind the brain in which the neurohormone accumulates

Corium, the elongate basal part of the front wing of Hemiptera

Cornea, outer covering of a compound eye, of a visual element (ommatidium) in particular

Cornicles, a pair of dorsal tubes on the posterior region of the abdomen of aphids which secrete a waxy substance

Costa, a longitudinal vein extending along the anterior margin of the wing

Coxa, basal division of leg which joins it to the body

Cremaster, hooklike process on end of abdomen of pupae of Lepidoptera

Crochets, spines on tip of prolegs of caterpillars

Crop, dilated part of the alimentary canal behind the esophagus for the reception of food

Ctenidia (sing. *ctenidium*), row of stiff spines on head and thorax of fleas

Cubitus, a longitudinal vein of an insect wing behind the media, usually two-branched

Cuneus, a triangular piece at apex of corium of the hemelytron, and separated from it by a suture (Hemiptera)

Cuticula, outer covering of the body wall of an insect composed of a noncellular layer of chitin

Deutocerebrum, the middle part of the brain which controls the antennae

Diapause, a period of suspended activity and morphological development commonly occurring in many insects during cold or dry seasons

Discal cell, a cell located in the basal or central part of a wing of an insect

Discoidal area, the middle of an area or a field such as in the wing of an insect

Ecdysone, the growth and molting hormone of the prothoracic glands

Ecology, the total relationships of all plants and animals in their environment, involving the organic as well as the inorganic

Ecosystem, a self-containing habitat in which living organisms and the physicochemical environment interact in an exchange of energy and matter to form a continuing cycle

Ectoderm, a germ layer which gives rise to the body wall, nervous system, stomodaeum, proctodaeum, tracheal system, and many glands

Ectohormones, see pheromones

Ectoparasite, a parasite living upon the body of the host

Egg-calyx, enlarged portion of oviduct at the bottom of the ovarioles

Ejaculatory duct, tube through which the spermatozoa pass from the vasa differentia

Elytron (pl. *elytra*), a horny, veinless front wing of Coleoptera, Dermaptera, and some Homoptera

Embolium, a narrow part of the corium, separated by a suture, along the costal margin in front wing of Hemiptera

Empodium (pl. *empodia*), a single, padlike or bristlelike structure often present between the tarsal claws of insects, either between paired pulvilli or alone

Endocuticula, the inner layer of the cuticula

Endoderm, the germ layer which gives rise to the mesenteron or ventriculus

Endoparasite, parasite living within the body of the host

Epicuticula, the thin nonchitinous outside covering of the exocuticula

Epimeron, the posterior sclerite of a thoracic pleuron

Epipharynx, a mouthpart attached to the inner surface of the labrum

Episternum, the anterior sclerite of a thoracic pleuron

Eruciform, resembling a caterpillar, with cylindrical body and with both thoracic legs and prolegs

Esophagus, that part of the digestive tract between the mouth and the crop

Exarate pupa, a pupa with the appendages free and not glued to the body

Exocuticula, the outer layer of the cuticula

Exoskeleton, a skeleton on the outside of the body

Exuviae (no sing.), cast skin of immature stages of arthropods

Facet, the lens which forms the base of the visual element, the ommatidium, visible on the surface of the compound eye

Femur (pl. *femora*), the middle or third leg division between the trochanter and the tibia

Filiform, threadlike or hairlike; that type of antenna with the segments quite uniform in size

Flabellum, lobe at end of glossa in bees

Flagellum, the apical part of the antenna, attached to the pedicel

Frenulum, a bristle or a group of bristles arising from the humeral angle of the hind wing in many Lepidoptera and extending underneath the front wing

Frons or *front,* that region of the head lying between the eyes and the clypeus

Furcula, a springing organ on the ventral surface of the abdomen of Collembola

Galea, the outer lobe of the maxilla, attached to the stipes

Ganglion, a bundle of nerve cells, supplying nerves to that part of the body where located

Gaster, that part of the abdomen of ants behind the petiole

Gena, that part of the head below the compound eye and to the side of the frons; the cheek

Genus, a group of closely related species, the first name of a scientific name

Glabrous, smooth, devoid of hairs

Glossa (pl. *glossae*), one of the paired lobes of the labium between the paraglossae

Grub, a thickset, usually sluggish larva with well developed head and thoracic legs

Gula, a sclerite on the ventral surface of the head

Gynandromorph, an abnormal individual with secondary sexual characteristics of both males and females

Habitat, area or region in which an organism is found

Haltere or *halter* (pl. *halteres*), small, knobbed organ, one on each side of the metathorax, representing the hind wing of the Diptera

Hamuli, minute hooks on the anterior margin of the hind wings of Hymenoptera, with which the front and hind wings are held together

Heart, chambered dorsal blood vessel which propels the blood forward through the aorta

Hemelytron (pl. *hemelytra*), front wing of true bugs (Hemiptera)

Hemimetabolous, pertaining to incomplete metamorphosis, as in the Ephemeroptera, Odonata, and Plecoptera

Hemocoele, general body cavity in which the blood flows

Hemolymph, lymphlike nutritive fluid of insects and other related forms

Hermaphrodite, individual in which characteristics of both sexes are combined

Hibernaculum, an overwintering case constructed by a larva as a place for overwintering

Hibernation, dormancy in the winter or cold weather

Holometabolous, pertaining to complete metamorphosis with egg, larva, pupa, and adult stages

Honeydew, a sweet liquid excreted from the anus of a number of Homoptera

Hypermetamorphosis, a form of complete metamorphosis in which the larval stages vary morphologically

Hypodermis, the cellular layer of the body wall which secretes the cuticula

Hypostome, a structure with recurved teeth located in a median position and arising from the basis capituli (in ticks)

Ileum, anterior part of the hindgut between the ventriculus and the colon

Imago, an adult insect

Instar, the stage of an insect between successive molts

Instinct, a chain of coordinated reflex actions, each occurring in its turn

Intercalary vein, a supplementary longitudinal wing vein lying between two preexisting veins

Jugum, a fingerlike process extending from the base of the front wing underneath the hind wing (Lepidoptera)

Labellum (pl. *labella*), the modified tip of the labium of a number of Diptera

Labium, the lower lip of an insect's mouthparts

Labrum, the upper lip of an insect's mouthparts

Lacinia, inner lobe of the maxilla arising from the stipes

Lamella (pl. *lamellae*), a platelike structure

Lamellate, pertaining to leaflike or platelike structures or segments

Larva, the immature stages between the egg and the pupa of an insect with complete metamorphosis; the six-legged stage or first instar of a tick or mite

Ligula, the distal lobes of the labium, the glossae and the paraglossae

Maggot, a legless dipterous larva without a well defined head capsule

Malpighian tubes, long blind tubes of excretory function arising from the anterior end of the hindgut

Mandibles, the paired primary jaws of an insect's mouthparts

Maxillae, the paired secondary jaws of an insect's mouthparts

Media, fourth longitudinal vein of the wing, approximately in the middle of the wing with not more than four branches

Mentum, the distal part of the labium bearing the ligula and palpi

Mesenteron, the midgut or ventriculus of the digestive tract

Mesoderm, germ layer which gives rise to the heart, gonads, muscular system, and the fat body

Mesosternum, ventral sclerite of the mesothorax

Mesothorax, the second or middle segment of the thorax

Metamorphosis, changes in form in development

Metasternum, ventral sclerite of the metathorax

Metathorax, the third and last segment of the thorax

Micropyle, opening in an egg through which the sperm enters to effect fertilization

Midgut, the mesenteron or ventriculus

Molt, the shedding of the skin

Moniliform, segments rounded, beadlike (e.g., moniliform antennae)

Mutualism, living together in close association of organisms of different species

Myiasis, disorder produced by invasion of dipterous larvae

Naiad, an aquatic nymph of insects with hemimetabolous development

Neotenin, the juvenile hormone inducing formation of larval characters

Neuron, nerve cell

Niche, the status or place of each species within a community

Nodus, the stout cross vein near the middle of the front margin of the wing of a member of the Odonata

Notum, the dorsal part of a body segment

Nymph, the young of insects which do not have a pupal stage; immature stage of ticks and mites which have eight legs

Obtect pupa, pupa which has the legs and wings glued to the body, as in Lepidoptera

Occiput, that part of the head that lies behind the vertex, eyes and genae

Ocellus, simple eye of an arthropod with a single lens for the entire eye

Ommatidium (pl. *ommatidia*), the visual unit of a compound eye

Ootheca (pl. *oothecae*), the covering or case of an egg mass of certain Orthoptera

Operculum, a cover or lid

Order, a group composed or related families

Osmeterium (pl. *osmeteria*), eversible saclike structures provided with scent glands, usually borne on anterior region of the body of caterpillars of certain butterflies

Ostia (sing. *ostium*), openings on the sides of the heart through which the blood enters

Ovariole, one of the egg tubes which collectively form the ovary

Ovary, a mass of tubes lying one on each side of the body cavity of the female insect in which the eggs are developed

Oviduct, tube leading from the ovary through which the eggs pass to the vagina

Oviparous, reproducing from eggs laid by the female

Ovipositor, egg laying organ of the female insect

Ovoviviparous, the production of living young by the hatching of the eggs before they are laid

Paedogenesis, reproduction in the sexually immature or larval stage

Palpi (sing. *palpus*), segmented appendages borne on the maxillae and also on the labium

Palpifer, small lobe or sclerite articulated to the stripes which bears the maxillary palpus

Palpiger, small sclerite on the labium which bears the palpus

Paraglossa (pl. *paraglossae*), one of the paired lobes borne on the distal end of the labium, to the side of the glossae

Parasite, an animal smaller than its host upon or within which it lives continuously for at least a part of its life cycle; the host is not immediately killed by its attacks

Pars intercerebralis, median part of the protocerebrum

Parthenogenesis, reproduction from eggs without fertilization

Paurometabolous, development in which the young resemble the adult, live in the same environment, and have the same food habits

Pectinate, comblike in appearance (e.g., pectinate antennae)

Pedicel, the second segment of the antennae

Pedipalpi, the second paired appendages of an arachnid.

Penellipse, in the caterpillar proleg, the figure formed by the crochets in a uniserial circle with a part of them absent

Pharynx, that part of the foregut between the mouth and the esophagus

Pheromones, substances secreted to the outside, causing specific reactions

Phoresy, a relationship in which one insect is carried on the body of another larger insect, but the former does not feed on the latter

Phylum, one of the major divisions of the animal kingdom

Plankton, population of microscopic plant and animal life found floating or drifting in water

Pleuron, the lateral side of a thoracic segment

Plumose, feathered (e.g., plumose antennae)

Polyembryony, the production of two or more embryos from a single egg

Postgena, that part of the head which extends downward and back of the gena

Postlabium, the basal or proximal part of the labium

Predator, an animal usually larger than the prey, which may be devoured in one meal

Prelabium, the distal part of the labium comprised of the prementum, the ligula, and the palpi

Prementum, region of the labium bearing the palpi and ligular lobes

Prepupa, a quiescent stage between the larva and the pupa

Proboscis, any extended structure of the mouthparts

Proctodaeum, the hindgut extended from the ventriculus to the anus

Proleg, a fleshy abdominal leg of some insect larvae

Pronotum, dorsal surface of the prothorax

Propodaeum, the first abdominal segment in the Hymenoptera which is joined to the thorax

Prothorax, the first of the three thoracic segments

Protocerebrum, the first part of the insect brain which supplies nerves to the compound eyes and ocelli

Proventriculus, the gizzard, the posterior part of the foregut which joins the ventriculus

Pseudotrachea (pl. *pseudotracheae*), a structure having the appearance of a trachea; a false trachea

Pteropleural bristles, bristles located on the pteropleuron of Diptera

Pulvillus (pl. *pulvilli*), padlike structures between the claws of the tarsi

Pupa (pl. *pupae*), the quiescent stage between the larva and the adult in holometabolous development

Puparium (pl. *puparia*), the larval skin which serves as a covering for the pupa in the higher Diptera

Pupiparous, giving birth to mature larvae which are ready to pupate

Pygidium, the dorsal surface of the last abdominal segment

Pyloric valve, a valve at the junction of the ventriculus and the proctodaeum

Radius, the third longitudinal vein of the wing which is divided into not more than five branches

Rectum, posterior part of the proctodaeum or hindgut

Reflex, the simple reaction in an animal following a stimulus or a set of stimuli

Retinula, the sensory part of the ommatidium, composed of seven or eight elongate cells which surround the rhabdom

Rhabdom, the optic rod lying in the axis of the retinula

Rostrum, snout or beak

Salivary glands, open into the mouth, secreting digestive material

Scape, the first segment of the antenna

Scarabaeiform larva, a grublike larva, cylindrical, curved and with short thoracic legs, but no prolegs

Sclerite, a plate of the body wall of an insect, bordered by sutures or membranes

Sclerotized, of the cuticula, hardened in definite areas

Scutellum, a posterior sclerite of the thoracic notum

Scutum, the middle sclerite of a thoracic notum, anterior to the scutellum

Seminal vesicles, pouchlike structures in which seminal fluid of the male is stored

Serrate, sawlike (e.g., serrate antennae)

Seta (pl. *setae*), a hairlike appendage

Setaceous, bristlelike, that type of antenna which gradually tapers to a point distally

Spermatheca, receptacle in the female which receives and stores the sperm of the male

Spinneret, a structure from which silk is spun

Spiracle, an outside opening to the tracheal system

Sternum, the ventral part of a body segment

Stigmal plate, in ticks, the plate which surrounds the spiracle

Stipes, the second segment or part of the maxilla

Stomodaeum, the foregut of an arthropod

Stylus (pl. *styli*), a short, slender process on the ventral surface of the abdomen of Thysanura

Subcosta, longitudinal vein of wing extending parallel to the costa

Subesophageal ganglion, the ganglion located below the esophagus

Submentum, the postlabium, the basal sclerite of the labium

Superposition image, image produced by superposition or overlapping of points of light from a number of facets

Supraesophageal ganglion, insect brain located above the esophagus

Suture, a groove or seam in the cuticula between sclerites

Synecology, the study of animals and plants as a whole with a combination of all environmental factors within a community

Synergist, compounds mixed with others producing toxic effects greater than the sum of the components used separately

Taenidium (pl. *taenidia*), a spiral chitinized thickening in the wall of a trachea

Tarsus (pl. *tarsi*), the distal division of an insect's leg attached to the tibia and consisting of one or more segments

Tegmen (pl. *tegmina*), the thickened or parchmentlike front wing of Orthoptera

Tenaculum, a structure on the ventral side of the abdomen of Collembola which holds the furcula or springing appendage

Tergum, the dorsal region of a body segment

Testis (pl. *testes*), sex organ of the male which produces the sperm

Tibia (pl. *tibiae*), the fourth division of an insect's leg between the femur and the tarsus.

Trachea (pl. *tracheae*), an air tube lined with taenidia

Tracheole, a terminal branch of the trachea, not chitin lined

Triploblastic, with three germ layers, ectoderm, mesoderm, and endoderm from which the systems of organs develop

Tritocerebrum, the third part of the insect's brain which innervates the labrum and the frontal ganglion

Triungulin larva, the first larval instar of Strepsiptera and certain beetles

Trochanter, the second division of an insect's leg between the coxa and the femur

Trophyllaxis, exchange of food materials between insects

Tympanum, a membrane covering the auditory organs

Vagina, structure formed by the union of the oviducts of the female reproductive organs which opens to the outside

Vas deferens (pl. *vasa deferentia*), sperm duct of the male

Ventriculus, the midgut or stomach of an insect

Vermiform larva, a wormlike, legless and headless larva

Vertex, the top of the head, between the eyes and anterior to the occiput

Vestigial, the nature of a degenerate or atrophied organ

Viviparous, producing living young, and not laying eggs

Weismann's ring gland, lies behind the brain encircling the aorta in larvae of cyclorrhaphous Diptera, source of puparium-forming hormone

A SELECTED BIBLIOGRAPHY

A list of references given below is not by any means a complete bibliography of the subject material in the text. It is offered as a further source of information for both the teacher and student. A number of the texts listed contain excellent bibliographies. Other bibliographical sources are: *Biological Abstracts*, Philadelphia, Pa.; *Index to the Literature of American Economic Entomology*, Baltimore, Maryland, the Entomological Society of America; *The Review of Applied Entomology Series A and B*, London, England, the Imperial institute of Entomology; *Abstracts of Entomology*, Philadelphia, Pa.; *The Agricultural Index*, New York, H. W. Wilson Co., and *Annual Review of Entomology*, Palo Alto, California, Annual Reviews Inc.

Most of the detailed information on insect pests is found in bulletins and other publications of the United States Department of Agriculture and State Agricultural Experiment Stations. Many of these publications may be obtained free or at little cost.

GENERAL AND ECONOMIC ENTOMOLOGY

Anderson, Roger F., *Forest and Shade Tree Entomology*, Wiley, New York, 1960, 428 pages.

Bishopp, F. C., *et al.*, "Insects," *U.S.D.A. Yearbook*, Government Printing Office, Washington, D.C., 1952, 780 pages.

Borror, Donald J., and DeLong, Dwight M., *An Introduction to the Study of Insects*, rev. ed., Rinehart, New York, 1964, 819 pages.

Borror, Donald J., and White, Richard E., *A Field Guide to the Insects of America North of Mexico*, Houghton Mifflin, Boston, 1970, 404 pages.

Brues, C. T., Melander, A. L., and Carpenter, F. M., *Classification of Insects*, Harvard College Museum of Comparative Zoology Bulletin, vol. 108, Cambridge, Mass., 1964, 917 pages.

Chamberlin, W. J., *Entomological Nomenclature and Literature*, 2nd ed., Edwards, Ann Arbor, Mich., 1946, 135 pages.

Chu, H. F., *How to Know the Immature Insects*, W. C. Brown, Dubuque, Iowa, 1949, 234 pages.

Clausen, C. P., *Entomophagous Insects*, McGraw-Hill, New York, 1940, 688 pages.

Comstock, J. H., *An Introduction to Entomology*, Comstock, Ithaca, N.Y., 1940, 1064 pages.

Cotton, R. T., *Insect Pests of Stored Grain and Grain Products*, rev. ed., Burgess, Minneapolis, Minn., 1963, 318 pages.

Craighead, F. C., *Insect Enemies of Eastern Forests*, U.S.D.A. Miscellaneous Publication 657, Government Printing Office, Washington, D.C., 1950, 679 pages.

Davidson, R. H., and Pears, L. M., *Insect Pests of Farm Garden and Orchard*, 6th ed., Wiley, New York, 1966, 675 pages.

Dennis, Clifford J., *Laboratory Manual for Introductory Entomology*, W. C. Brown, Dubuque, Iowa, 1966, 101 pages.

Doane, R. W., Vandyke, E. C., Chamberlin, W. J., and Burke, H. E., *Forest Insects*, McGraw-Hill, New York, 1936, 463 pages.

Ebeling, Walter, *Subtropical Fruit Pests*, University of California Press, Berkeley, 1959, 436 pages.

Essig, E. O., *A History of Entomology*, Macmillan, New York, 1931, 1059 pages.

Essig, E. O., *College Entomology*, Macmillan, New York, 1942, 900 pages.

Essig, E. O., *Insects and Mites of Western North America*, Macmillan, New York, 1958, 1050 pages.

Ewing, H. E., *A Manual of External Parasites*, Charles C. Thomas, Springfield, Ill., 1929, 225 pages.

Felt, E. P., *Plant Galls and Gall Makers*, Comstock, Ithaca, N.Y., 1940, 364 pages.

Fenton, F. A., *Field Crop Insects*, Macmillan, New York, 1952, 405 pages.

Folsom, J. W., and Wardle, R. A., *Entomology with Special Reference to Its Ecological Aspects*, 4th ed., Blakiston, Philadelphia, Pa., 1934, 605 pages.

Fox, Richard M., and Fox, Jean Walker, *Introduction to Comparative Entomology*, Reinhold, New York, 1964, 450 pages.

Frost, S. W., *Insect Life and Insect Natural History*, 2nd rev. ed., Dover, New York, 1959, 526 pages.

Furman, Dean P., *Manual of Medical Entomology*, National Press, Palo Alto, Calif., 1961, 122 pages.

Graham, S. A., *Principles of Forest Entomology*, 2nd ed., McGraw-Hill, New York, 1936, 410 pages.

Horsfall, William R., *Medical Entomology*, Ronald, New York, 1962, 467 pages.

Howard, L. O., *A History of Applied Entomology*, Smithsonian Miscellaneous Collections, vol. 84, Publication 3065, Washington, D.C., 1930, 564 pages.

Imms, A. D., *A General Textbook of Entomology*, 9th ed., Dutton, New York, 1957, 886 pages.

Imms, A. D., *Insect Natural History*, Collins, London, 1947, 317 pages.

James, Maurice T., and Harwood, Robert F., *Herm's Medical Entomology*, 6th ed., Macmillan, New York, 1969, 484 pages.

Jaques, H. E., *How to Know the Insects*, 2nd ed., W. C. Brown, Dubuque, Iowa, 1947, 212 pages.

Keen, F. P., *Insect Enemies of Western Forests*, U.S.D.A. Miscellaneous Publication 273, rev., Government Printing Office, Washington, D.C., 1939, 210 pages.

Kellogg, V. L., *American Insects*, 3rd ed., rev., Holt, New York, 1914, 694 pages.

Leach, J. G., *Insect Transmission of Plant Diseases*, McGraw-Hill, New York, 1940, 615 pages.

Lutz, F. E., *Field Book of Insects*, 3rd ed., Putnam, New York, 1948, 510 pages.

McKenzie, Howard, *The Armored Scale Insects of California*, Bulletin of the California Insect Survey, vol. 5, University of California Press, Berkeley, 1956, 209 pages.

Mallis, Arnold, *Handbook of Pest Control*, 4th ed., MacNair-Dorland, New York, 1964, 1148 pages.

Matheson, Robert, *Entomology for Introductory Courses*, 2nd ed., Comstock, Ithaca, N.Y., 1951, 629 pages.

Matheson, Robert, *A Laboratory Guide in Entomology for Introductory Course*, Cornell, Ithaca, N.Y., 135 pages.

Matheson, Robert, *Medical Entomology*, 2nd ed., Comstock, Ithaca, N.Y., 1950, 612 pages.

Metcalf, C. L., and Flint, W. P., *Fundamentals of Insect Life*, McGraw-Hill, New York, 1932, 581 pages.

Metcalf, C. L., Flint, W. P., and Metcalf, R. L., *Destructive and Useful Insects*, 4th ed., McGraw-Hill, New York, 1962, 1087 pages.

Morgan, Ann H., *Field Book of Ponds and Streams*, Putnam, New York, 1930, 448 pages.

Osborn, Herbert, *Fragments of Entomological History*, Columbus, Ohio, published by the author, 1937.

Painter, R. H., *Insect Resistance in Crop Plants*, Macmillan, New York, 1951, 520 pages.

Patton, W. S., and Evans, A. M., *Insects, Ticks, Mites and Venomous Animals of Medical and Veterinary Importance*, pt. 1, Medical, H. R. Grubb, London, 1929, 785 pages.

Patton, W. S., *Insects, Ticks, Mites and Venomous Animals of Medical and Veterinary Importance*, pt. 2, Public Health, H. R. Grubb, London, 1930, 740 pages.

Pennak, Robert W., *Fresh-Water Invertebrates of the United States*, Ronald, New York, 1953, 769 pages.

Peterson, Alvah, *Entomological Techniques*, 10th ed., Edwards, Ann Arbor, Mich., 1964, 435 pages.

Peterson, Alvah, *Larvae of Insects Part I, Lepidoptera and Hymenoptera*, 1962, 315 pages. *Part II Coleoptera, Diptera, Neuroptera, Siphonoptera, Mecoptera, Trichoptera*, Edwards, Ann Arbor, Mich., 1960, 416 pages.

Pfadt, Robert E., *et al.*, *Fundamentals of Applied Entomology*, Macmillan, New York, 1962, 668 pages.

Pierce, W. D., *Sanitary Entomology*, Gorham, Boston, 1921, 518 pages.

Quayle, H. J., *Insects of Citrus and Other Subtropical Fruits*, Comstock, Ithaca, N.Y., 1938, 583 pages.

Richards, O. W., *The Social Insects*, Philosophical Library, New York, 1953, 219 pages.

Ross, H. H., *A Textbook of Entomology*, 3rd ed., Wiley, New York, 1965, 539 pages.

Smart, John, *Insects of Medical Importance*, British Museum (Natural History), London, 1965, 303 pages.

Stoll, N. L. (Chairman), *International Code of Zoological Nomenclature*, 1964, International Trust for Zoological Nomenclature, London, England, 1964, 176 pages.

Swain, R. B., *The Insect Guide, Orders and Major Families of North American Insects,* Doubleday, Garden City, N.Y., 1948, 261 pages.

Sweetman, Harvey L., *Recognition of Structural Pests and Their Damage,* W. C. Brown, Dubuque, Iowa, 1965, 384 pages.

Tietz, Harrison Wm., *Illustrated Keys to the Families of North American Insects,* Burgess, Minneapolis, Minn., 1963, 206 pages.

Torre-Bueno, J. R. de la, *A Glossary of Entomology,* Science Press, Lancaster, Pa., 1937, 336 pages.

U.S. Public Health Service, *Pictorial Keys: Arthropods, Reptiles, Birds and Mammals of Public Health Significance,* Atlanta, Georgia, 1966, 192 pages.

Usinger, Robert L., *Aquatic Insects of California,* University of California Press, Berkeley, 1963, 508 pages.

Ward, Henry B., and Whipple, George C., *Fresh-water Biology,* Wiley, New York, 1918, 1111 pages.

Wardle, Robert A., *The Problems of Applied Entomology,* McGraw-Hill, New York, 1929, 587 pages.

PRINCIPLES OF INSECT CONTROL AND ECOLOGY

Andrewartha, H. G., and Birch, L. C., *The Distribution and Abundance of Animals,* The University of Chicago Press, Chicago, 1954, 782 pages.

Borkouec, Alexej B., *Insect Chemosterilants,* vol. VII in Advances in Pest Control Research, Interscience, New York, 1966, 144 pages.

Brown, A. W. A., *Insect Control by Chemicals,* Wiley, New York, 1951, 817 pages.

Chapman, R. N., *Animal Ecology,* McGraw-Hill, New York, 1931, 464 pages.

Claussen, C. P., *Biological Control of Insect Pests in the Continental U.S.,* U.S.D.A. Tech. Bull. No. 1139, Government Printing Office, Washington, D.C., 1956.

DcOng, E. R., *Chemistry and Uses of Insecticides,* Reinhold, New York, 1948, 345 pages.

Dethier, V. G., *Chemical Insect Attractants and Repellents,* Blakiston, Philadelphia, Pa., 1947, 289 pages.

Insect-Pest Management and Control Principles of Plant and Animal Pest Control, vol. 3, Publ. No. 1695, National Academy of Sciences, Washington, D.C., 1969, 508 pages.

Jacobson, Martin, *Insect Sex Attractants,* Wiley, New York, 1965, 154 pages.

Kilgore, U. W., and Doutt, R. L., *Pest Control, Biological Physical and Selected Control Methods,* Academic, New York, 1967, 477 pages.

LaBrecque, G. C., and Smith, C. N., *Insect Sterilization,* Appleton-Century-Crofts, New York, 1967, 422 pages.

Metcalf, R. L., *Organic Insecticides, Their Chemistry and Mode of Action,* Interscience, New York, 1955, 392 pages.

O'Brien, R. D., *Insecticides, Action and Metabolism,* Academic, New York, 1967, 332 pages.

Proceedings of the FAO Symposium on Integrated Pest Control, nos. 1, 2 and 3, 1965, Food and Agriculture Organization of the United Nations, Rome, Italy, 1966.

Rabb, R. L., and Guthrie, F. E., *Concepts of Pest Management,* North Carolina State University, Raleigh, 1970, 242 pages.

Scientific Aspects of Pest Control, A Symposium, Publ. No. 1402, National Academy of Sciences, National Research Council, Washington, D.C., 1966, 470 pages.

Shepard, H. H., *The Chemistry and Action of Insecticides,* McGraw-Hill, New York, 1951, 504 pages.

Smith, Carroll N., *Insect Colonization and Mass Production,* Academic, New York, 1966, 618 pages.

Smith, Kenneth M., *Insect Virology,* Academic, New York, 1967, 256 pages.

Sweetman, H. L., *The Biological Control of Insects,* Comstock, Ithaca, N.Y., 1936, 461 pages.

ANATOMY, PHYSIOLOGY, AND PATHOLOGY

Beament, J. W. L., Treherne, J. E., and Wigglesworth, V. B., *Advances in Insect Physiology,* vol. 1, 512 pages, 1963; vol. 2, 364 pages, 1964; vol. 3, 382 pages, 1966; vol. 4, 415 pages, 1967; vol. 5, 362 pages, 1968, Academic, New York.

Beck, Stanley D., *Insect Photoperiodism,* Academic, New York and London, 1968, 288 pages.

Chapman, R. F., *The Insect's Structure and Function,* American Elsevier, New York, 1969, 819 pages.

DeBach, Paul, *Biological Control of Pests and Weeds,* Reinhold, New York, 1964, 930 pages.

Dethier, V. G., and Elliot, Stellar, *Animal Behavior,* Prentice-Hall, Englewood Cliffs, N.J., 1961, 118 pages.

DuPorte, E. Melville, *Manual of Insect Morphology,* Reinhold, New York, 1959, 224 pages.

Lees, A. D., *The Physiology of Diapause in Arthropods,* The University Press, Cambridge, England, 1955, 151 pages.

Menaker, Michael, *Biological Clocks,* BioScience vol. 19 no. 8, American Institute of Biological Sciences, Washington, D.C., 1969, pages 681–689, 92.

Patton, Robert L., *Introductory Insect Physiology,* Saunders, Philadelphia, Pa., 1963, 245 pages.

Richards, A. Glenn, *The Integument of Arthropods,* University of Minnesota Press, Minneapolis, Minn., 1951, 411 pages.

Rockstein, Morris, *The Physiology of Insecta,* vol. 1, 640 pages, 1964; vol. 2, 905 pages, 1965; vol. 3, 692 pages, 1964, Academic, New York.

Roeder, Kenneth D., *et al., Insect Physiology,* Wiley, New York, 1953, 1100 pages.

Snodgrass, R. E., *Anatomy of the Honeybee,* Comstock, Ithaca, N.Y., Associates, 1956, 334 pages.

Snodgrass, R. E., *Principles of Insect Morphology,* McGraw-Hill, New York, 1935, 667 pages.

Steinhaus, Edward A., *Principles of Insect Pathology,* McGraw-Hill, New York, 1949, 757 pages.

Wigglesworth, V. G., *The Principles of Insect Physiology,* 6th ed., Methuen, London, England, 1965, 741 pages.

NEAR RELATIVES OF INSECTS (SPIDERS, MITES, AND TICKS)

Baker, E. W., and Wharton, G. W., *An Introduction to Acarology,* Macmillan, New York, 1952, 465 pages.

Banks, Nathan, *A Revision of the Ixodoidea or Ticks of the United States*, U.S. Bureau of Entomology Bulletin, Technical Series No. 15, Government Printing Office, Washington, D.C., 1908, 60 pages.

Cloudsley-Thompson, J. L., *Spiders, Scorpions, Centipedes, and Mites*, Pergamon, New York, 1958, 228 pages.

Comstock, J. H., and Gertsch, W. J., *The Spider Book*, Comstock, Ithaca, N.Y., 1948, 740 pages.

Gertsch, W. J., *American Spiders*, Van Nostrand, New York, 1949, 285 pages.

Hooker, W. A., Bishopp, F. C., and Wood, H. P., *The Life History and Bionomics of Some North American Ticks*, U.S. Bureau of Entomology Bulletin 106, Government Printing Office, Washington, D.C., 1918, 239 pages.

Nuttall, G. H. F., *et al.*, *Ticks, a Monograph of the Ixodoidea*, pt. 1, 1908; pt. 2, 1911; pt. 3, 1915; pt. 4, 1926, pts. 1–3, 550 pages; pt. 4, 302 pages, Cambridge University Press, Cambridge, England.

Prichard, A. E., and Baker, E. W., *A Revision of the Spider Mite Family Tetranychidae*, Pacific Coast Entomological Society, San Francisco, 1955, 472 pages.

Tuttle, Donald M., and Baker, Edward W., *Spider Mites of Southwestern United States*, The University of Arizona Press, Tucson, Ariz., 224 pages.

EPHEMEROPTERA (MAYFLIES), ODONATA (DRAGONFLIES), AND PLECOPTERA (STONEFLIES)

Burks, B. D., *The Mayflies or Ephemeroptera of Illinois*, Illinois Natural History Survey Bulletin 26, Urbana, Ill., 1953, 216 pages.

Frison, T. H., *Studies of North American Plecoptera*, Illinois Natural History Survey Bulletin 22, Urbana, Ill., 1942, pp. 235–355.

Morgan, A. H., *A Contribution to the Biology of Mayflies*, Annals of Entomological Society of America 6, Entomological Society of America, College Park, Maryland, 1913, pp. 371–426.

Needham, J. G., and Claasen, P. W., *A Monograph of the Plecoptera or Stoneflies of America North of Mexico*, Thomas Say Foundation, Lafayette, Ind., 1925, 397 pages.

Needham, J. G., Traver, J. R., and Hsu, Y., *The Biology of Mayflies*, Comstock, Ithaca, N.Y., 1935, 759 pages.

Needham, J. G., and Westfall, M. J., Jr., *A Manual of the Dragonflies of North America (Anisoptera)*, University of California Press, Berkeley, 1955, 615 pages.

Tillyard, R. J., *The Biology of Dragonflies*, Harvard University Press, Cambridge, Mass., 1917, 396 pages.

ORTHOPTERA (COCKROACHES, GRASSHOPPERS, ETC.) AND ISOPTERA (TERMITES)

Blatchley, W. S., *The Orthoptera of Northeastern America*, Nature, Indianapolis, Ind., 1920, 784 pages.

Hebard, Morgan, *The Blattidae of North America, North of the Mexican Boundary*, Entomological Society of America Memoirs, No. 2, Philadelphia, 1917, 284 pages.

Hebard, Morgan, *The Dermaptera and Orthoptera of Illinois*, Illinois Natural History Survey Bulletin 20, Urbana, Ill., 1934, pages 125–279.

Kofoid, C. A., *Termites and Termite Control*, 2nd ed., University of California Press, Berkeley, 1934, 795 pages.

Krishna, Kumar and Weesner, Francis M., *Biology of Termites*, vol. 1, 1969, 597 pages; vol. 2 in preparation, Academic, New York.

Morse, A. P., *Manual of the Orthoptera of New England*, Boston Society of Natural History Proceedings, vol. 35, no. 6, 1920, pp. 203–556.

Synder, T. E., *Catalogue of Termites (Isoptera) of the World*, Smithsonian Institution Miscellaneous Collections, vol. 112, Washington, D.C., 1949, 490 pages.

Snyder, T. E., *Our Enemy the Termites*, rev. ed., Comstock, Ithaca, N.Y., 1948, 257 pages.

Uvarov, B. P., *Locusts and Grasshoppers*, Imperial Bureau of Entomology, London, 1928, 352 pages.

MALLOPHAGA (CHEWING LICE), ANOPLURA (SUCKING LICE),
HEMIPTERA (TRUE BUGS), AND HOMOPTERA (APHIDS, SCALES, ETC.)

Blatchley, W. S., *Heteroptera or True Bugs of Eastern North America, with Special Reference to the Faunas of Indiana and Florida*, Nature, Indianapolis, Ind., 1926, 1116 pages.

Britton, W. E., et al., *The Hemiptera or Sucking Insects of Connecticut*, Connecticut State Geology and Natural History Survey, pt. 4, Hartford, Conn., 1923, 807 pages.

Ewing, H. E., *Taxonomy, Biology, and Distribution of the Gyropidae*, U.S. National Museum Proceedings, no. 63, 1924, pp. 1–42.

Ferris, G. F., *Atlas of the Scale Insects of North America*, series 1–7, Stanford University Press, Stanford, Calif., 1937–1950.

Ferris, G. F., "The Mallophagan Family Monoponidae," *Parasitology*, no. 16, 1924, pp. 55–66.

Ferris, G. F., *The Sucking Lice*, Pacific Coast Entomological Society, San Francisco, Calif., 1951, 320 pages.

Kellogg, V. L., *A List of Mallophaga taken from Birds and Mammals of North America*, U.S. National Museum Proceedings, no. 22, 1899, pp. 39–100.

MacGillivray, A. D., *The Coccidae*, Scarab Co., Urbana, Ill., 1921, 502 pages.

Patch, E. M., *Food-plant Catalogue of the Aphids of the World, Including Phylloxeridae*, Maine Agricultural Experiment Station Bulletin 393, Orono, Me., 1938, 431 pages.

Van Duzee, E. P., *Catalogue of the Hemiptera of America, North of Mexico, Excepting the Aphididae, Coccidae and Aleurodidae*, University of California Publication, Entomology, Technical Bulletin, vol. 2, 1917, 902 pages.

COLEOPTERA (BEETLES) AND STREPSIPTERA (STYLOPIDS)

Blatchley, W. S., *An Illustrated and Descriptive Catalogue of the Coleoptera or Beetles of Indiana (Exclusive of Rhynchophora)*, 2 vols., Nature, Indianapolis, Ind., 1910, 1385 pages.

Blatchley, W. S., and Leng, C. W., *Rhynchophora or Weevils or Northeastern North America*, Nature, Indianapolis, Ind., 1916, 682 pages.

Boving, A. G., and Craighead, F. C., *An Illustrated Synopsis of the Principal Larval Forms of the Order Coleoptera*, Brooklyn Entomological Society, New York, 1931, 351 pages.

Dillon, Elizabeth S., and Dillon, Lawrence S., *A Manual of Common Beetles of Eastern North America*, Row, Peterson, Evanston, Ill., 1961, 884 pages.

Leconte, J. L., and Horn, G. H., *Synopsis of North American Coleoptera*, Smithsonian Institution Miscellaneous Collection, 26(507), 1883, 567 pages.

Leng, C. W., *Catalogue of the Coleoptera of America, North of Mexico*, John D. Sherman, Jr., Mount Vernon, N.Y., 1920; five supplements 1927–1947; 470 pages.

Pierce, W. D., *A Monographic Revision of the Twisted-winged Insects Comprising the Order Strepsiptera*, U.S. National Museum Proceedings 54, 1918, pp. 391–501.

LEPIDOPTERA (MOTHS AND BUTTERFLIES) AND
TRICHOPTERA (CADDISFLIES)

Comstock, J. H., and Comstock, A. B., *How to Know the Butterflies*, Comstock, Ithaca, N.Y., 1936, 311 pages.

Dyar, H. G., *A List of North American Lepidoptera and a Key to the Literature to this Order of Insects*, U.S. National Museum Bulletin No. 52, 1902, 723 pages.

Forbes, W. T. M., *The Lepidoptera of New York and Neighboring States, Primitive Forms, Microlepidoptera, Pyraloids and Bombyces*, Cornell University Agricultural Experiment Station Memoir 68, Ithaca, N.Y., 1923, 729 pages.

Forbes, W. T. M., *Lepidoptera of New York and Neighboring States, Geometridae, Sphingidae, Notodontidae and Lymantriidae*, pt. 2, Cornell University Agricultural Experiment Station Memoir 274, Ithaca, N.Y., 1948, 263 pages.

Forbes, W. T. M., *Lepidoptera of New York and Neighboring States, Noctuidae*, pt. 3, Cornell University Agricultural Experiment Station Memoir 329, Ithaca, N.Y., 1954, 433 pages.

Holland, W. J., *The Butterfly Book*, Doubleday, New York, 1931, 424 pages.

Holland, W. J., *The Moth Book*, Doubleday, New York, 1913, 479 pages.

Klots, A. B., *A Field Guide to the Butterflies*, Houghton Mifflin, Boston, 1951, 349 pages.

McDunnough, J. H., "Check List of the Lepidoptera of Canada and the United States of America," *Southern California Academy of Science Memoirs*, Los Angeles, Calif., pt. 1, 1938, (Macrolepidoptera), 274 pages; pt. 2, 1939 (Microlepidoptera), 171 pages.

Ross, H. H., *The Caddis Flies or Trichoptera of Illinois*, Illinois Natural History Survey Bulletin 23, Urbana, Ill., 1944, 326 pages.

Seitz, A., *Macro-Lepidoptera of the World*, vol. 5, The American Rhopalocera, F. Lehmann, Stuttgart, 1924, 1139 pages.

DIPTERA (FLIES) AND SIPHONAPTERA (FLEAS)

Aldrich, J. M., *A Catalogue of North American Diptera*, Smithsonian Institution Miscellaneous Collections, vol. 46, Washington, D.C., 1905, 680 pages.

Baker, C. F., *A Revision of American Siphonaptera or Fleas*, U.S. National Museum Proceedings 29, Washington, D.C., 1904, pp. 365–469.

Betten, Cornelius, et al., *The Caddis Flies or Trichoptera of New York State*, New York State Museum Bulletin 292, University of the State of New York, Albany, 1934, 576 pages.

Carpenter, S. J., and La Casse, W. J., *Mosquitoes of North America*, University of California Press, Berkeley, 1955, 360 pages.

Curran, C. H., *The Families and Genera of North American Diptera*, New York, published by the author, 1934, 512 pages.

Fox, Irving, and Ewing, H. E., *The Fleas of North America*, U.S.D.A., Miscellaneous Publication, No. 500, Washington, D.C., 1943, 128 pages.

Hall, D. G., *The Blowflies of North America*, Entomological Society of America, Thomas Say Foundation Publication, vol. 4, Baltimore, 1948, 477 pages.

Hubbard, C. A., *Fleas of Western North America*, Iowa State College Press, Ames, Iowa, 1947, 533 pages.

Lane, J., *Neotropical Culicidae*, vols. 1 and 2, University of Saõ Paulo, Saõ Paulo, Brazil, 1953, 1112 pages.

Matheson, Robert, *Handbook of the Mosquitoes of North America*, 2nd ed., Comstock, Ithaca, N.Y., 1944, 314 pages.

Russell, P. F., Rozeboom, L. E., and Stone, Alan, *Keys to the Anopheline Mosquitoes of the World*, American Entomological Society, The Academy of Natural Sciences, Philadelphia, Pa., 1943, 152 pages.

Stone, Alan and others, *A Catalog of the Diptera of America North of Mexico*, U.S. Government Printing Office, Washington, D.C., 1965, 1960 pages.

West, L. S., *The House Fly*, Comstock, Ithaca, N.Y., 1951, 584 pages.

Williston, S. W., *Manual of the Families and Genera of North American Diptera*, 34d ed., James T. Hathaway, New Haven, Conn., 1908, 405 pages.

HYMENOPTERA (WASPS, BEES, ETC.)

Creighton, W. S., *The Ants of North America*, Harvard University Museum of Comparative Zoology Bulletin, vol. 104, Cambridge, Mass., 1950, 585 pages.

Grout, R. A., ed., *The Hive and the Honey Bee*, rev. ed., Dadant & Sons, Hamilton, Ill., 1961, 556 pages.

Muesebeck, C. W. F., Krombein, K. V., Townes, H. K., et al., *Hymenoptera of America North of Mexico—A Synoptic Catalogue*, U.S.D.A. Agricultural Monographs, no. 2, Government Printing Office, Washington, D.C., 1951, 1420 pages.

Rau, Philip, and Rau, Nellie, *Wasp Studies Afield*, Princeton University Press, Princeton, N.J., 1918, 372 pages.

Root, A. I., *The ABC and XYZ of Bee Culture, An Encyclopedia Pertaining to Scientific and Practical Culture of Bees*, revised by E. R. Root, H. H. Root, and M. J. Deyell, Medina, Ohio, A. I. Root Co., 1950, 703 pages.

Viereck, H. L., et al., *The Hymenoptera, or Wasp-like Insects of Connecticut*, Connecticut State Geology and Natural History Survey Bulletin 22, Hartford, Conn., 1916, 824 pages.

Von Frisch, Karl, *Bees: Their Vision, Chemical Senses and Language*, Comstock, Ithaca, N.Y., 118 pages.

Wheeler, W. M., *Ants: Their Structure, Development and Behavior*, Columbia University Press, New York, 1926, 663 pages.

MINOR GROUPS

Banks, N., "A classification of the Psocidae," *Psyche* **36**, 321–324 (1929).

Chapman, P. J., "Corrodentia of the United States of America, I, suborder Isotecnomera," *New York Entomological Society Journal* **38**, 219–290 (1930).

Gourney, Ashley B., "A synopsis of the order Zoraptera, with notes on the biology of *Zorotypus hubbardi*," *Washington Entomological Society Proceedings* **40**, 57–87 (1938).

Mills, H. B., *A Monograph of the Collembola of Iowa*, Iowa Collegiate Press, Ames, 1934, 143 pages.

Moulton, D., *Synopsis, Catalogue, and Bibliography of North American Thysanoptera*, U.S.D.A. Bureau of Entomology Technical Series no. 21, Government Printing Office, Washington, D.C., 1911, 56 pages.

Ross, Edward S., *A Revision of the Embioptera, or Web-spinners of the New World*, U.S. National Museum Proceedings, vol. 94, 1944, pp. 401–504.

Watson, J. R., *Synopsis and Catalogue of the Thysanoptera of North America*, University of Florida Experiment Station Bulletin 168, Gainesville, Fla., 1923, 100 pages.

INDEX

505

75 76 9 8 7 6 5 4